Practical
SMALLFARMING
in New Zealand

Practical SMALLFARMING *in* New Zealand

TRISHA FISK

REED

Published by Reed Books, a division of Reed Publishing (NZ) Ltd, 39 Rawene Rd, Birkenhead, Auckland. Associated companies, branches and representatives throughout the world.

ISBN 0 7900 0501 8

Cover photographs by Graham Meadows
Cover design by Clair Stutton

First published 1989
Reprinted 1990, 1992, 1993
Revised edition 1996
Reprinted 2001

Printed in Singapore

To Mum, Reg and Razzle

Acknowledgements
A lot of people assisted in this book and without their support and encouragement — and often very real practical help — it would not have grown into what it is now. But special thanks to Neil Rennie for making it all possible; Alan and Sue Clarkson for keeping me on the right track and getting me there on time; Drew Brownson, Tom Lindsay, Rose Buckingham, Janine Dieben for their time and suggestions; Hugh Stringleman at NZ Rural Press for use of photofiles; Alan P.K. for his help developing prints; and all my friends who offered suggestions, model animals or just encouragement at times when it was needed.

Contents

Introduction

Getting back to Mother Nature and living 'the good life' is a romantic and idealistic notion many people share. But the reality of smallfarming is more often mud, gumboots, rescuing cold lambs in the middle of a wet night and having a goat eat something poisonous and not knowing what on earth to do about it.

This book is for realists — for those who want some space, to get away from the rat race, but who want to know how to do it right.

Just as we have practical manuals on the care of cars to help us fix problems and keep them ticking over, so we need a manual for the smallfarm, a nuts and bolts guide to keeping land and animals alive, healthy and paying their way.

Most New Zealanders still have fairly close ties with the land. But visiting a farm in the school holidays won't provide the information you need for running your own show. When do you put the ram out? How do you help a cow that is down? How do you castrate a goat? Ryegrass staggers, milk fever, sleepy sickness — words you have probably heard before, but what do they mean?

There is a lot written about the romantic side of alternative living, the joys of self-sufficiency and so on — enough to feed your enthusiasm until you want to keep pigs, chooks, bees, make homebrew and put up fences. Then you need to know the practicalities involved so you can do it and not just dream about it. That is what this book is all about.

I'm a country kid. I grew up on a farm. I even worked on a farming magazine and learnt all the right words, but when it came to the crunch of running my own place, my ignorance often appalled me. If I was this bad, how were all the other good lifers, without even my experience, getting on?

I didn't have to talk to many to realise a lot of them weren't getting on at all and those who were, were doing so by good luck rather than good management. Ignorance might be bliss for people but it is a bit rugged on all the animals out there living at the mercy of their owners.

So this book is in part for people. It's a practical guide to help those with neat ideas realise them. It is also for the vets of the world, who must get driven to distraction by the cries for help from new chums to farming life.

And of course it is for the animals. If this book helps somebody, somewhere, avoid causing unnecessary illness or suffering to their stock, then it will all have been worthwhile.

A farm is a single whole — soil, trees, garden, grass and stock. All are intertwined and interdependent. Knowing a lot about animals will not help you farm them well if you don't understand the rest of the story. For this reason I have left the livestock section until last. Before getting into animals, understand your land first, then you will be more likely to pick a farming venture to suit.

For those of you just toying with the possibility of getting away from it all, the chapter on buying land will give you some idea of what to look out for and help you select a place that can live up to the dreams you have.

I have included chapters on trees and the garden for those more interested in growing plants than livestock. But even if animals are your main interest, you need to understand what makes the grass grow — after all, that is what your stock will eat.

Finally there is the livestock section. There is enough information here to help you keep a veritable zoo, and hopefully keep you, and the zoo, alive.

Go for it!

1

Part 1: The land

1. Buying

This chapter is for those dreaming of a smallfarm and idyllic country lifestyle who haven't actually got there yet. I cannot stress enough the importance of selecting the right property. Better to borrow a bit and get the land you want, than to buy a place that will never live up to your expectations or provide the living and lifestyle you desire. I've seen too many forays into alternative living end up in heartbreak and unhappiness.

So before buying think through what you want to do with the land. Be it to farm animals, plant trees or both, first read the chapters concerned to see what they require.

On top of that take into account:

- Locality and access. Is it in a region you want to live? Don't just go out into the wop wops because land is cheap there if you actually like a bit of contact with the big smoke or need a town for work, for schools or for stimulation.

- Size. Is the farm large enough for all the activities you have planned? Or is it too big? More land means more to do, and if you work off the farm and have limited time and energy to devote to it, then too big a place will just be a worry and a drag. Better to have a couple of hectares you can enjoy than a couple of hundred you cannot cope with. But if all the family want pet horses, pet sheep and pet cows, make sure there is enough grazing for all and any likely offspring.

- Soils. Get an idea of the predominant soil types. Are they stable, reasonably fertile? Did the previous owner ever topdress? (If it is scrub covered then the vigour of the trees will indicate natural fertility.)

- Is the topography acceptable? Some people like flat farms, others prefer hills and a varied landscape. Consider if the nature of the land will prevent you from any preferred farming activities. Steep land is not much use if you plan to get into horticulture, while flat land might be wasted on pine trees or cashmere goats.

- Altitude. This will affect average temperatures and climate.

- Aspect. This is very important. Land that lies to the north and east is generally warmer than land lying south. Soil temperatures on a south slope in the Manawatu could be as low as a flat paddock in Gore.

- Climate. Is there adequate rainfall? Local rainfall figures can be quite different to figures for the overall region, so check with neighbours. Ideally, try to find someone in the area who has kept rainfall records. If there are hills to windward they could get all the summer rain. Then maybe those north faces will not be so desirable after all if there is insufficient moisture to keep them green. Sunshine hours will also affect temperature and grass growth. How does the land lie in relation to the prevailing winds? Is there shelter, either from hills or tree plantings? Canterbury, Manawatu and Hawke's Bay for example, are all affected by hot, dry nor'westers.

- Water. Does the farm have permanent water sources, either springs or streams? Are they reliable? Is water piped for stock or is that a development cost you face?
- Improvements. Consider the fences and buildings. Are there any? If not, can you afford them as well as the purchase price? If they are already there, are you paying through the nose for them? Are they in reasonable condition, and how long until they need to be replaced? Is the house what you want and where you want it? Is there electricity, telephone and vehicle access?
- Land cover. Is the land in grass, scrub, timber trees, weeds or what? How much work or money is involved in getting it into the state you want?
- Weeds and vermin. Any gorse, blackberry, Californian thistles, rushes or sedge? How difficult or expensive will those weeds be to eradicate? Are rabbits or possums major pests in the area? Are there wild goats, pigs or deer? (Some people do have them. The question is do you want them and will they interfere with your plans for the land?)
- Tenure. Don't automatically assume land is freehold. Of New Zealand's 26.9 million hectares only about 10.9 million are freehold. The rest falls under a variety of Crown and private leasehold arrangements, everything from pastoral leases to endowment lands, leases under Education Lands Act, Mining District leases, special tenures and L.I.P. (leasehold in perpetuity). For most people freehold is the most desirable tenure. It is the most complete estate which can be held and is subservient only to the interest of the Crown (e.g. The Public Works Act). If you are looking at leasehold land consider the length of the lease and the rental. Is it fixed or likely to escalate? Is there any right of renewal? Is there any right of purchase? Is the lease transferable, i.e. can you sell it if you want to?

- Valuation and rates. The Valuation Department values land every five years for rating purposes, taking into account market values for similar land in the area and also any improvements. The valuation will be divided into the unimproved value (just the land) and the improved or capital value. Counties vary on how they apply their rates, some setting a rate on every dollar of the unimproved value, others on the capital value. Besides the general rates, there may also be special rates levied for catchment boards, water supply, drainage and so on. Some counties apply a uniform annual charge to all properties as well as the rate on the value. Before buying a property find out what the rates are. If it is in a very desirable area, they might be more than the land can support from a smallfarming income.

Buying land

Well, you have found *the* property. You've decided where the orchard is going, what colour to paint the barn and the kids have put in their orders for ponies and goats — so how do you go about getting everything signed and sealed?

Under private sales the buyer and seller agree on a price, then a contract to sell is signed. This is a simple document available at most stationers. It usually includes an agreement by the seller to sell and to give possession by a certain date, and an agreement by the purchaser to buy, accompanied by a deposit (usually about 10 per cent of the purchase price plus Stamp Duty). A date of settlement is agreed on, everybody signs the document, and their signatures are witnessed. Note: Stamp Duty is not payable on your first farm, providing that farming is your main source of income.

These agreements can be made conditional, for example on the buyer selling a property first to obtain the money needed to buy the property in question. They are usually conditional for a few days in any case to give the purchaser time to search the title. If you have a solicitor acting for you he or she will take care of this. But if you are acting for yourself then you can do your own 'search' of the Land Transfer Register.

All land is registered under the Land Transfer

system. The whole country has been surveyed into Land Districts. They have their own central office in the main town and each Land District is divided into a number of Survey Districts, usually named after the locality. The Survey Districts are further divided into 'blocks' and these into 'rural sections'. The Department of Survey and Land Information can show you maps of the Land and Survey Districts.

Each property will be described, its area should be marked and its legal description noted. Each parcel of land will have its own 'Certificate of Title' which will include a sketch of the land with a statement showing the area, description and its present owner. So long as you know the location of the block and can identify it on a survey plan for the area, or you know the owner's full name, then you will be able to find the Certificate of Title. These are kept at the Lands and Deeds division of the Department of Justice.

The Certificate of Title will show whether there are any mortgages or unpaid rates on the land, how often it has been sold in the past and any easements on it. (These may be right of way easements for adjoining properties or drainage easements for the local council. Check the implications of any easement before you buy.)

You can even find out what a property previously sold for as each transfer or change of ownership marked on the Certificate of Title will have a registered number of the transfer and the date. With this number you can look up the Register of Transfers and these will show the sale price.

A similar system of registering titles exists for leasehold land, with a copy of the Certificate of Title held by the District Land Registrar. So check the title and be sure the land is unencumbered by rates, covenants or easements you cannot live with. Remember it is *buyer beware!*

The solicitor acting for the seller arranges for the title to be produced at the Land Transfer Office on the day of settlement. The office will supply a transfer form to be filled in by the seller. The signatures must be witnessed by a JP or solicitor. Then either the transfer document or the contract to sell must be stamped at the Stamp Duties office and the Stamp Duty paid with the money put up by the buyer. This is usually 1 per cent of the purchase price up to $50,000, 1.5 per cent for the excess over $50,000 to $100,000 and 2 per cent for the excess over that.

The buyer and seller (or their solicitors) meet on the agreed date of settlement and the buyer must have the balance of the purchase price, usually in a bank cheque. The buyer pays the registration and land transfer fees, the land transfer is signed and witnessed and lodged at the Land Transfer Office, and the transfer legally takes place from that moment. Once the alterations have been made to the title it is returned to the new owner (or their solicitor). This may take a few days.

Most people employ solicitors to do their conveyancing for them. But there is no reason why you should not act on your own behalf, though if it is not a straightforward 'clear' title then you would be advised to get legal help. Conveyancing fees vary slightly between solicitors, but are usually related to the value of the property being sold, as is the cost of the transfer registration. Check with the Land Transfer Office or your solicitor for their latest charges.

Finding land for sale

Visit real estate agents in the area to find out what properties they have on their books. If you buy through an agent it is the seller who pays the agent's fees, unless you have commissioned them to find you a particular property. Alternatively check the advertisements in the local papers. Some people may prefer to sell privately this way and avoid paying an agent's fees. Lastly, talk to the locals — at the pub, in the local store. They may know of blocks to suit and owners willing to sell even if the fact hasn't been advertised.

Buying farm equipment

Going out and buying tools and machinery for your farm is like buying new toys. But plan your purchases; don't act like a kid in a toyshop and grab the first neat thing you see.

Decide your priorities — tractor, chainsaw,

fencing tools, sprayer, drenching gun — whatever. Don't rush out and buy a tractor because you think all farms should have one. If your place is small or steep then it may be money wasted. And why spend hundreds of dollars on a shearing plant for a couple of pet sheep if a neighbour is willing to shear them? Each property and situation will be different, but you can be sure of one thing, and that is that farm equipment is seldom cheap. On a smallfarm it will take even longer for the gear to pay for itself than it would on a big farm.

Discuss it with neighbours. Maybe you can come to an agreement on who buys what. In my area, one family has bought the tractor and maintains it, another the rotary slasher. I have a shearing plant and no handpiece but friends have a handpiece and no plant . . . it all works out in the long run.

The other consideration is whether to buy new or second-hand. Farm equipment doesn't stay looking new for long and if there are serviceable items going at lower prices at auctions and clearing sales, then go for them. But check out the new prices first; some old country codgers are pretty proud when it comes to bidding at auction and refuse to give up on an item even after it has gone over new price. Don't be intimidated at auctions, either. Often the biggest and burliest get to stand nearest the items being bid on, and unless you worm your way into the auctioneer's sight he might not realise you are bidding. Most auctions require payment on the day, in cash, unless you make arrangements with the auctioneers beforehand about paying by cheque. Don't travel miles to an advertised auction without first checking that the item you are interested in is still up for bids. Between the time of inserting the advertisement and the sale day the farmer might have sold it privately and it's damned annoying to get there and learn you travelled for nothing.

Some things are better bought new. If it is a bit of equipment you are going to be using regularly, such as a chainsaw, then shout yourself a good quality new one, complete with guarantee. It may prove cheaper in the long run than always having to repair someone else's tired old cast-off.

2. Fencing

To avoid the uncertainty of wondering if your prize buck has found his way onto the roadside to play with the traffic, or if your favourite cow is in danger of finding an unsuitable boyfriend in the neighbour's place, make fences a top priority. By law you must keep boundary fences to a stock-proof standard. On a road boundary you have to bear the cost alone, but an adjoining landowner should front up with half the money for a boundary fence that needs replacing or repairing. If one of you is hopelessly hard up and just cannot afford it, a good kiwi alternative is for one party to supply the materials and the other the labour. If you do opt to build the fence and want to stay friends with your neighbour, don't take forever over it and do a good job.

Fence types

There are numerous fence types. Different parts of the country tend to favour different styles; even some of the terms used differ according to where you are. Ask a Northlander to throw you a dropper and you are likely to get a fist in the mush, while in the South Island a batten is what you do down to the hatches when the nor'wester starts blowing.

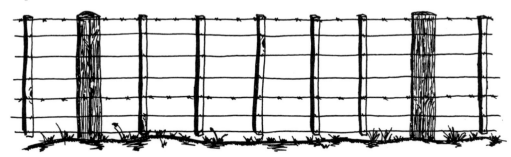

Fig. 1 **Seven wire and battens.**

Fig. 2 **Netting.**

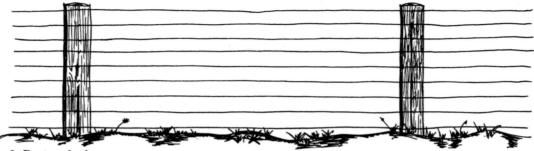

Fig. 3 **Post and wire**.

Seven wire and battens

This is the traditional North Island fence with posts every four metres, seven wires, sometimes one or two of them barbed, and five battens between posts. (See Fig. 1.) This fence is strong, stockproof, suited to all terrain, and expensive. But if well built from good materials it should last 40 to 50 years.

Netting

High tensile netting (see Fig. 2) with posts spaced at 5 m and three battens between them is slightly cheaper. However, netting can be a bit trickier to erect.

Post and wire

An even cheaper alternative, this fence uses more wires and fewer battens. To be effective the posts need to be 4 m apart, with nine or ten wires strained tight. (See Fig. 3.)

Materials

It takes just as much grunt to put up a fence with shoddy materials as with good, but the end product will not last as long. So go for good stuff. Do it once and do it right.

- *Wire.* The traditional number eight wire fence has been superseded by modern high tensile wires, basically because of cost. Price is based on weight, so a roll of 12.5 gauge (2.5 mm diameter) goes further than a roll of old fashioned number eight (4 mm) — 648 m as against 253 m. So for nearly the same price you can fence much further. But high tensile can be a cow to work with. Drop the end of your wire and watch it 'boing' back up the hill, usually after poking you in the eye. Try bending it into a knot and learn just what high tensile really means. Get a roll of mild steel number eight when you buy your high tensile. It is still best for footing posts and tie backs, and has many other applications around the farm. There is not much that cannot be fixed with a bit of number eight and an old drench container!

- *Posts.* There are concrete, steel and wooden posts of all shapes and sizes. Personally I'd say forget the concrete. They are not as strong as equivalent-sized wooden posts and if you prefer the look 'au naturel', then concrete just does not fit in. Steel standards might be okay for a quick job or for dry inland areas, but elsewhere the rust gets them too quickly. If you go for wooden posts, go for decent ones. There is a choice of full rounds from big number ones down to number threes. The latter are quite good for sharpening and ramming in by hand but as they only come from little trees they are mostly sapwood. Number twos and ones can be sharpened and driven if you are one of those lucky people who has access to a tractor-driven rammer. But if you want to get fit and strong and healthy and do it by hand I recommend half rounds. They come from a bigger tree, so have more heart wood than an equivalent-sized round post, and they have a nice flat face to work to.

- *Battens.* These come in many varieties, ranging from the traditional wooden batten to clip-on wires, clip-on strips of galvanised iron, plastic, polythene pipe and many more. Price, maybe looks, and personal prejudices will dictate your choice.

• *Staples.* There are big staples for posts and small ones for battens. Ask for the right ones. They also come barbed or smooth shanked. Tests show that barbed staples hold better in dry posts but smooth hold better in green. Either way make sure they are galvanised. Hammer them in skewed rather than perpendicular, and drive them in until they barely touch the wire.

Tools

Fencing is honest work and there is really no way of cheating. But you can make the job go smoother by having the right tools. (See Fig. 4.) These are:

a. A good hammer.

b. A pair of fencing pliers — those funny looking things like a cross between a hammer, a parrot's beak and wire cutters.

c. A spade. The best type for fencing is the trenching spade. It has a narrow blade so can fit down a post hole, and is good and heavy.

d. A posthole borer. Type depends on your soil. A mechanical one is excellent in free soil but hard work in puggy clay, and dangerous if there are likely to be tree roots around. A simple hand borer with an almost flat face is excellent in clay.

e. A spinning jenny. This can be an elaborate collapsible job, such as those the stock firms sell, or you can make a simple one yourself. (See Fig. 4.) Mine has been going for years. Put the arms section on top of the half round, shove a piece of pipe, or use the end of the rammer, through both parts and into the ground, and howzat, one spinning jenny!

f. A rammer. This is probably the secret of a good solid fence. I weigh in at 48 kg and couldn't flatten an earthworm if I didn't have the right rammer. There are several available on the market. The best will be the heaviest with the smallest ramming head. The handle should be solid steel, then it can double as a crowbar.

g. A saw. A small chainsaw is best. It is easy to tote around and can be used to either clear scrub out of the way or top posts and shape stays.

h. A wire tension meter. Make this up using a 1.1m long piece of gate timber. Place a nail at each end so they are 1 m apart and hammer them halfway home. Get hold of a small spring balance able to measure up to 28 lb or 12.5 kg. Make a mark 12 mm off the true line between the nails. (See Fig. 4.) Hook the wire on one side of the nails holding the bar along the fence and use the spring balance to pull the wire to the 12 mm mark. Read off the balance, multiply that by 20 and you know the strain on the wire in either pounds-force (1bf) or kilograms-force (kgf). (See Table 1 on page 15.)

i. A chisel. One between 38 and 50 mm wide will do.

A netting and wire fence, well stayed at the angle post.

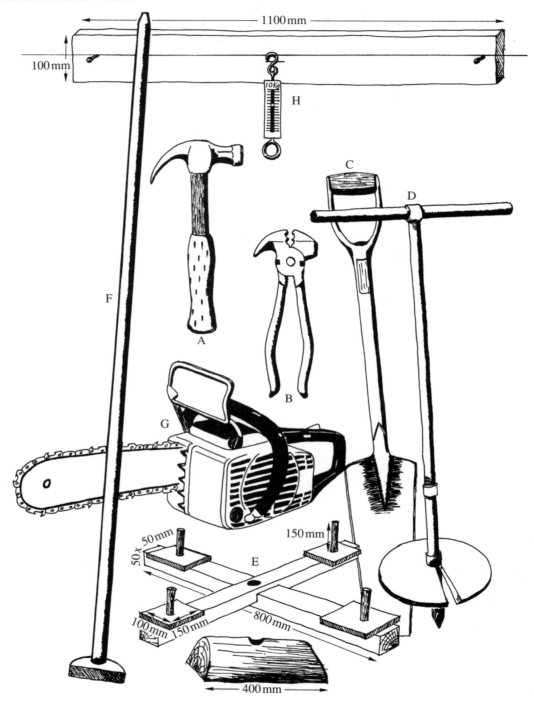

A — hammer; B — fencing pliers; C — spade; D — posthole borer; E — spinning jenny;
F — rammer; G — chainsaw; H — tension meter and spring balance.

Fig. 4 **Tools for fencing**.

Fence building

Clearing the line

First step is to clear the line. If it is a boundary then you will have no choice about where it goes. If it is an internal fence remember stock management is easier if the paddocks are similar sizes. Note where the stock trails are to take advantage of them for gate layout, and on hills try to fence down contours rather than around them or stock might try jumping out of the upper paddocks. (See Fig. 5.)

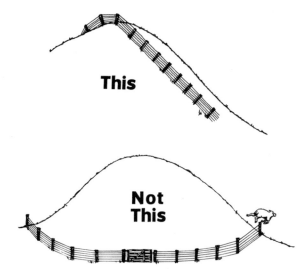

Fig. 5 **It is best to fence down contours rather than around them.**

Strainers

Next step is to put in the strainers. These are the big end posts and as they hold the strain on the wires they need to be strong, buried deep, and stayed properly. A number one strainer is about 250 mm across and 2.4 m long so needs a hole a bit over 1 m deep. The fencing experts all say foot strainer posts, although I don't. But if you want to be fussy about your fence I have included Fig. 6 to show you how.

Right, the hole has been dug and the strainer heaved in — now comes the hard bit (and you thought the digging was hard work!). I like to ram a strainer all the way around. That means putting

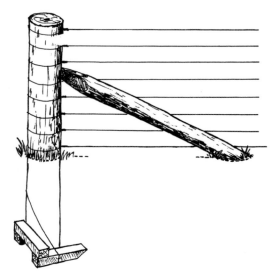

Fig. 6 **Footing a strainer post**.

the post in the centre of the hole, dropping a couple of spadefuls of dirt around it and ramming all the sides evenly, frequently checking the post for vertical (more frequently as you need more breathers). If the post is leaning over slightly *don't* push it back by hand or you will undo the last half hour's good work. Ram it back into position by pounding longer on the side the post leans to. Continue to fill up the hole, putting in about five centimetres of soil at a time and ramming it solid. If there are two of you working on the fence it is a good idea to stand either side of the post and take turns with the rammer.

Stays

Once the post is in it needs to be stayed. The stay is usually 1.8–2.4 m long and about 100–150 mm thick. The stay has to be shaped (squared) to slot into a square hole cut about half-way up the post on the line of the fence. Either a chainsaw or an axe will do to square the end (like sharpening a big pencil). Then saw off just the very tip at the correct angle so it will be snug against the post once the stay is angled about 20 to 30 degrees from the ground. (See Fig. 7.) Lean the stay in position, run a pencil line around the edge of it against the post and chisel out the hole marked. Make it 16 to 20 mm deep and slightly longer than

11

marked as this gap will be taken up once the stay is lowered into the ground.

The stay then has to be blocked. Usually a half length of a half round post will do, but use more if the ground is a bit soft. Dig a hole so the block can be laid down at right angles to the fence line and centred to where the stay will go. Angle the block so the stay end will eventually sit flush with it. Cut the stay (careful, is it the right length?) so that it is a bit too long and sits about half-way over the block. Dig a scarf (trench) so the ground won't get in the way once you lever the stay down into place. Fit the square end of the stay into the chiselled hole on the post and lay the other end on the block. Use a spade to lever it down (see Fig. 8) and thump it into position. Bury the block, fill in any excess scarf and replace the turf.

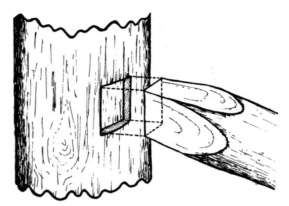

Fig. 7 **Fitting a stay**.

Alternative stay

Another technique is to use the horizontal stay. (See Fig. 9.) This is really only applicable where you are driving posts but avoids the need for a mortice and tenon joint, and stay block. The system uses two good posts each about 150mm wide and 2.3m long driven into normal fence height 3m apart on the line of the fence. A horizontal stay is fitted to the top by chainsawing out a small step for it to fit into and pinning it there with a 230mm length of 10mm steel rod. When pinning the stay to the second post leave the pin sticking out about 50mm. Make up a double loop of number eight wire, leading it from the base of the end strainer to the top of the second one. Insert a half length of batten or something like it for a twitch stick, wind the loop up good and tight, and lock the stick behind the stay.

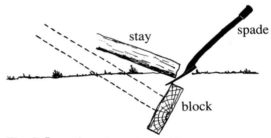

Fig. 8 **Levering stay into position**.

Angle posts

If the fence line you chose isn't completely straight it means putting in an angle post. If the switch in direction is 45 degrees or less a good solid 1.8m post will do. But if the angle is wider then you need to consider something a bit longer and stronger. Whichever it is the post still needs to be stayed (same method as for the strainer but this time the stay should be at the centre of the angle the fence wires will make). Now if you are thinking of running goats, a word of warning. Goats are

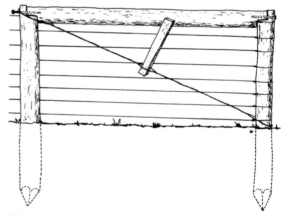

Fig. 9 **Horizontal stay**.

nimble things and it is kid's play for them to trot up along a stay and use that as a launch point to go over the fence. So to prevent this, at the strainers put the wire on the inside of the stays when you come to wire up. With an angle post come along later and fence off the corner and plant a tree in it or else use a tie back.

Tie backs

These are used on angle posts, where the terrain does not allow room for a normal stay, or where keeping goats in dictates that stays are unsuitable. Drive or ram a post or stake (about the size of a decent stay or bigger) 1 m into the ground about 1.8 m away from the post outside the fence, in the middle of the big angle the wires will make. Tilt the stake slightly away from the fence and cut it off a few centimetres above the ground. Bury a block against the stake on the side nearest the fence so that it will be at right angles to the tie back wire. Run a loop of number eight up around the fence post, stapling it securely about 50 mm from the top, and back down to the stake at ground level. Tie the loop off so it is continuous (see Figs. 10 and 11), slip a half length of batten or tea-tree branch between the two sides of the loop and wind away to tension the tie back.

Getting a line

Once the end strainers and angle posts are all in you are ready to run out a wire to get a line. It is easiest to run wires down a slope, so if you are working on hills put your spinning jenny by the top strainer. Load a coil of wire onto it, being careful to find the right end first. Most new coils of wire have a slip of card marking the start and whenever you cut the wire it pays to slip the card back on to the roll.

With the right end in hand and the roll securely on the spinning jenny, march steadily off in the direction of the bottom strainer, pulling the wire behind you. It is great to have someone standing by the jenny to make sure it turns smoothly and no wires jump off, but if you haven't got a fencing mate and it suddenly gets hard to pull, poke the

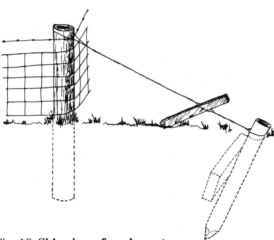

Fig. 10 **Side view of angle post**.

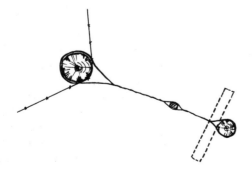

Fig. 11 **Plan view of angle post**.

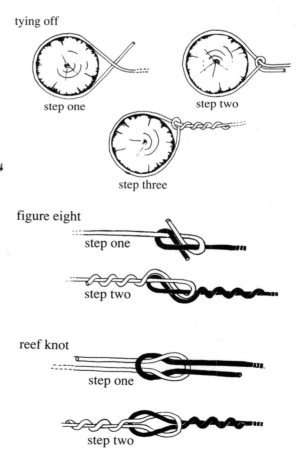

tying off

step one

step two

step three

figure eight

step one

step two

reef knot

step one

step two

Fig. 12 **Fencing knots**.

end you are towing into the ground to hold it and go back to the jenny and free any snarl ups.

Once you have reached the bottom strainer, tie the wire off around the post (see Fig. 12) and staple it loosely where the third wire from the top will be. Do the same at the angle posts (make sure the staples are only half in so the wire can run through them freely) and go back to the beginning. Pull out enough wire to get around the top strainer and still have about 600 mm to play with. Poke the end into the ground until you are ready to strain the wire up.

Straining a wire

You can either use permanent wire strainers which are little wind-up things that stay on the fence or chain wire strainers. (See Fig. 13.) These are gadgets which come in two pieces, each with a flexible snout which grips the wire. One side has a chain attached and the other has a couple of levers with claws for grabbing the chain on the first bit, and a handle to work the levers back and forth.

If you are using chain wire strainers (see Fig. 13) the procedure is as follows.

Sling a short length of wire around the post and staple it at the height the wire will eventually be. Tie it off and tie a small loop (A) in the loose end. Attach half of the strainers (B) onto the short wire, slipping the loose end into the slot on the strainer snout. Next, rescue the end of the fence wire (C) you had poked in the ground and slip the other half of the strainers (D) onto it at a point where the chain is able to join up with the other part of the strainers, and the fence wire can slide into the loop of the short wire. Slip the chain onto the claws and

gradually work the handle to walk the claws along the chain, sliding the fence wire through the loop as it is pulled up.

At this stage leave the strainers holding the wire while you put in the line posts. Once it is tight enough (check with your tension meter) tie it off. Then work the strainers backwards to ease the tension from them onto the wire, and remove the strainers.

If using permanent strainers this is the procedure. Pull the wire around the top post. Put a staple in loosely to hold the wire at the right height, pull it up as tight as possible by hand and tie it off. Fit the strainer gadget, wind it up enough to get the wire pulled tight, and put in the pins. Now you have a line to put your posts to.

Line posts

Now it is just a matter of wandering along and digging holes at 4–5 m spacings, dropping in a post and filling the holes in again. If you are using half rounds put the flat side facing the wire. The face of the post must end up being vertical with the line wire just sitting loosely against it. If you position the hole carefully you can usually place the round edge so it is hard up against the back side of the hole. Before beginning ramming, sprinkle a bit of soil down the back, and this will get rammed automatically as you ram the front flat side. The sides of the post must be at right angles to the ground even on sloping ground. By the time you have rammed half the hole or less that post should be in so solid you cannot budge it.

Footing posts

Posts in hollows must be footed and posts on rises left about 25 mm higher out of the ground to allow for any effect strain on the wire will have. There are as many ways to foot posts as there are fencers. Basically the object is to attach a block of durable timber to the bottom of the post, bigger than the post itself so that once the earth is rammed over the whole lot, the post is less likely to be pulled upwards. The method I like is to attach firmly a piece of leftover stay or a post cutoff to the bottom of the post so it sticks about 80 mm out from the face and about as much on each side. (See Fig. 14.) You have to dig the hole a bit bigger than

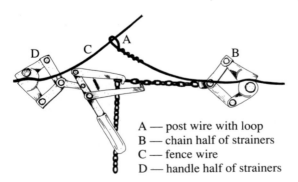

A — post wire with loop
B — chain half of strainers
C — fence wire
D — handle half of strainers

Fig. 13 **Chain wire strainers**.

Fig. 14 **Footing a post**.

usual to get the whole shebang down, then ram it all as usual. It is worth the extra time and trouble, as otherwise the fence lifts and stock learn they can walk out under it.

Running out the wires

With all the posts in place you can run out the rest of the wires. I like to run out a wire, attach it at the bottom end, staple it loosely on the way back at any high or low points and angle posts, strain it up and tie it off. Real fencers seem to prefer running out all wires at once. If you do it that way poke the ends into the ground so that the bottom wire is closest to the strainer and top wire furthest away to reduce the risk of crossing wires.

Final strain

Table 1 lists the recommended final strains for both 4 mm number eight and 2.5 mm high tensile wires. If the strainers settle slightly there will be a more marked slackening effect on a short section than on a long fence so you tighten the short strains up more to begin with. Take care not to overstrain. The figures given are well within the wire's breaking strain but wire also has a yield point (about 75 per cent of breaking strain), and once tensioned beyond this it loses a lot of its elasticity. Strain the second wire from the bottom first, then the third from the top, then strain the other wires from the bottom up.

Hand ramming posts — a good way to get fit.

Wire type	Fence length (metres)	Recommended tension		Tension meter reading	
		kgf	lbf	kg	lbs
4 mm mild (No. eight)	100	480	1050	24	52.5
	1600	165	365	8	18
2.5 mm H.T. (12.5 gauge)	100	270	600	13.5	30
	1600	140	320	7	16

Table 1. **Wire tensions**.

Finishing the fence

To finish the job attach the battens if you are using them. When stapling wooden battens put the batten on the other side of the wires from yourself and drop the sharp end of your rammer into the ground immediately behind it. Then hold the rammer up parallel against the batten. While you are stapling the batten is held securely and there is no jarring. You can tidy up the fence by bevelling the top edge of the strainer posts with your chisel, and sawing all the line posts off flat and equidistant from the top wire.

Electric fences

Electric fences are quicker and cheaper to erect than conventional and once stock have learned about them they will not argue with a hot wire. Nor will most people, so they can be a hindrance to your own movements around the farm.

With all electric fences the object is not to put up a physical barrier to your animals but a mental one. They get such a wallop from it they never want to touch that damn wire or tape ever again. You can end up pretty well conditioned yourself!

It is very important that when animals are first introduced to a hot fence it is working really well. It might not matter if it develops a short later in the year when they have learnt not to touch it, but be sure to get it cleaned up before the next lot of young stock are born or new stock bought in so they can be properly conditioned too. Get a good system going to begin with and maintain it.

There is nothing magical about an electric fence and you do not have to be an electrician to rig one up. The basic idea is that you want wires to divide up portions of your farm and you do not want stock to cross them. Well, those wires must be isolated (insulated) so that the only thing they connect directly to is the power terminal on the electric fence unit. They must have insulators at every post and batten and be completely insulated from the end post or strainer and clear of grass, scrub and weeds along their length. If there are several hot wires, connect them up to each other and make sure the joins have plenty of overlap so the current can cross easily.

The next thing to do is to decide what to use for an earth, the opposite end of the circuit. (See Fig. 15.) Connect a wire from the earth terminal on the fence unit to something which has very good contact with the ground. On a small length of temporary fence a bit of steel pipe rammed about 1 m down into the ground will suffice. On a permanent fence you can leave the bottom wire unelectrified and connect the earth wire to it. Usually there are enough rushes and grass growing up to the low wire to ensure good ground contact.

The closer the ground contact is to where the animals are, the quicker and more instant the shock will be. So it is no good having a fence unit back home in the garage and an earth peg just outside the window if the fence is 2 km away, as when stock touch the hot wire, the voltage has to travel through them, through the ground and all the way to the earth peg, and all the way back through the ground to the animal again. They might have already pushed through the fence by then, or if the ground is dry, the voltage could get lost on the way back. So the best idea is to run two wires (lead out wires) from the fence unit out to the fence. One is connected to the power terminal on the unit and to the hot wires and the other is connected to the earth terminal on the unit and a peg in the ground near the fence or the bottom unelectrified wires.

Electric fencing alone is not really suitable as a boundary fence. But by running an outrigger around a conventional fence (that is, simply a hot wire mounted on insulated pegs which hold it about 300 mm off the existing fence and at about snout level for the type of stock it is to hold) you get the benefits of a physical barrier but the added discipline of an electric shock.

For internal subdivision electric fences are fine. The usual system is one to three wires for cows and horses, four to five wires for sheep and goats, all electrified or with the bottom wire left as an earth. For cows use three hot wires a hammer length apart on posts every 25 to 30 m on even slopes. The wires are only strained to 70 kgf. For sheep use five wires with posts every 50 m and insulated battens every 10 m. On uneven ground put an extra post at each change in slope.

The wires are mounted on battens, posts or

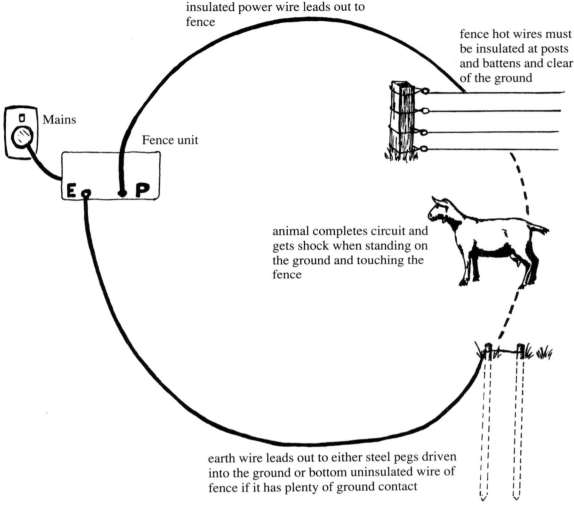

insulated power wire leads out to fence

fence hot wires must be insulated at posts and battens and clear of the ground

Mains

Fence unit

animal completes circuit and gets shock when standing on the ground and touching the fence

earth wire leads out to either steel pegs driven into the ground or bottom uninsulated wire of fence if it has plenty of ground contact

Fig. 15 **Electric fence circuit**.

stakes which either have insulators attached or are of wood which has natural electrical resistance (insultimber). You can make your own insulators by cutting dense plastic pipe from 10 to 20 mm diameter into 50 mm lengths. Thread these onto the wire while the fence is being built. (You must not slit them and slide them on later as in wet conditions that slit will short the fence out.) There are several brands of plastic and polythene insulators on the market.

For tying off the end posts you can either put a wire loop around the strainer and attach the fence wire to the loop via an insulator, plastic or ceramic

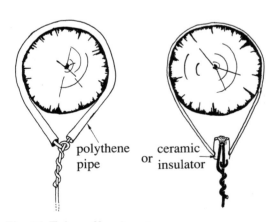

polythene pipe or ceramic insulator

Fig. 16 **Tying off end posts.**

(see Fig. 16), or else tie the wire off as you would for a conventional fence, but sheath it in polythene pipe where it would otherwise touch the post.

For a permanent electric fence I recommend using 12.5 gauge wire. Should you want to replace the fence with conventional then the posts and wire can be retained.

Temporary fences

If you just want to temporarily break a paddock into smaller units, as with break feeding, it is easiest to use one of the many temporary electric fence systems on the market. There is a choice of coloured wire or coloured tape. The latter is more expensive but more visible so both you and the animals are less likely to accidentally blunder into it.

There are various types of standards, ranging from the old-fashioned pig tail (a steel standard with one to three loops on it, each loop insulated with plastic) to fancy flexible plastic stakes and glass-fibre standards. The glass-fibre is rigid, but some types require a special cap before they can be hammered into the ground and the glass can splinter, which is rough on the hands. Plastic stakes are generally very visible and easy to push in by hand, but they can warp. The old pig tail standard will last and last, but cannot carry enough wires to hold small stock. Another alternative is flexinet. It is a netting made of hot wires and has its own standards which are easy to push in. It is ideally suited for break feeding sheep, especially on uneven ground, but it is expensive.

Testing a fence

Well, you have built a beautiful electric fence, installed the fence unit and thrown the switch. Now comes the $64 million question, is it working?

I *hate* electric fences, but sometimes on a farm you have to do what you have to do. Well, there is a cheap way and an expensive way. The cheap way is to get a blade of grass about 150 mm long, wet it and wet your fingers, then holding the grass at one end, plop the other end on the hot wire. All being well you should get a very slight kick or tingle. If not, move the grass up gradually so that your hand is nearer the wire. If you are still getting nothing try kicking your gumboots off as they

Three-wire electric — enough to hold cattle or horses.

could be insulating you. If you still have no joy you have a fault somewhere.

The expensive way is to buy a voltmeter. It is a little gadget about the size of a cigarette pack with a clip that hooks onto the hot wire and a lead that runs to a pin you poke in the ground and it gives a neat little digital readout.

Troubleshooting

If there is no kick at all, check the obvious first: that the power board has not disconnected you for not paying your power bill, that the unit is connected and switched on, and that no one has chopped your lead-out wires when scotching thistles. Next, walk the fence and see that the hot wires are not shorting on anything and if it still doesn't work suspect your earth contact. Connect it to a longer section of uninsulated bottom wire, or if using a pipe in the ground, throw a bucket of water over it.

Gates

Wooden gates are the ultimate. They look nice, they are durable and easy to make. You can buy them pre-made. You can also buy galvanised iron gates which are fine if you like looking at something like the inside of a cage. If it is not already too late I suggest you make your gateways at least 3 m wide as one day you might want to get some heavy machinery or a large truck through.

Making a wooden gate

Use 100 mm x 25 mm timber. Decide on the length and height of gate you want and its design. (See Fig. 17.) For a 3 m gate you need:

- six 3 m horizontals
- five 1.1 m uprights
- four 450 mm hinge supports
- two diagonals.

Assemble the gate on a flat piece of ground. Measure the diagonals from corner to corner to check everything is square, then nail it up. Use a bolt and nut at each corner but don't put the bolts on the hinge end until you are ready to fit the hinges. Some manufactured wooden gates use nuts and bolts at each joint, but I think that is overkill. Lay the diagonals where you want them, mark the angles, saw on the mark and nail in place. At the hinge end tack the off-cut pieces in place, the off-cut that goes next to the diagonal will have to have an angle cut in it to butt in tight. Bolt on the hinges. Check they are in line. Stand the gate up and nail the remaining 3 m length along the top.

Hanging a gate

Manoeuvre the gate into the gateway, block it up to about the height and position you want it, prop it in place and mark off on the strainer where the gudgeons (big hinge pins) will go. Note that the screw-in part of the gudgeon is lower than the lip the gate will sit on. Select a bit the same size as the central part of the gudgeon, but not as wide as the thread. Drill a hole, then wind in the gudgeon, positioning it so that the gate can open back against a fence on the side you want. A big crescent spanner with a large hole in the handle, or a ring spanner is handy for winding the pin in. Alternatively, use a spare unattached hinge.

Positioning the gudgeon pins properly takes practice, because how the two end up in relation to each other affects how the gate will lie and open. Basically you can adjust the height of the opening

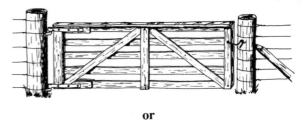

or

Fig. 17 **Wooden gates.**

end of the gate by screwing the bottom pin in or out.

Taranaki gates

Otherwise known as ten-minute gates because they take only ten minutes to make but supposedly just as long to open and close. It is true they are quick and cheap to make, but if done properly they should also be stockproof and easy to use. Basically the gate is just like a short section of fence which can be detached from its strainer at one end. You can use number eight, high tensile or even barbed wire to make them from, but number eight is probably easiest.

Cut seven or eight strands of wire the length of the gateway with about 450 mm extra at each end to play with. Lay them on the ground at equal spacing right next to the gateway as if they were the gate rails and the gate had just been laid down. Staple a very strong batten or small post to all the wires at each end so it points to a spot about 100 mm inside each gatepost. Twist each wire around the post and tie it off neatly. Lay more battens across the wires about 600 mm apart. Staple them on.

Next decide which end of the gate you want to open. On the strainer at the other end attach loops top and bottom around the post and big enough to poke the end upright of the gate into. Staple in place, then pull the gate towards the other post and again make a loop top and bottom long enough so that you can stretch the gate to reach them without too much effort. This is the secret of a good Taranaki. If the loops at this end are too short you will find it too hard to close. If it is too sloppy the gate will be too slack and the stock can push under it. Once you've got the loops the right length, hook the gate in (always putting the bottom in first) and put a staple on the inside of the upright top and bottom so that the loop has to be flicked over the staple before coming off. (See Fig. 18.)

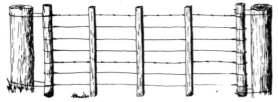

Fig. 18 **Taranaki gate**.

Yards

First consider what the yards will have to do. Are they for sheep or goats only, or for cattle as well, or for shearing in, or milking the cow in? How many animals will they have to hold? On a smallfarm and small budget I believe in multi-purpose yards. This simply means, if you are running large and small stock, make the yards strong enough to hold the big ones and stockproof enough to hold the small.

Rails can be anything from half-round posts to 150mm x 50mm or 150mm x 25mm planks, or strong, straight tea-trees. The posts need to be closely spaced (about 1.8m apart), and if the yards are to hold cattle they should be as massive and sunk as deep as a strainer.

Yard design

First requirement is a small holding paddock next to the yards. This must be big enough to hold all the animals and for them to be happy to go into it. The paddock should be funnel-shaped leading into the first main pen, or alternatively the gate into the pen should be in a corner of the holding paddock. How many pens depends on what you want to do and how many ways you might want to sort stock. I think the optimum for a small holding is three pens, one twice as big as the other two and also a narrow crush pen-cum-drafting race. (See Fig. 19.)

Arrange gates so stock move from the holding paddock into the large pen and from there can be directed either into the crush or one of the secondary pens. *Always* put stock in one end of the yards and let them out the other way or else they

Life on the smallfarm is impossible without a small set of yards.

two pens

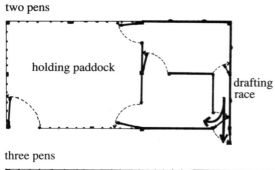

holding paddock

drafting
race

three pens

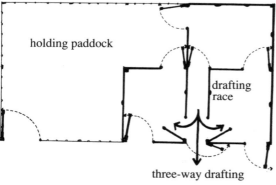

holding paddock

drafting
race

three-way drafting

Fig. 19 **Yard design**.

will learn to run in and straight back out again next time you try to pen them.

A long skinny pen about 750mm wide can double as a crush for drenching sheep and also as a bail for holding a cow. In this case have a few slip rails handy which can be poked through the rails behind the animal. (See Fig. 20.)

The only other consideration is where to put the yards. Take into account the value of having power handy, road or truck access, and maybe a tree, both for shade and to act as a gantry for raising killed stock.

Fig. 20 **Confining a cow in a crush pen**.

3. Earth and water works

Farm plumbing

Stock need clean water available at all times. The ideal is a network of troughs supplying every paddock. There is no point spending heaps on beautiful fences if you have to leave the gates open so the animals can find their way back to the dam. And it is positively unhealthy for stock to have to drink from some slow moving or stagnant stream which they stand in, pug up and lift their tails in. That same source kept dug out, fenced and the water piped to a trough may be fine.

New Zealand is generally well off for water and most regions have their share of springs and small streams. If you are on flat land you may have to rely on pumping up artesian (underground) water or the local irrigation or community stock water scheme.

But if the land is rolling it may have its own springs. Try to find out from neighbours and people familiar with the area if the streams, springs and dams are reliable. Will they last all year or will they dry up and disappear underground in the hottest months just when you need them most? A small dam built at an unreliable source may store enough to last through the dry months until the water flows again.

Whatever your source, if you are likely to alter the rate or pattern of flow in a river or stream by tapping into it, you'd better check with your local water catchment commission about any regulations or requirements you must meet. The rules are designed to ensure the water resources are not wasted and, if the source is limited, that everyone gets a fair share. The catchment people are generally pretty helpful unless you are being greedy.

Put a trough half-way through a fence and it can serve two paddocks.

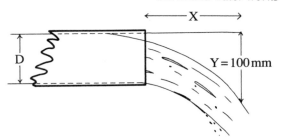

It is easy to measure how much water is coming from a particular source at a particular time (see following), but only by taking regular measurements over a few years will you know just how reliable that source is.

Fig. 21 **Measuring flow from horizontal pipe.**

Measuring flow

Springs

Most farms will have springs welling up out of the ground somewhere. To determine the flow, tap into the spring. Clear the ground around where the water wells up, and if possible sink an open-ended drum or large section of pipe well down into the soil so the water wells into the drum. From the top of the drum, feed the water into a pipe large enough to carry all the flow.

The easiest way to measure flow is to get a large pail (about 10 litres) and use a watch or stop watch and see how long it takes to fill the pail. If a 10 litre pail takes 20 seconds to fill you have 0.5 litres/sec or 30 litres a minute.

If there is more water coming out than you can hope to catch in a pail then you can determine flow by the trajectory of the water. Ensure that you are getting all the flow from the source and direct it into a pipe big enough to take the flow. Make sure the pipe is horizontal, then measure X and Y co-ordinates as shown in Fig. 21, and then apply those figures to the graph (Fig. 22) to determine flow.

Small streams

Use either the float timing method (fairly approximate) or weir measurement. For the float timing method find a uniform stretch of the channel about 20 m long. Measure the cross-sectional area of the stream, i.e. depth and width. Then toss a float into the midstream and see how long it takes to cover a known distance of that 20 m stretch. The float velocity gives the speed of the surface water in the stream. To get the average velocity of the water at all depths, multiply float velocity by 0.8 then compute the discharge as follows:

$$Q = A \times V$$

where Q is the discharge in m^3/sec;
A is the cross-sectional area of the stream in m^2;
V is the average velocity in m/sec.

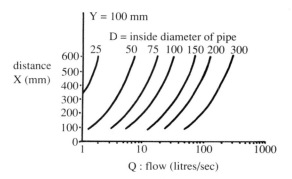

Fig. 22 **Flow rate of water discharging horizontally.**

The more accurate alternative for small streams is to build a triangular weir (see Fig. 23) then set it into the stream bed at right angles to the flow and seal around it with mud, so all the water goes over the crest. The notch should be horizontal and high enough above the stream bed so the head of water which spills over it is only a third of the height of the weir wall. The water must be able to fall freely

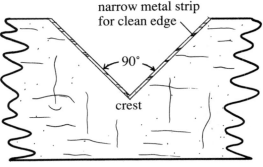

Fig. 23 **Triangular weir.**

23

over the top. Water upstream of the weir should be tranquil (not exceeding a velocity of 0.152 m/sec.)

Measure the head over the crest with a staff gauge sunk down to the stream bed, then calculate the discharge from Table 2 or the formula:

$$Q = 1.34 \, H^{2.5}$$

where Q is the discharge in m^3/sec;
H is the head over the crest in metres.

Head over weir crest (mm)	Discharge over weir (litres/sec)
60	1.3
90	3.6
120	7.2
150	12.6
200	24.2
245	40.5
290	62.1
320	79.6
350	99.7
380	122.7

Table 2. **Weir measurement**.

Having determined the flow in the stream or spring, next consider what sort of pipe and feed system you need to get it to the house, garden or stock troughs. If the spring is well above the house or trough then you can use a gravity feed system. If it is below the level you want the water at, then you need to look at pumping it up: by electric pump (is power available to the site?); by windmill (is it exposed enough to get wind?); or by water wheel or water ram (is there enough water to drive the wheel or ram?).

Gravity feed system

To design a suitable system you need to calculate:
1. Output required (in litres/minute).
2. Length of the pipe (the distance from the house or trough to the source).
3. Head height (vertical height of the water source above the end-use point. This determines the pressure in the pipe and is measured as m/head.)

The easiest way to determine the head height is to get a hand-held sight level. Measure the height from your eye to the ground level then start at your house, or wherever you are bringing water to, and follow any route that will take you to the water source. Sight horizontally through the level to an object you can identify, then walk and stand there and sight again, each sighting taking you an eye-height higher. Once you reach the source, multiply the number of sightings by your eye-height and you have the height of the intake above the house. To convert the head in metres into pounds pressure per square inch divide the height by 0.704. (The correct metric measure for pressure is the kilo-Pascal, but since there are 7 kP to 1 p.s.i. you end up with big numbers and most people prefer the old Imperial units.)

How much pressure do you want? From Table 3 for polythene pipe you should be able to calculate what diameter pipe you need to get the required amount of water at the required pressure. When considering pressure remember you don't want to have to wait half an hour to fill the kettle or for the trough to take all night to give the cows a drink. Try for 50–60 p.s.i. That will give a good squirt out of the tap but is not likely to blow the pipe to pieces. If you don't have sufficient head to get pressure you can put a pump in to boost it.

Once you have worked out from the tables what size pipe you need then go one bigger, as you will find once you have a system in you will want to run water here, there and everywhere, and it will be annoying if after all that trouble the pipe isn't quite big enough. If you are working with polythene or PVC pipe, check the class with your supplier. Different classes handle higher pressures than others. See Table 4 for details of pressure levels for low density polythene.

Laying the pipe

If you have chosen galvanised metal pipe then you've probably got the sort of money to get contractors in to lay it. But for the poorer do-it-yourselfer polythene pipe is quickest, cheapest and simplest. It is preferable to bury the pipe at least 450 mm deep. Sunshine can act to break it down, particularly if the water is still and heats up inside. Bury it and you don't have to worry about this, or

Length of pipe (m)	Pressure in metres head									
	6	15	30	45	60	6	15	30	45	60
					Equivalent p.s.i.					
	8.5	21.3	42.6	64	85	8.5	21.3	42.6	64	85
	Delivery from 12 mm					*Delivery from 25 mm*				
15	15.3	25.2	37	46.2	54.5	100	174	265	333	399
30	10.2	17.2	25.3	31.8	37.5	66.6	115	174	220	260
60	7.1	11.9	17.5	21.9	25.7	44.7	76	117	148	174
150	4.2	7	10.3	12.8	15.1	27	45	67	82	96
300	2.9	4.8	7.1	8	9.6	19	31	45	57	67
600	2	3.3	4.8	5.6	6.7	13	21	31	37	45
1200	1.2	2.1	3.1	3.5	4.3	8.9	15	21.5	26.5	31
	Delivery from 38 mm					*Delivery from 50 mm*				
15	284	424	697	856	1015	598	1003	1515	1913	2273
30	189	318	468	583	689	409	689	1023	1288	1515
60	133	217	316	390	454	284	481	712	890	1060
150	80	133	193	239	278	174	293	431	545	640
300	55	92	135	167	195	119	199	292	364	424
600	39	64	92	115	135	81	134	197	246	288
1200	27	43.5	64	78	92	56	93	134	169	197

Table 3. **Water flow through low density polythene in litres per minute.**

12 mm	130 p.s.i. or 50 m head
25 mm	90 p.s.i. or 64 m head
38 mm	70 p.s.i. or 50 m head
50 mm	70 p.s.i. or 50 m head

Table 4. **Pressure levels for low density polythene.**

the water overheating or freezing. In a frost zone bury it at least 300 mm or one cold morning there will be no water. In some areas the frost depth is less, so check your local MAF.

If you have a tractor and can hire a mole plough then this is a quick way to pull pipe in if the route is drivable. Lay the pipe along the line first. As the tractor drives along the plough opens a slit in the earth about 450 mm deep (you can adjust the depth), and the pipe is fed over the tractor into the slit. If you're not going any great distance you may get away with a shallower trench dug by hand. If the route is through bush the pipe will not be exposed to sun damage but in cold areas suspend it half a metre above the ground to reduce the risk of it freezing.

Air locks

These are the bane of farm water systems. But if the system is properly designed they needn't occur. They usually result from the pipe meandering over hills and dales with outlets to troughs and the like on the way which allow air into the system. The bubble gets as far as the next rise and gets stuck. So if you need to draw water off *en route*, do so at the top of rises. If the rises aren't suitable spots for troughs then put the troughs where you want them, but put in a couple of valves in the line at rises. Then you can go and open these to let any air in the system out.

Too much head

You may have just read the bit about maximum pressure in the pipes and looked at the minor mountain your water is to come from and realised you have too much head. No problem. You just need to break the section up. Tap the stream or spring as mentioned earlier, run a pipe part way down the hill and into a storage or holding tank there. Then feed from that tank on to your house or farm supply and measure the head from the tank height.

Water intake

A good intake will ensure you get good water through the pipe regardless of flooding or silt in the spring or stream. Work on the principle that still water drops its silt. If tapping from a stream, make a little wall in the stream side so that water has to back eddy up towards the intake pipe. Some of the load will be dropped before it gets there, though you will have to clear the silt dropped at the entrance from time to time. (See Fig. 24.) Then feed your intake pipe from the stream, or from the open-ended drum sunk around a spring source, into a holding tank. Anything from 50 to 400 litres will do. The tank must have a plug at the bottom which you can open periodically to empty out the sediment which falls to the bottom. The intake for the farm or house supply should be well up the side of the tank. (See Fig. 25.)

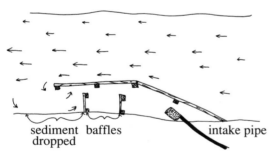

sediment baffles   intake pipe
dropped

Fig. 24 **Tapping a stream**.

How much do you need?

There are no hard-and-fast rules here. Animals can drink lots but on the other hand if the grass is lush and full of moisture they may not go near the trough for days. Use common sense, ensure there is enough water there or that the trough can fill fast enough to give all the animals a drink so they do not have to fight over it, and make water available to every paddock.

26

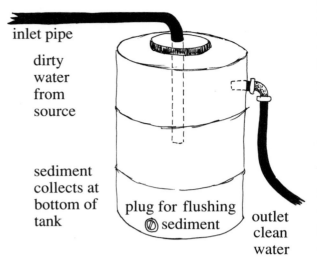

inlet pipe

dirty water from source

sediment collects at bottom of tank

plug for flushing sediment

outlet clean water

Fig. 25 **Intake sediment trap**.

You can cut down on the number of troughs needed by placing them half-way through fences so they supply two or even three paddocks. Try to site them somewhere that is free draining. If this is not possible, dump a truckload of metal or lime

Stock category	litres/head/day
Friesian cow in milk	70
Friesian dry stock	45
Big beef breeds, dry stock	45
Angus cow in milk	65
Angus dry stock	40
Jersey cow in milk	55
Jersey dry stock	35
Calves	25
Ewes	4
Goats in milk	20
Goats dry stock	4
Horses	65
Pigs	40
Rabbits	2
Average household	230
Garden /m^2	4
Firefighting	
Minimum	9000 litres/house
Recommended	22,000 litres/house

Table 5. **Maximum stock water requirements**.

rock around the trough so it does not end up a pugged, damp spot, perfect for the spread of disease.

You can buy ready made concrete troughs, though you will need vehicle access to get them into position. Alternative are old baths, or you can build your own troughs. Pour a solid concrete bottom and either make wooden shutters and pour square sides, or build up a frame of mesh and chicken netting and slap plaster on to it, poking it well into the mesh.

If the stream or water source is below most of your property then you will have to pump that water to a header tank and from there gravity feed it around. Electric pumps are fine but they require electricity and that means power bills. Look at the possibility of a windmill, a waterwheel or a hydraulic ram.

Draining land

A few areas set aside for the frogs are fine, but if they cover most of the best flat land you want to farm or plant an orchard on, then drainage is essential. The type of drain you opt for will depend on what you are prepared to spend and on soil type. (See Fig. 26.)

Open drain

This is the cheapest — simply an open trench dug down to the water table and then falling evenly away to the nearest stream or sea. Batter or slope the sides back so they do not collapse into the drain. They will last longer if you can keep stock fenced out and if the drains are very steep and deep, the stock might last longer too!!

Bush drain

The next cheapest alternative. Dig the trench at least 900 mm deep. Put in a 600 mm layer of branches with fine leaves and twigs at the top to stop soil filtering down into the bigger wood. If you have a cheap metal source, use about 450 mm of scrub then 150 mm of coarse shingle. Finally back-fill the top-soil. This sort of drain should be effective for up to five or ten years. By then the wood will have decayed, but it may be long

enough to get trees established which can then take over the task of drying the soil out.

Mole drain

This requires a tractor with a mole plough. The 'mole' is a torpedo-shaped bar which the plough pulls through down to the required depth and is then 'ripped' through the soil behind the tractor. The rip or slit closes over but the tunnel behind the mole remains for about five to ten years. It works best in heavy or clay soils. Use this system in conjunction with tile or Novaflo drains (see following) in a herringbone pattern, with the tile or Novaflo drain as the backbone and the mole drains the 'ribs' feeding into it.

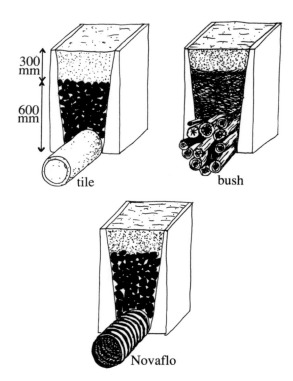

Fig. 26 **Types of drains.**

Novaflo

This is a trade name for the corrugated plastic pipe with lots of slits in it. Dig the trench, put down a shallow layer of shingle for the pipe to lay on, run out the pipe, then cover it with a good 300 to

Open drains — cheap and nasty, but effective.

Laying tile drains.

450mm layer of shingle up to 20mm in diameter. Keep the pipe in the centre of the trench and make sure it falls steadily to the outlet. Any bumps or humps will become sediment traps and eventually block the pipe. Then back-fill dirt over the shingle.

You can also buy filter sock to slip over the Novaflo to stop sediment entering the pipe and thus make the drain last longer. To join Novaflo simply cut a length 300mm long and slit it open down one side. Butt the two ends to be joined together and snap the slit length over them.

Tile drains

These are the most expensive but most permanent option. The pipes are naturally porous, letting water but not sediment through. Lay as with Novaflo above. The more shingle around the pipe the more effective it will be.

How many drains?

Heavy soils with a high clay content will need more drains than light or sandy soils as the water cannot percolate so far. You can guess how far

apart to put your drains or ask advice from MAF or the local catchment or drainage board or test it yourself. Put in one drain and over a few months see how wide an area it drains. That will give you the spacing. Of course if you plan on a herringbone pattern using mole drains as well as tile or Novaflo then the main drains can be spaced further apart. Use Table 6 as a guide.

Getting an even fall

It is vital that the gradient is always downhill. Any rises in a drain become sediment traps and may eventually block up all that good work. A fall of 1:80 or 1:120 is ideal.

First step is to ascertain what is level. Bang in a couple of stakes about 1.8m apart at the spot you are draining from and attach some clearly visible board horizontally between the stakes. Bang in a couple more stakes at the spot the drain will run out to and have another board ready to nail up to these. Next have someone with an Abney level or hand-held sight level look from the crossbar at the top of the drain-to-be towards you while you slide the second crossbar up and down the stakes until

Soil type	Soil permeability	Effective drainage distance (m) each side of a pipe at a drain depth of	
		0.6–0.9	0.9–1.2
Sand	med/high	15–23	23–46
Sandy loam	medium	12–15	15–23
Loam	med/low	11–14	12–15
Clay loam	low	6–9	8–11
Clay	very low	4–5	5

Table 6. **Soil types and drainage distances**.

they tell you when the tops of the two bars are level. Mark that on the stakes. Then decide how much fall you want in the drain over its length. If you want 600 mm of fall then nail the second horizontal board 600 mm below the 'level' mark you earlier put on the stakes.

Now decide how deep the drain is to be. Make yourself a staff long enough for one end to sit on the bottom of the drain and for a crossbar to be put at the other end where it will be in line with the tops of the two horizontal boards you nailed up. So if you want a 900 mm-deep-drain, and the top of the first horizontal board is 800 mm above the ground, then your staff needs to be 900 plus 800 = 1.7 m long.

Now you go along digging the trench. Take your staff with you and get someone to sight along the tops of all three bars. When they are all in line you know you are on target with the fall line. If you don't have someone to sight for you put in another crossbar behind the one at the top of the drain. Line it up with the two you already have then use the two top bars to sight your staff up with. (See Fig. 27.)

Farm tracks

Aim for tractor or four-wheel-drive access into each paddock, if not all over it. Jobs will be much easier if you can cart materials at least into the vicinity of the work, be it fence posts, seedlings or letting the knackers pick up a dead horse.

The time to plan your tracks is before you start fencing. If you are hiring the local bulldozer then the driver will usually have the experience to advise you. Just remember it may be better to put all your money into one well-built and well-placed track which is always passable, than to spread it around over lots of tracks which are impassable half the year and scour out in heavy rain.

Watch where your stock walk. If your track follows a similar line the stock will shift along more readily. Make the tracks and gateway as wide as possible. Not only will they be safer to travel on but you will be able to get heavy machinery in if it's needed. (It is annoying to have to knock a gate post out to let the manure truck in!) So 3 m is the absolute minimum; better to make your gateways 3.6 m and be sure.

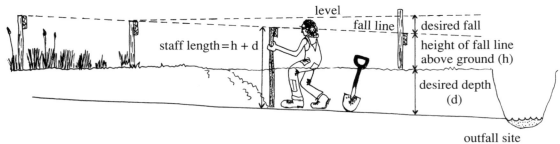

Fig. 27 **Checking fall in a drain as it is dug**.

Metalling farm tracks

It doesn't take much rain to make a track slick and dangerous. If it is a track you don't expect to use much then just grass it over. Sprinkle a bit of fertiliser on with the seed to get the grass away well on the bare ground. Where the route will get enough traffic to wear the grass out, you may need to metal it to ensure access at all times. But this doesn't come cheaply. In the Far North, for example, metal is like paving roads in gold, so try to find lime-rock or river shingle as a cheaper alternative.

To put 100mm on the track allow about $1 m^3$ of metal per 3.3m of track. So a truck which holds 9 m^3 of metal should manage to cover about 30m of track. You can make it go a bit further by shoving a 200 litre metal drum upright in the middle of the truck's tail-gate before it starts dumping. Then you end up with two rows, hopefully a wheel distance apart.

The first time you metal a track order good-sized, coarse shingle as a decent foundation. It may be bumpy at first but is less likely to be pressed down into the mud and lost. In later years you can put a skiff of fine stuff on top and end up with a nice, smooth, and permanent road.

Watertables

These are the ditches on the side of the track or road. Without them water will pool on the track or run down it in minor rivers, gouging out a path as it goes until the old wheel ruts become major trenches. Get the bulldozer driver to shape the track so it is quite convex on top. This encourages water to run off to the side. And then clear along the side so the 'gutter' water can run freely away into the paddock. If there is a bank beside the track and the water cannot escape without crossing the track, then put in a culvert to carry it under the track. Just a shallow Novaflo drain will do.

Don't think you will save money by not putting in culverts and watertables. You will only end up having to get the bulldozer back in to clean up the tracks once they have scoured out, and still have to pay to do the culverts and watertables. So put them in in the first place.

Part 2: The plants

4. Pasture principles and fertiliser

Too often smallfarmers make the mistake of thinking that farming just needs an understanding of animals. But the fact is you are taking over a whole system, including the land and the pasture it grows — the grasses, clovers, herbs and weeds as well as stock.

You will probably have heard through the MAF, farming magazines and radio programmes about 'stock units' and 'stock per hectare', with the emphasis being on area as the critical factor in determining how many sheep, goats or camels you can run. But that is only part of the story. It is pasture the animals eat, so it is how much pasture you can grow that will be the limiting factor. Of course area comes into the equation, but so does soil fertility, grazing management, climate, terrain and aspect.

Like any plant, pasture requires bulk amounts of nitrogen, phosphorus, potassium and calcium to grow (and various trace elements which will be mentioned later). These are all called nutrients. Mother Nature has set up a pretty effective nutrient cycle with lots of give and take between the animals, the plants and the environment.

Simply put: the sun and rain give to plants; some of these give to animals as fodder; others break down and decay and give to the soil. Animals in their turn give manure and blood and bone to the soil, and some nitrogen back to the air; the soil gives nutrients back to the plants. So on and on it goes, round and round, until humans come along and stuff it all up by taking a regular crop of animals or wool off to the auction, or raking all the horse dung the horse so carefully returned to the pony paddock and concentrating it all in the vegetable garden.

Thus the idea of fertilising is to correct any imbalances we may be causing, to compensate any land for treatment it has suffered in the past, or to build up fertility in poor soil.

But pasture management must be considered even before you get around to putting on fertiliser. If you were ever in charge of the lawnmower around your old town place then you will probably have noticed that once the lawns were mown really short and trim they stayed that way for a while. Then, just when you were starting to think they had grown a little, they would suddenly shoot away and become the embarrassment of the neighbourhood.

Well, when pasture is chopped down by lawnmower or by stock it takes a while to get going again because, as well as taking up nutrients from the soil and soil micro-organisms, pasture takes energy from the sun through photosynthesis. And the less leaf left on the plants the harder it is for them to absorb and use that sunshine. So if you keep that pasture mown or chewed down hard all the time, the plants get weaker and weaker as they can't photosynthesise effectively and will take longer to recover.

Look at Fig. 28, and you can see that pasture grows in three different stages. The first is slow tentative growth after the plants have been badly chewed out. Most of the leaf has been eaten so photosynthesis is slow. The second stage is the most rapid growth as there is plenty of leaf to absorb the sunlight and none is wasted on bare ground. In the last stage, growth slows down again as more leaves get shaded and plants start competing for light. A lot of the leaves will die off.

The time taken between these stages will vary according to the season, the climate and soil fertility. But the thing to realise is that regardless of where you are and what time of year it is, your pasture grows most when in the second stage, so try to keep it there. This means never grazing paddocks shorter than 30 to 50 mm and letting them recover back to 120 to 150 mm before regrazing.

If stock start getting a bit choosy about just what they will and won't eat you can break the rules in autumn or early winter and chew the paddock out hard then. This will encourage the grasses to tiller (subdivide into more plants) and the sward to become more dense so there is no gap between plants. But after a hard grazing, spell the paddocks long enough for them to get back into the second stage growth. Fertile ground recovers more quickly than tired land and obviously if the weather is right the pasture will come away more quickly again. So while it may only take about 30 to 40 days in Northland before a paddock is ready to regraze it may take 90 to 100 days in winter in Southland.

Fencing ties pasture management in with stock carrying capacity, as more subdivision means better grazing control, and the feed available is used better.

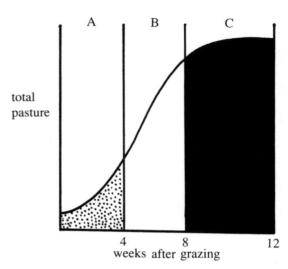

Fig. 28 **Pasture growth after grazing**.

Fertilisers

Another variable you can influence is soil fertility. Every farm and even parts of a paddock may be different and to get the best out of any money you are prepared to put into fertiliser you should have your soil analysed.

In this book I am not trying to preach one sort of philosophy above any others. The choice ranges from biodynamic farming to a simple organic approach or the conventional system using artificial fertilisers to replace elements taken out. Basically organic growers feed the soil so the plant can find all the food it requires in a balanced form. The inorganic approach is to feed the plant directly to put maximum weight on the crop, be it vegetables or grass. I can only put the options before you and let you make the choice. After all, it is your land and your lifestyle. Some of you may be into holistic 'natural' methods and others of you very busy people who just want the most time-efficient methods.

Artificial fertilisers

Most chemical fertilisers are soluble salts which tend to bypass soil micro-organisms and feed plants directly. Their solubility makes them susceptible to leaching in heavy rain so they have

Fertiliser	Nitrogen (N)	Phosphorous (P_2O_5)	Potassium (K_2O)	Sulphur (S)
Superphosphate	0	9	0	11
15% Potassic	0	7	0	9
30% Potassic	0	6	15	7
Urea	46	0	0	0
Sulphate of ammonia	21	0	0	24
DAP	18	20	0	2
Muriate of potash	0	0	50	0
Longlife super	0	11	0	8

Table 7. **Artificial fertilisers**.

to be applied regularly. Some of them may be harmful to worm life and others acidify the soil, particularly sulphate of ammonia and superphosphate.

Unless you have had your soil tested and know of a particular deficiency it is wise to stick to one of the more balanced mixes.

Organic fertilisers

These are generally slower-acting and are targeted at building up the soil, which will in its turn feed the plants. The best known organic fertilisers are probably the seaweed and fish-based extracts like Plant Plasma and Maxicrop. There is continuing controversy about the effectiveness of these and I cannot offer any hard evidence for or against them. If you do want to use them I suggest you have a go; monitor the response and decide for yourself. Some farmers have adopted a policy of alternating between these organic fertilisers and chemical ones with the aim of ensuring the soil still gets a bulk dose of NPK, but also gets the 'tonic' effects of the sea-based extract.

There are also organic mineral fertilisers. Rock

A four-wheel-drive lime spreader.

Fertiliser spreading.

phosphate is one, reverted superphosphate another. This is super which has reacted with dolomite or lime to form dimagnesium and dicalcium phosphates which are not as readily soluble as ordinary super so stay in the soil longer before leaching out. Blood and bone is an excellent organic fertiliser, rich in nitrogen and potassium, but it is expensive. Commercially available organic fertilisers are usually made from mixes of cement kiln dust, blood and bone, sewage sludge, reverted super and animal manures.

Biodynamic mixtures

Besides organic fertilisers there are the biodynamic formulas which come from the philosophy and teachings of Rudolph Steiner. This is a very specialised field and even more controversial than organics. Below are a couple of the formulas used, but for those interested there are some biodynamic contacts listed in Appendix B.

Preparation 500

This is made by filling a cow horn with fresh, green dung and burying it over the winter months. The resulting substance is then mixed with 10 litres of pure warm water, stirred very thoroughly and sprayed over about half a hectare. It is said to promote root development and to stimulate soil micro-organisms and help in the release of trace elements. It is best applied in overcast conditions in the late afternoon and should only be used in spring or autumn on moist soil.

Preparation 501

This is made from a silica-rich rock like quartz, finely ground and mixed to a paste with water, and buried in a cow horn over the summer. The material is mixed to a spray and applied to pasture two weeks after Preparation 500 has been put on. For this one pick a sunny day and spray early in the morning.

How much fertiliser to apply

If you are using organic type fertilisers these tend to stay in the soil so even if you put on more than is required it will not be wasted. But too much artificial fertiliser may literally be money down the drain.

Soil type, climate and farming pattern all influence how much your land needs. If you are planning on an intensive dairy type operation you may need to put on 500 kg/ha of super a year. But if you are casually grazing sheep on steep hillsides and only want to hold soil fertility at its present levels then 125 kg/ha may be sufficient. But because each situation is different, my advice is that you get your land tested, explain your particular requirements to the advisory officer and get a tailor-made fertiliser programme.

When to apply it

On good rye and clover pasture a general guide is:

- In autumn until June in the warm parts of the North Island, or else in a split application, putting phosphorus on in autumn and potassium in early spring. Where sulphur leaches quickly add sulphur to the autumn super.
- In warmer parts of the South Island and cool parts of the North Island apply fertiliser in late summer to mid-autumn and if sulphur leaches rapidly use a split dressing, putting phosphorus and sulphur on in late summer and potassium in early spring.
- In the cooler parts of the South Island (Southland, Otago and most of Canterbury) apply phosphate and sulphur where needed in late summer or early spring. If potassium is also needed, apply that in early spring.

On semi-improved hill country topdress late summer where subterranean clover is dominant or in early spring if you wish to encourage perennial clovers.

On unimproved hill country timing is not so important, so topdressing can be made to fit in with other farm chores.

Methods of application

Your choice here depends on terrain, area to be covered and your bank balance. If the land is flat to rolling then ground spreading by truck or tractor is cheaper than aerial spreading and quicker than hand spreading.

If the land is very rugged, and your farm a reasonable size, you can get it flown on but for this you need access to a landing strip and a fertiliser bin. If your block is a bit small for the plane and too steep for a truck you may have to go back to the old-fashioned pioneer method of tossing it about by hand. I did four ha of my block this way one year. It took about two and a half days, and was rather monotonous but it did enable me to concentrate the fertiliser where it was needed most. The following year I got the spreader truck in. If spreading by hand, wear a filter or handkerchief over nose and mouth.

Most fertiliser companies have their own ground-spreading trucks. If the stuff has to be trucked to your property anyway it is very convenient if the same vehicle can run around and spread it for you. If there are a few steep pockets or inaccessible corners, the driver can deposit a heap nearby for you to spread by hand later.

Some farmers have their own tractor-driven spinner spreaders which hook up to the power-take-off on the back of the tractor. You may be able to beg, borrow or hire the equipment and maybe farmer as well and put it on that way. If spreading by hand or by tractor, order fertiliser in 50 kg bags, which is easier to handle than a bulk supply.

Stock transfer of fertility

Even on a small block you will notice that animals heavily graze some areas then wander off to their favourite camp-site, usually on a ridge or under some trees, where they drop their own manure so you end up with infertile flats and very fertile camp-sites. This is known as stock transfer of fertility. The solution is to fence in a way which forces animals to stay and camp where they graze. But if this is not practical the only answer is to compensate when you apply fertiliser. Don't put it on the camp-sites, they get plenty anyway, and put heavier concentrations on the flat areas where the animals do most of their grazing.

Trace elements

These will show up in a soil test. A shortage in one or other trace element can lead to a deficiency disease in stock, and may even affect you if you only eat home grown produce. Deficiencies tend to cover quite a wide geographical area so your local veterinarian or MAF advisor should be able to tell you of any known local shortages. If in doubt have

your soil analysed. Most elements like copper, boron, molybdenum, selenium, cobalt, magnesium and zinc can be added to fertiliser and put on at the same time.

Fertiliser for vegetables

All plants require nitrogen, phosphate, potash, sulphur and calcium, but in different degrees. So before applying a fertiliser to the garden consider what you are growing and what elements it likes lots of (see also Chapter 5).

- Nitrogen. Helps build up leaf and green matter which is good on crops like lettuce, cabbage (and grass) but a hindrance on root or fruiting crops. Too much nitrogen on these will only encourage the plants to grow rank rather than develop good tubers or set fruit. A deficiency of nitrogen on leaf crops will show up as leaves turn pale yellow starting at their stems. In brassicas the leaves turn pink, then orange. Gardeners can accidentally cause nitrogen deficiencies by adding too much carbon-rich organic matter like sticks, sawdust and straw to soil. These will rob nitrogen as they decompose.

  One of the easiest ways to add nitrogen and get it to plants quickly is via a liquid tea or 'magic mix'. For this just tip a bucketful of horse, cow or sheep dung into a 200 litre drum of water. Leave it for a week, then ladle out the tea. Depending on how strong the brew is, dilute it slightly then use it to water plants, or add a few cupfuls to each plant just after they have been watered. Dried blood from blood and bone also contains high levels of nitrogen and is fairly mild in its action. Sulphate of ammonia contains 21 per cent nitrogen but it is severe on plants and soil micro-organisms. It also adds to soil acidity so use sparingly. Urea is 46 per cent nitrogen. It does not burn plants and may be used as a liquid spray over the foliage for quick results. Rain is perhaps the best source of nitrogen, bringing it down out of the atmosphere. Plants will pick up after a shower of rain in a way they never respond to your watering.

- Phosphorus. Stimulates root development and helps crops mature early. A deficiency will show up as stunted carrots, with purple colouring on their older foliage. Lettuces will grow

Crop	Nitrogen (N)	Phosphorus (P)	Potassium (K)
Bean	1	2	2
Beet	3	4	3
Brassicas	3–4	3–4	3–4
Carrots	2–3	2–3	2–3
Celery	3–4	3–4	4
Cucumber	3	3	3
Lettuce	4	4	4
Onion	3	3	3
Parsnip	2	2	2
Peas	2	3	3
Potatoes	3–4	4	4
Spinach	4	4	4
Sweetcorn	2–3	2–3	2–3
Tomato	2–3	3	3
Turnip	1	3	2

1 = low requirement, 2 = low to medium, 3 = medium to high, 4 = very high

Table 8. **Plant requirements for the three main nutrients.**

poorly and cabbage shows purple markings in the centre of the leaf. Sweetcorn likes a lot of phosphorus and will show purple streaks down its leaves if deficient.

Superphosphate is the most common form of phosphate available. However, the sulphur in it does increase soil acidity. Alternatively use reverted super which is slower acting, or else fish meal, poultry manure and blood and bone.

- Potassium. Potash forms part of the cell membranes in plant tissues and is involved in protein, enzyme and amino acid synthesis. Clays are normally well supplied in potassium but sandy soils may be deficient. If there is an excess of nitrogen or phosphorus the plants' ability to take up potassium can be affected and cause an apparent deficiency. Affected plants will have leaves that look scorched around the edges, tomatoes will ripen patchily, potatoes will die back too early and beans will appear susceptible to brown spot.

Superphosphate and many other commercial fertilisers contain potassium. It is also found at 5 per cent concentrations in wood ash and is in animal manures, bone meal, seaweed meal and comfrey.

- Calcium. Used in the plant cell walls and also in the make-up of enzymes. It is important as a neutraliser for acid soils and makes a lot of minerals more readily available to plants.

Calcium comes from lime (see next section). Dolomite lime contains magnesium as well. Ground lime-rock is slow acting and does not harm soil organisms but quick lime may.

Liming

As well as a regular fertiliser programme you need to consider liming: high rainfall, poor drainage, heavy stocking and applying artificial fertilisers all add to soil acidity and it is lime which corrects an imbalance. Acidity is measured on a pH scale which tests the concentration of hydrogen ions. The scale goes from 0 to 14; seven is neutral, below is acidic and above alkaline.

On farm land ground lime-rock is the most common form used. It is the cheapest, does not burn the soil and is slow acting. Thus one application of 1 to 2 tonne/ha should maintain soil pH for several years. How much to put on will depend on the soil's natural acidity, climate and stocking rate. If your soil is to be tested for mineral content, get

Soil type	pH level	Crop
Acid (no lime)	5–6	Potato, rhubarb, parsley, kumara.
Slightly acid	5.5–7	Beans, brussels sprouts, corn, cabbage, cucumber, parsnip, peas, radishes, swedes, turnips, tomatoes, strawberries.
Neutral	6.5–7.5	Asparagus, beetroot, carrot, cauliflower, celery, leek, lettuce, onion, spinach.
Slightly alkaline (lots of lime)	7–8	Artichoke, garlic, passionfruit.

Table 9. **Compatibility of vegetables with pH levels**.

advice on a liming programme at the same time. Adding lime will generally promote clover growth and 'sweeten' pastures. Peat and clay soils tend to need more lime to alter their pH than do sandy soils.

Put lime on a few months before other fertilisers, because if it is applied at the same time as superphosphate the two can interact, and the super will revert and become less soluble. Likewise do not apply lime and blood and bone at the same time as chemical reactions between them mean some of the nitrogen could be lost as ammonia gas.

Ideally, pasture and the vegetable garden should range from a pH of 5.5 to 7.5. Most garden shops sell a simple pH testing kit, but to get a reasonably accurate indication take several soil samples from about 10 cm below the surface.

If the soils are too acid, calcium and magnesium will be in short supply for plants. Alkaline conditions lead to the locking up in the soil of iron, manganese, boron, copper and zinc. So aim to get the pH near neutral; reduce acidity by adding lime, reduce alkalinity by adding a sulphate fertiliser, or in the vegetable garden add compost or peat moss.

How much

Clay soils generally need more lime than sandy soils. In the vegetable garden add about 120 g lime/m^2 clay and about a quarter as much for sandy soil. Wood ash has about three quarters of the liming effect of lime and also contains other nutrients. In following years about 25 g/m^2 will do as a maintenance dressing. For pasture that equates to about 1.2 tonne/ha as an initial dressing and 1 tonne/ha every four years after that.

What likes lime

In the vegetable garden you will learn that some plants like the minerals available to them in acid soils while others prefer those found in alkaline, so it is a good idea to keep part of your garden unlimed each year to cater for all. (See Table 9.)

5. The garden

The vegetable garden can feed the family and the pigs, and grow titbits for the chooks and other stock. In return the farm or farm animals contribute to the garden with manure and compost materials.

The first thing to decide about your garden is what you expect to get from it and how much time you have to put into it. You may prefer to have just a small plot which grows fresh vegetables for the table, but this means bulkier crops like potatoes, carrots and onions have to be bought in.

An alternative is to incorporate several plots, sown in rotation, in the farm management system.

Such a system could be as follows:

Year 1: Grazing for stock, later for the pigs which can root it up.
Year 2: Bring it into cultivation with root crops.
Year 3: Follow up with legumes (peas, beans, clover, or lucerne).
Year 4: Finish with the heavy feeders, the brassicas such as cabbage and broccoli for the house or swedes and turnips for stock. Also the marrows, pumpkins, tomatoes and the like for home eating.
Year 5: Back into grass again.

A system like this should provide the household with enough vegetables to last all year and some stock feed supplements, but it does require a lot of work and fencing costs.

Selecting a site

Space and terrain are the main factors to consider here, as you can alter the soil and microclimate. Try to find a sunny, reasonably well-drained spot to save yourself some work. Shelter would also be an advantage but you can always add it later. If the plot is naturally sheltered you only need to fence it to keep stock out, but if you want a warmer microclimate make the fence double as a windbreak using shelter cloth or close palings. The fence must not shade plants so shelter needs to be lower and more open on the northern side.

Soil improvement

Whatever your soil type you can work it to improve both its texture and fertility.

Volcanic soils

These make an excellent garden base as they have a loamy, friable texture and are easy to work. However, phosphate can become locked up in them so regular addition of a phosphatic fertiliser is needed for healthy plants. Mulching with straw or compost will help stop the soils drying out in summer.

Clay soils

Clay's poor structure means it gets waterlogged in winter but dries out rock hard in summer. Don't despair. Clays are generally rich in nutrients and the addition of plenty of organic matter and sand will both physically break up the clay structure, improving drainage and aeration, and also encourage the bacteria and micro-organisms which make all those nutrients available to the plants.

Sandy soils

These are loosely structured and easy to work. They drain well and hold their warmth but the soil does dry out quickly. They tend to be infertile, as nutrients are leached or washed out quickly. Digging in large amounts of organic matter will improve water retention and mulching with straw

Raised beds can be a feature of your garden.

will reduce surface water loss. To combat leaching of nutrients, fertiliser, compost or manure must be added regularly.

Silt soils

Usually found on valley floors. They are easy to work but tend to be infertile due to leaching. Add lots of organic matter or compost to bulk the soil up and improve fertility, and mulch worked ground to stop wind erosion and surface caking.

Peaty soils

Peats are based on decayed plant matter rather than rock. If they have had a lot of water lying on them in the past they may be infertile due to leaching. Add lime and compost to counteract acidity and build up fertility. If the soil needs draining take care to not let the peat dry out too much, as this leads to shrinkage and the soil can be hard to re-moisten.

Loams

These vary considerably but are probably the best gardening soil. Generally they contain about 5 per cent or more organic matter and both clay and sand, so they are open-structured and rich in

minerals. Regular addition of organic matter will maintain the good structure, improve fertility and encourage earthworm activity.

Stony soils

On most stony ground the topsoil is thin, crumbly and weakly structured, so water drains through quickly and the land dries out in summer. Dig in lots of organic matter to improve water retention and build upon fertility.

Wet soils

Some low-lying plains have poorly drained peaty loams or silty loams. These soils need to be drained (see Chapter 3), and straw, compost or un-treated sawdust dug into the sub-soil. Lime should be added to combat the soil's strong acidity and compost or fertiliser to supply plant nutrients.

Organic matter and humus

Organic matter comes from anything which has lived and died. Humus is decayed organic matter. Whatever your soil type it will benefit from adding humus.

There are three main ways of adding humus to soil: green cropping, composting and mulching.

To green-manure your land, plant it in a quick-growing crop such as peas, beans, lupins, clover or mustard. When the plants are just about to flower, pick a day when the soil is fairly moist and just dig those plants into the soil. That ground will be ready to replant in about six weeks.

Composting is the most popular organic method. Making compost is no more than gathering up organic material, and mixing it so worms and other micro-organisms can get in and speed up the breakdown process. There are several types of manufactured compost bin available, but you can build a perfectly effective one yourself. It is simply a wooden bin divided into three compartments, which means one bin can be maturing, one is ready for use and the third can be for filling. (See Fig. 29.) It is a good idea to be able to cover the bin against heavy rain which might cool the heap off and slow down decomposition.

Heap up your organic material (see following sources) next to the bin and try to keep it covered to stop it getting soggy and setting up anaerobic (smelly) decay. Almost anything which has grown and died can be used in the compost heap. Stalky, dry materials contain carbon while soft, green-leaved material and animal manure contain nitrogen. The best breakdown occurs when there are about 3–10 parts by volume of carbon containing material and 1 part of nitrogen-containing material.

Start with a layer of sawdust, mixed with a bit of lime and old compost, laid at the bottom directly onto the soil. Follow this with layers 150 mm deep of carbon material and 50 mm of nitrogen material. Sprinkle a handful of lime over each layer. Repeat the layers until the bin is full and moisten the heap as it is built up. A heap should heat up after a couple of days (up to 70°C), and this helps speed decomposition. If the heap fails to heat up or turns soggy and smelly it is best to take it apart and rebuild it using some fresh material added to the old.

After a couple of weeks the heap will have cooled and you may turn it to bring the undecayed matter from the top and sides into the centre. You do not have to wait until the compost is as dark

Fig. 29 **A homemade compost bin divided into three compartments**.

and crumbly as peat before you use it, but the material should have darkened and lost its original structure. If used too soon the compost could rob the garden of nitrogen as it breaks down.

The third way of introducing organic matter is mulching: spreading layers of partly decomposed material on top of the soil around plants, and just leaving it to gradually decay and get mixed in through worm activity. Mulching helps stop soils drying out, can reduce frost damage to plants and suppresses weeds.

The disadvantages are that as it decomposes, the mulch may rob the soil of nitrogen and the bottom of the mulch layer may become soggy, encouraging plant stems to rot. So be prepared to add nitrogen, especially if you are using woody material like sawdust or hay. The alternative is an inorganic mulch such as black polythene sheeting. This helps raise the soil temperature and stops weed regrowth. Plant seedlings can be poked in through slits in the polythene and if used carefully it should last several seasons.

Organic materials
On the farm

- Manures. Sheep manure is richer in nitrogen and potash than horse or cow dung, and fowl manure is richer still. Note that the fresher the manure the more likely it is to burn plants so should be put through a compost heap first.
- Hay. Makes an excellent mulch but may contain a lot of weed seeds so scatter it in the chook run first, let them clean up the seeds and enrich it with their dung.
- Autumn leaves. These can be slow to decompose which is good if you want them to break up heavy soils.

- Pine needles. These tend to be a bit acid, so add lime with them.
- Sawdust. Always use untreated sawdust, preferably well-aged. For compost, mix 6 parts of sawdust with 1 of fowl manure and 1 of lawn clippings and sprinkle all liberally with blood and bone and lime. Keep the mix moist and turn weekly for a month then fortnightly for five months.
- Stable straw. Best composted first to kill weed seeds.

Off the farm

- Brewery wastes. Spent hops make good mulch if you can get them.
- Grass clippings. Let them wilt and dry out a bit before using.
- Newspaper. Use only sparingly in the compost heap as it needs a lot of nitrogen to decompose. But it makes a good mulch. Weigh it down with sawdust or bark chips.
- Seaweed. Adding seaweed will greatly improve the health and vigour of plants as it is rich in minerals and trace elements. Chop and put through the compost heap first.

Earthworms

These are nature's great mixers. Surprisingly the large New Zealand native worms are not much use to the gardener; it is the small English worm that does the work. These were introduced with the pioneers and have spread sufficiently so that most of the country has adequate worm populations. But if you are breaking in new bush you may have to introduce worms. Dig up some turfs from the nearest rich pastureland, especially the ground immediately under a cow or horse pat. Take the worms home and put in a box with soil and lots of organic matter and let them breed. Or put them direct into your garden after adding organic matter to it. Watch out if using artificial fertilisers and pesticides as these can burn and kill worms. You can also add worms to the compost heap once it has cooled down to speed decay.

Raised beds

If you want small, intense garden plots raise the beds. The soil will drain better, and the 'fence'

around each bed means you can add a lot of organic matter and keep it there, building up a deep layer of rich workable soil which makes plants healthier and weeds easier to pull. To raise the bed simply build a wooden fence about 300 to 450 mm high. If using new timber do not use boric-treated timber, but tanalith or celcure-treated timber is okay. The plots should be in long rectangles so you can reach over them to weed without having to trample on and compact the bed. (See Fig. 30.)

Fig. 30 **Rectangular raised beds make weeding easy**.

When to sow

This will depend on your climate. I have loosely grouped vegetables into cool, warm and inbetween season crops. Just where the limit lies for your garden may take a couple of seasons to find out. Save yourself some wasted effort and talk to the long-standing locals. Cool season crops like temperatures between 10 to 20°C. They can tolerate colder conditions but may not grow much until the soil warms again.

These are the winter vegetables in the mild areas and spring and autumn vegetables in cold regions: artichokes, asparagus, broad beans, broccoli, brussels sprouts, cauliflowers, onions, peas, spinach, turnips and swedes.

Intermediate crops can be grown all year in some parts of the country. They prefer temperatures from 15 to 25°C. Some, particularly the root crops, may run to seed if sown late in autumn, leaving insufficient time to bulk up before the cold weather. Others, like the green-leafed vegetables, may run to seed in warmer districts in summer. In-between crops include: beetroot, cabbages, carrots, celery, chicory, mustard, leeks, lettuces, parsnips, radishes, rhubarb and silverbeet.

Warm season crops are mostly susceptible to frost and like temperatures above 20°C. They are usually summer salad and barbecue fare: beans, capsicums, chokos, cucumbers, eggplant, melons, marrows, potatoes, pumpkins, squash, sweetcorn, kumara and tomatoes.

Crops for stock

Turnips, swedes and other brassicas are commonly grown as stock feed. Turnips sown in spring will mature in 60 to 75 days and can be fed off as a drought supplement. Or a late sowing in autumn may be saved as a winter feed in milder areas.

You can also sow some leguminous crops such as red clover, lucerne, and peas which will enrich the soil with nitrogen. However, if feeding red clover to cows, only give them access to a little at a time to avoid bloat, and give them plenty of roughage as well.

If you are running pigs you may want to put in a crop of marrows, squash or cucumbers. All carry on producing for several weeks. Squash, if stored somewhere dry with plenty of air circulation will last most of the year. Pigs fatten well on lightly cooked squash.

Maize is also easy to grow in bulk as pig, horse or chook fodder. But don't plant it too close to your sweetcorn or the two may cross-pollinate and you will end up eating maize yourself.

Experiment with growing wheat for chook feed. Winter wheat is planted in autumn and then shoots up quickly the following spring for an early crop. Spring-sown wheat will ripen later in the summer.

Insects and diseases

Various bugs, slugs, snails, fungi, viruses and birds will be competing with you for the goodies you grow in the garden. There are many ways of tackling them. At the outset let me emphasise that if you grow strong healthy vegetables in the first place then, like healthy people, they will be able to resist a lot of disease and pest attacks.

Walk into any gardening store and you will find a huge range of chemical pest controls, vegetable

sprays, fruit tree sprays, insecticides, fungicides, and herbicides — all promoted as the normal, sensible way for a clean garden. But many of us grow our own produce to get away from the chemicals commercial growers might be using. There is a strong school of thought that suggests those chemicals might not be good for us, or for our soils and the garden ecosystem, so in case that's right, keep those chemicals as a last resort. There are several simple home-made controls worth trying first.

The main thing in pest and disease control is to take care of the basics:

- Make sure the garden is well drained, as wet soils encourage slugs, snails and wireworms and also promote root rot and fungal infections.
- Time your plantings so crops are harvested before the main bug seasons, which differ in each district.
- Rotate your crops so that a pest does not get a go at the same crop in one plot year after year.
- Water regularly. If plants have dried out to wilting point they may suffer root damage and these areas will be susceptible to fungal infections.
- Keep the garden weeded as some weed plants are host to insect and fungi pests.
- Physically protect your plants. For instance, use fine mesh to keep white butterfly from cabbage and other brassicas.
- Trap slugs and snails with saucers of old beer.
- Try some form of companion planting. In most home vegetable gardens the sheer diversity of plants can act as a deterrent to pests getting out of hand but there are some plant associations which are definitely helpful. Generally speaking strong smelling plants appear to deter insect pests; for instance onions, radishes, and chives help protect carrots, lettuce and tomatoes. Marigolds discourage blackfly and cabbage caterpillar if planted among beans and cabbages. Their roots also secrete a substance which inhibits soil nematodes.

Sprays and dusts

If you still have trouble with a blight or insect plague try one of these home-made sprays:
- Seaweed spray. Pulp and soak seaweed or else

buy a drum of concentrated extract. Many gardeners have found a regular spraying with seaweeds keeps insects and pests at bay, possibly due to either the increased health of the plants, or the smell of the seaweed, or the stickiness of it.

- Garlic spray. A fungicide. This can be made by soaking 74 g of chopped garlic in 110 ml of mineral oil (from a chemist) for a day. Add a pint of water containing 6 g of soft soap then dilute with 20 parts of water to spray.
- Elder spray. Another fungicide. The common elder tree (*Sambucus nigra*) contains a weak hydrocyanic acid. Simmer the leaves for 15 minutes and use the cooled tea diluted as a spray.
- China berry spray. This ornamental tree, *Melia azedarach*, also known as bead tree or Indian lilac, has clusters of fragrant, purple flowers and poisonous berries. The leaves can be boiled for 20 minutes and the cooled tea used against mildew and fungi.
- Soft soap spray. Available from a chemist (made with potassium carbonate instead of caustic soda as in ordinary soap), soft soap can be dissolved 50 g at a time in 4.5 litres of water, left to cool and sprayed to protect cabbages against caterpillars.
- Chilli pepper and Condy's crystals spray. Both deter pests if mixed with water as a spray.
- Pyrethrum spray or dust. This can either be bought as a liquid or you can make your own by drying and grinding the flowers (*Chrysanthemum cinerariaefolium*). Add the powder to talc or gypsum and use as a dust. Note that pyrethrum is deadly to bees.
- Rhubarb spray. Cut 1 kg of leaves and boil in 3 litres of water for half an hour. Dissolve 180 g of soft soap in 2.5 litres of water and mix with the rhubarb extract. This spray deters aphids.
- Derris dust. This comes from tropical plants which contain rotenone. It acts as a nerve poison on insects.
- Bordeaux mix. Dissolve 250 g of copper sulphate in 22 litres of water. Mix 150 g of freshly burned quick-lime with a little water until it is creamy, then add to the copper sulphate solution. It is effective against potato blight but must be sprayed on before the blight appears to ensure a bumper crop.

Garden friends

- Birds clean up insect pests. Silvereyes pick up codling moths, thrushes get the slugs and snails, while sparrows eat aphids.
- Hedgehogs go for slugs and millipedes.
- Centipedes eat slug eggs.
- Ladybirds love aphids.
- Lacewings eat thrips, mites, caterpillar eggs, scale insects, leafhopper nymphs, aphids and mealybugs.
- Wasps. Some species lay eggs in insect eggs and when hatched wasp larvae eat the food of the host larvae.
- Frogs and lizards eat aphids, grasshoppers, scale insects, moths, caterpillars and even snails.

6. Trees

Growing trees and having pasture for animals should not be considered mutually exclusive. Trees will contribute more to animal wellbeing than they will take away in grazing space. Trees also help stabilise soil. Depending on the species, trees can supply nitrogen, produce cash crops of timber, fruit and nuts, provide nectar and pollen for the bees, and homes for the birds, and. . . they just look nice. At the end of this chapter are tables listing most of the main native and exotic species, and indicating what they can offer the smallfarmer.

Erosion control

We all know that erosion is undesirable. Nobody enjoys looking at unsightly scars with valuable topsoil disappearing down into gullies and out to sea. But do we all realise how long lasting the effects are? A study undertaken by the Soil Conservation Centre at Aokautere suggests pasture growth is still down 80 per cent on scars that are six or seven years old! And after 50 years pasture growth is still down about 23 per cent compared with the immediate area.

If you have steep paddocks where erosion could be a problem, you have a choice: either blanket plant it in trees, or plant it thinly and graze stock underneath. This is known as two-tier farming and experiments so far suggest you can run as many animals, and they will do as well, if there are up to 100 stems/ha. More trees than that and the grass will be shaded. If you use timber species, they will actually grow faster on pasture at low density spacings than in a densely planted forestry site.

Erosion isn't limited to steep hillsides. Wind erosion can be a problem wherever ground gets dry or is not protected with vegetation. Tests on a worked paddock in Canterbury suggest the wind could strip away up to 5 tonnes of soil/ha/day, and even more in a severe blow. Similar losses have been recorded in Hawke's Bay.

Then there are the riverbeds, exposed coastal sites and unstable soil types. If erosion is already occurring it is up to you as guardian of the land to halt the process.

If wind erosion is the problem, then consider planting trees for shelter (see following

Grass growth on scars like these may never fully recover.

44

Stream bed erosion.

paragraphs). If erosion is water based, then quick-growing species that will rapidly push their roots out and hold the topsoil are needed. We aren't talking chicken feed here. On average 5 tonnes of sediment flows down the Manawatu River every minute. That is nearly 3 million tonnes/yr and the rate is much higher when the river is in flood. Much the same could be said for many of New Zealand's rivers.

So how do trees stop erosion? In a forest the canopy cushions the fall of water. The surface area of all those leaves and stems is considerable, so it takes a lot of rain before drops actually fall to the ground. Then they have to penetrate the litter layer, itself a giant sponge with an enormous surface area. Water that finally reaches the soil level can do little damage as its momentum is lost and the soil particles it reaches are so bound together with the roots of all the plants they cannot be dislodged.

Shelter

Grass will benefit just as much from protection from cold or hot drying winds as kiwifruit.

Transpiration or water usage by any plant (the flow of moisture up through the plant from the soil and out into the atmosphere), can be greatly reduced if wind speed over the plant is cut down. This also helps stomata on the plant leaves to stay open longer, so the rate of photosynthesis and of plant growth will be greater. Shelter will cut down moisture loss from the soil; protect the crop, even grass, from being blown flat, battered and damaged; stop blossoms being removed; and prevent bees and the like from being discouraged from working.

If you are farming animals, shelter takes on even greater importance. The chill factor of even the lightest breeze multiplies the effect of cold, particularly if the wind is combined with rain. For instance, if, on a calm frosty morning, the thermometer has just reached $-7°C$, then that is bad enough for your stock. But add a 24 kph breeze and the wind chill factor can drop that to a frigid $-21°C$. If the animal is wet as well, that chill factor will be further increased. The colder an animal is the more it has to eat to maintain its body temperature without using up its own body fat reserves. Some farmers have recognised the value of shelter enough to tender quite competitively for the grazing of forest land over winter. They know they will have to feed out less to stock sheltered under the trees.

Principles of shelter belts

A dense belt will act like a brick wall, so the area effectively sheltered will be very narrow, and there will be a lot of turbulence in the lee of the belt. But a more open shelter belt (between 40–60 per cent solid) will filter the air flow and reduce the wind speed over a much wider band of the lee side. (See Figs. 31 and 32.) So don't plant a wide, dense belt of trees. Keep it narrow, with just two or three rows of trees — maybe a tall species with a shorter one next to it.

Height of the shelter trees will determine how far downwind the air flow is reduced. The taller the trees, the further the shelter effect will be. In good belts the sheltered area will extend 10 to 20 times the height of the belt. The length of the belt is also important. If it is too short, the wind will just curl around the ends. Ideally it should be 20 to 25 times the mature height of the belt. Shelter belts need to be uniform along their length. Any gaps act to funnel the wind.

Selecting shelter belt sites

Remember your belt will have to be fenced to protect it from stock. To get as much sun as possible on both sides the belt should run in a north–south line. If you need to plant the belt east-west across prevailing winds use deciduous trees to let the sun through in winter.

Selecting the species

There is no reason shelter belts cannot be multiple use; either timber for future cash crops, trees suitable for firewood, trees for animal fodder, or trees to provide nectar or pollen for the bees. If doing a double or a triple row of shelter trees consider planting a quick-growing one in conjunction with a slower one. For instance, if you want to take timber off the belt, plant pine trees, eucalypts or poplars which will come away rapidly, and put a slower growing conifer in front of them. Then once the timber crop is removed there will still be a shelter belt in place.

If you are in a very exposed situation, you may

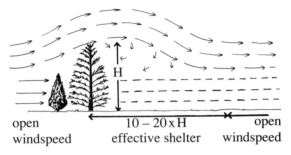

Fig. 31 **Permeable belt.**

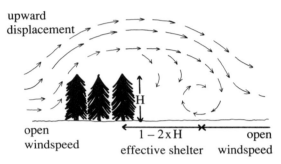

Fig. 32 **Impermeable belt.**

A mature shelterbelt of poplars and Lawsoniana cypress.

46

need to plant something hardier than trees first. Flax or pampas grass are hard to beat. At 3.6m high they are only low growing, but the shelter behind them may be enough to get your trees started.

Planting for shelter

Obviously the closer you plant trees in the shelter belt, the sooner it will be effective. If using cuttings from poplars or willows, they can be poked in between 0.5 and 1 m apart. Slower growing evergreens should be planted at about 2 m spacings, likewise for pines and eucalypts.

How many rows you put in will also affect how close each tree should be planted. The more rows, the wider the gap you can allow between each plant and still have an effective screen if the rows are staggered.

If you are in snow country some of the principles change, as snow carried over a shelter belt may drop and form drifts in the lee side of the belt. That is probably where your stock will want to cluster to keep out of the bite of the wind. Reduce this drifting effect by making the belt wider, eight to ten rows, so snow will be caught in it and the lee side will stay clear. Put lower or slower growing species near the centre to help trap the snow. This is quite a woodlot so go for timber producing trees which can recompense you for the area taken out of grazing.

Shade

Dairy cows will spend much less time eating once the temperature is over 21°C. If they aren't eating they aren't making milk. Likewise, beef cattle will not put on as much meat, and hot panting sheep are neither healthy nor happy. So give them shade. This is true for all of New Zealand because the whole country at some time of the year gets its fair share of days over 21°C.

Once you've gone on to read about timber, pollen and nectar sources, fodder trees and landscaping, you may have some definite ideas about what sort of trees you want on the place. But when providing shade, you don't want it so concentrated that the animals camp in one spot so the

The tall shape of poplars makes them ideal for farm shade as stock will camp well out from the trunk and move with the sun so no ground gets over-used or spoiled.

ground gets soiled and is a disease trap. This can happen with evergreen species, particularly those that branch close to the ground. By contrast, taller trees, or trees that have been pruned up to about 4 m, present a long narrow band of shade that moves as the sun progresses over the sky, so the stock have to get up and move too. That means the ground is not over-used and soiled. A deciduous tree will also let sunlight through in winter, encouraging grass growth right up to the bole.

Fodder trees

In a drought tree prunings make good emergency fodder. Poplars and willows are the best. Prune poplars and willows in January or February before the leaves start to dry off too much. Once stock have developed a taste for tree prunings you will have to take extra care to keep them fenced out of woodlots. Stock nibble at most trees. Just because they eat it doesn't mean it is good for them. If in doubt check with your veterinarian or MAF advisor. Also read Appendix D for plants that definitely are poisonous.

Stock will also eat fruit, nuts or tree beans. The sound of an apple falling is enough to start a horse, cow, goat and sheep stampede around my place.

Also consider walnuts, pecans, chestnuts, hazelnuts, figs, plums, pears and even mulberries to provide some fodder for you! Check with your local nurseries which species will do all right in your situation.

Trees for bees

Pick your trees carefully and you may provide a year-round supply of bee fodder so your bees can produce lots of that good sweet stuff. Several species provide pollen or nectar, yet are also good timber trees or valuable for landscaping, erosion control or shelter. Shelter in itself is a help to the bees. After all it takes something like 160 000 bee trips to produce 1 kg of honey — which means a lot of tired bees if they are flying into a stiff wind.

Bees require pollen for protein and nectar for their carbohydrates and energy. The most critical period is early spring when the number of bees in the hive will be expanding rapidly but the main flow of nectar will not have started. If planting with your bees in mind, consider what times of the year bee fodder is shortest in your area and pick tree species to fill the gap. Most trees produce both pollen and nectar, but some provide more of one than the other.

Timber trees

Having, I hope, convinced you of the values of shelter and shade for your stock you should be prepared to put in at least some trees. Make them timber-producing species and watch your dollars growing. I have long thought it would be a nice idea for landowners, at the child-rearing stage of their lives, to go out and plant 2 ha of timber trees when each baby was born. What a 21st present that would be! It is one way you could give your children a good start in life without having to break your own bank balance.

You need to consider if you want 'quick'

A well-pruned stand of young pines.

returns and thus trees worth felling in 20 to 30 years' time, or if you want trees that will be a family heritage. Climate will affect which species you can grow, and how quickly they will mature. Other farming factors come into the choice. Do you want to graze stock under the growing trees, use the thinnings for firewood or posts, feed prunings to your stock, and how much maintenance can you give while the trees are growing? Any glance through a tree book will show up countless species valued for some specialised form of woodwork. Okay, if you want to make cricket bats, grow cricket willow. But the more common species are more likely to find a ready market as mills will know how to deal with the timber.

Planning the woodlot

Once you have decided what species to plant you next need to determine the area you have available. Draw a plan of the area. Do this by counting the paces along each side and work out the angles between sides (you can do this using a compass to determine the orientation of each side). Revive your rusty mathematical talents and use isosceles triangle formulas to work out the area.

Because even trees of the same species can grow at different rates and shapes, foresters normally plant far more than they will need for the final crop. This way they can thin out the poor-formed individuals as the woodlot grows. That means starting with about 2000 trees (stems)/ha, normally planted 2 m apart in rows 2.5 m apart. These are thinned down to only 200 stems/ha by the time they are ready for felling.

That means a lot of thinning out which you may feel is a big waste. If you are going for a less common timber tree which is costing a lot more to buy in the first place, or you can be sure of the quality of the tree stock, consider putting them in at wider initial spacings; do likewise for two-tier farming, where you will run stock under the trees once they are established above grazeable height. Start with about 500 stems/ha and thin out within a few years as soon as the form of the trees is obvious. Leave just a few more than the final crop of 200 stems/ha to allow for any wind damage or disease.

Managing a woodlot

To get timber worth the trouble of extracting and milling you need to prune and thin the woodlot whether you started with 2000 stems/ha or 500.

Pruning

Pruning is removing the lower branches from a timber tree so that it grows a good length of clear trunk. It is done in stages as the tree grows. The object is to get wood clear of knots. When a log is milled, each board will have a knot in it where a branch grew. But if that branch had been cut off flush with the trunk when the tree was quite small, new wood would have grown out and over the branch stump — a process known as occlusion. Thus while there would be a small knot right in the middle of the stem, the new, outer layers of the trunk would be clear and knot free. (See Fig. 33.)

Begin pruning when the trunks are slightly thicker than a beer bottle (you'll need a few of those out there to get through the job anyway). Prune up to about 2 m the first time. The tree will probably be between 4–6 years old and about

Fig. 33 **A cutaway view of the tree trunk after pruning to show how clear timber occludes over stubs.**

5–6 m tall. Cut the branches off with a saw or pruners as close to the trunk as possible without damaging the skin of the trunk around the branch. Then leave the trees alone for a couple of years. Once they are 7–8 m high, prune up to about 4 m. Usually three prunings is enough. The third time the tree should be 10–11 m tall and 8–10 years old. Prune them up to 6 m.

Which trees to prune

If you put trees in at wide initial spacings (500/ha or less) then prune all the stems and only cut out the malformed stock. But if you planted densely (2000/ha) concentrate on only pruning the best 600 to 1000 and cut out the rest. At the second pruning only work on the best 240 to 440 trees. By the third pruning you will be concentrating on the final 200, but prune up to 300 thus leaving a few extra stems in to make up for any wind damage or disease.

Once you have finished each pruning you can then go through and chop down the unpruned trees. These are the thinnings. You can either thin to waste (just drop them on the ground and leave them to rot) or you can draw them out if they are big enough for posts or rails, or any good for firewood.

Selecting final crop trees

In selecting the trees you will concentrate your pruning and tending efforts on, look for:

dominance and vigour, condition of the leader (that is the uppermost tip of the trunk where you would tie the star if it was a Christmas tree), stem straightness, spacing from other selected trees and branch size. Let's look at these separately.

- Dominance and vigour. That just means you want to select the biggest, strongest trees in the vicinity. Dominant trees usually have their tops above the general canopy; they have thicker, stronger trunks and a good deep crown.
- Condition of the leader. This is important as it will determine what form the rest of the tree's growth will take. A single, straight, strong and healthy shoot is what you want. (See Fig. 34.)
- Stem straightness. Obviously a straight stem is best. Slight curves or kinks are okay if the tree is otherwise in good shape as these defects often straighten out as the tree grows. Stand at a point where the kink or curve is seen at its worst, and imagine a line from the middle of the trunk at its base up to the mid-point 6 m up the trunk. If the line stays within the trunk, the amount of kink is acceptable. (See Fig. 35.)
- Spacing. This is important, too. It is no good selecting 600 to 1000 of the best trees if they are all down one end of the woodlot. Look at the trees in groups of six and try to pick two or three out of those six.
- Branching habit. Once pruned, stubs of small branches are occluded or healed over quicker than big branches. Branches up to 8 cm diameter are acceptable.

Thinning timetable

Pines are the most common forestry species grown and the following timetable works well for them. If you want grass to grow under the final crop trees then you will thin out as soon as you have determined which will be the final crop, and let as much light into the ground level as possible. But if you want to get a bit of cash from the trees without waiting 20 or 40 years then plan your thinning operations so that the trees chopped out can be used or sold for posts.

At the first pruning thin to 1000 stems/ha, chopping out anything not big enough to yield a post. At the second pruning at 6–8 years the trees should

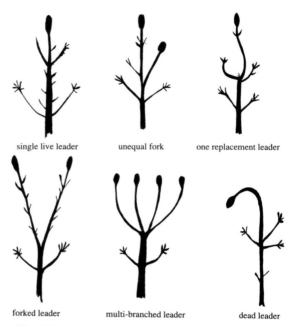

single live leader   unequal fork   one replacement leader

forked leader   multi-branched leader   dead leader

Fig. 34 **For selection for timber trees the top three are acceptable, the bottom three should be thinned out.**

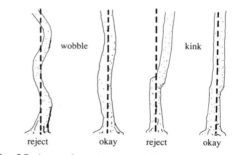

wobble   kink

reject   okay   reject   okay

Fig. 35 **Assessing stem straightness.**

average 150 mm in diameter measured 1.4 cm above the ground. So you will be thinning out about 600 or more 150 mm stems. (Don't be tempted to take the best out now, they have to go on growing for the final crop.) Then at 8–10 years the trees should be 300–350 mm in diameter and you will be keeping the best 200 or so to grow on for timber. The rest should be suitable for sale for posts.

Post thinnings should be debarked or peeled soon after they are cut down, cut to length and stacked so air can filter through to help them dry. They must also be sprayed with a fungicide to stop any mould developing. Mills and treatment plants will not take logs that show any white fungus growth.

Management for other species varies slightly. Douglas Fir take longer to reach the different pruning stages and final crop. Plant them 2.5 m by 2 m at the widest (no further apart as they have a tendency then to develop soft springwood). When they reach 8 m, prune to 4 m on the best 370. When they reach 11 m prune to 6 m. From about 30 years old you can start selectively logging the stand so that you thin out that 370 by about a third every ten years. If you want cash from them more often thin out about a sixth every five years.

Eucalypts tend to be crown shy, that is they will grow away from each other, if planted too closely and inhibit each other's growth. So space them widely initially or thin severely once they reach 10–15 m. Some species are self-pruning. If you are planting in scrubland just clear holes in the scrub rather than clear the whole area. The scrub will encourage them to grow tall and straight to the light. Make clearings about 6 m in diameter, plant two or three trees in each, and after a couple of years thin out, leaving just the best stem.

Poplars are so fast growing they should be pruned from about the third year on. when their diameter at breast height will be about 100 mm. Then prune every year or at least every second year, going up in lifts of about 2 m each time.

Stock protection

Stock and trees do not mix, at least not until the trees are a self-respecting height. If you're planting woodlots or big shelter belts they must be fenced off. It only takes a few seconds and a bite for a young tree to be worthless. So do it right.

If you want to plant individual trees around or through paddocks then there are as many ways of protecting them as there are farmers planting trees.

If you can afford it, a four-sided rail fence, creosoted a dark colour, looks great and works well. The rails must be far enough back from the

A tin drum and netting combined protect against both sheep and cattle.

Cheap but effective protection using hot wires and shade cloth.

This wooden protector lets stock graze close to the tree bole.

tree to stop larger stock leaning over and chomping the top branches as it comes up.

A 44-gallon-drum plonked over the top of a tree might not look too elegant, but it does work. Paint them all the same natural colour and they won't look so bad. Secure them to sharpened battens, stakes or posts about 50 mm off the ground. This allows air to circulate inside the drum and stops the little tree from cooking.

If you don't have drums you can make round barriers using a stiff mesh like a fine reinforcing mesh. If you are in a windy spot wrap a length of shade or shelter cloth around the hoop and lace it on. Staple it up the same as you would a drum. If kept about 50 mm off the ground sheep can push their noses in and graze almost to the tree trunk, thus stopping it becoming choked and overgrown.

There are some manufactured tree guards. One is a sleeve of plastic mesh. It is best for tall poles like willow and poplar and if pulled over the pole at planting time will stop stock nibbling the bark. However it does not stop them scratching on the pole and pushing it over or snapping it off. So the

mesh should be used with a couple of stakes.

If you have electric fences you may be able to run a hot wire out under the ground and then around the tree.

Once the trees have reached 5–6m it is probably safe to let the stock in amongst them. If you have goats though, check your tree species do not have palatable bark.

Besides farm animals, there are the wild pests to counter, especially hares, rabbits and possums. The best protection is to remove the pests. Shoot them, set traps, lay poison! Though remember traps and poison can also catch domestic pets.

If you border a rough, bush-covered area, then you may not be able to keep up with the number of pests that infiltrate. So the only option is to protect your trees. They are most attractive to pests when they have lush, soft, new growth in spring and early summer. You can make that greenery unattractive to them by wiping on a mixture of mutton fat and kerosene. It only takes a light smear to protect the young tree. You can run up and down the rows of a woodlot pretty quickly, wiping as you go. The trees should only need protecting this way for a couple of seasons, then they will be up above the rabbits and hares.

Planting

You've decided what trees you want, you've built the fences and stock barriers they need, so now you're all set to plant.

Preparing the site

If you are not planting in enormous numbers you can prepare the ground a month or so before you even get the trees. If you want to preplant spray, do it early, give the chemical time to take effect, then dig the hole, loosen the soil, chop up the turf and mix it into the soil.

If you are putting in a long shelter belt, consider ripping a couple of lines the length of the belt. This will loosen the soil, help water run into the planting zone, and break up any soil pans so the trees can get their roots down easily. If the soil is poor, now is the time to drop in a bit of blood and bone to enrich it or peat moss if it is too heavy.

How to plant

Bare-rooted trees

The sooner these are planted the better. Some will last up to a week or so if kept in the shade and moist, but the failure rate will increase with the time they are out of the ground. If you can't get to them straight away dig a trench in good soil somewhere that you can water them, put the trees in the trench *en masse* and heel the soil in around them.

Forestry planters just open a slit in the ground and bung the tree down in it, stamp the slit shut and move on to the next one. But if you want a good strike rate take a bit more time with each tree. Make one slit in the ground with your spade, make another slit about 70 mm closer to you and lean on the spade so the soil between the slits comes out. Chop it up, put the tree deep in the hole, scoop the loosened soil in around it, then pull the tree upwards till it is at the same level it was at in the nursery. Pulling it up like this makes sure the roots are all facing downwards and not caught up in a bundle or bent back upwards. Then firmly press the soil on each side of the tree. Don't stamp it to kingdom come, it won't do the tree or your knees much good.

Larger, bare-rooted trees often come with a bit of sack tied around the root ball. If the roots are already protruding don't pull the sack right off or you will damage the roots. Loosen it slightly and plant it too, as it will decompose and provide some humus for the soil. Dig a good big hole and loosen up the soil taken out. Put the tree in the hole at the same level it was at in the nursery, disturbing the roots as little as possible. But unwind any that are twisted or wound into a ball. Shovel the soil back in, hold the tree upright and firmly press the soil down.

Root trainer trees

Some forestry trees come in root trainers. There are different types. Peat pots are about the size of a yoghurt pottle. They don't have to be taken off the plant as they will decompose, but it pays to pull the bottom off so the roots can come out easily. Also remove some of the rim as if it sticks up above the soil it will act as a wick and soil moisture will be lost to the air.

Individual, plastic planter-bags must be pulled off before the tree is planted. The hard, plastic packs which hold four or five trees are hinged at the bottom and once open you can remove all four trees. The roots grow in an elongated plug and may poke out the bottom of the trainer or curl in a knot at the bottom. Chop these off before planting.

For bigger, container-grown trees, growing in their own soil, planting is much the same. Make sure your hole is big enough to allow you room to work. The soil you fill the hole in with should be loose and reasonably fertile. Cut off any roots that have wound around the inside of the container.

Poles

Willows and poplars can be planted as cuttings taken off older trees while they are dormant. Either dig a hole and plant as you would a bare-rooted tree, or else use a long fencer's crowbar to poke a hole down about 600 mm and push the pole firmly down.

Stake tall trees, at least for the first year or two until their roots are safely established.

When to plant

Plant bare-rooted, small, forestry trees at the end of winter — usually July/August.

Plant root-trainer, forestry trees before they start growing again in spring. July to September or even as late as October in the colder parts of the south.

Plant bare-rooted, big trees while they are still dormant in winter.

Plant container-grown, big trees almost any time so long as they get adequate moisture and are planted without disturbing the roots.

Poles should be cut when the adult trees are dormant in winter and planted before any green shoots show.

Care after planting

Removing competition

Small trees can suffer from grass competition. To prevent this you have four choices: plant and hope for the best; keep the grass cut or mown around the trees; mulch around the base; or spray grass regrowth.

Let me tell you a story about a guy who wanted to put in lots of trees and make up for the years he had spent chopping them down. The ground was preplant sprayed, a nice 2 m diameter circle around each spot. The trees were planted in spring and come summer were disappearing under grass regrowth. The experts all advised release spraying. This was done very carefully, using Roundup. He covered each tree while spraying around it, and only worked on still days to avoid drift onto other trees. The results after following all that advice? Each woodlot suffered a 40 to 50 per cent failure rate. I know — I filled in the blanks. The one woodlot that wasn't release sprayed had about a 4 per cent failure rate.

Now let me tell you another story set in the Far North, this time with kikuyu grass and blackberry as the villains, pine trees the goodies and yours truly the leading lady. I wanted to plant pines to choke out the baddies, but times were hard and there were no princes on white horses carrying cans of Roundup on the horizon. All the wise men said thou shalt preplant spray and release spray. Lacking a fairy godmother and magic wand, I cried and wrung my hands and planted the damned trees anyway. Now stock had been shut out of that ground for the weeks of hand wringing, so the baddies had got well away and were all tall and rank. When the trees were planted the very act of planting stomped down a circle of grass. And the baddies had been so evil and greedy they had almost outgrown themselves, so they were never able to get up and threaten to choke the trees. The bits that weren't trampled did no more than shelter the young trees and they are now growing straight and strong (and already begging to be pruned).

So the moral of these two stories is — I don't think you need to spray as much as the spray companies and some of the more academic experts suggest. Preplant spraying is, I think, a good idea. The sprayed grass will decompose and condition the soil. But after that, unless you are in a very dry area and the grass is threatening to rob all the available moisture, then I'd think twice about release spraying. If you are doing small-scale planting, preplant spray, then once the tree is in the ground put a mulch of newspaper, sacking or even black polythene around the tree, and weight it

Fig. 36 **Soften buildings by planting and use trees to link separate buildings together.**

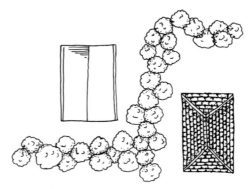

Fig. 37 **Screen buildings so only one style is visible in the same view.**

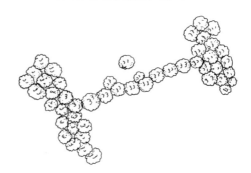

Fig. 38 **Use clumps of trees to break straight belts.**

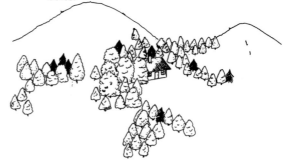

Fig. 39 **Nestle buildings in amongst trees.**

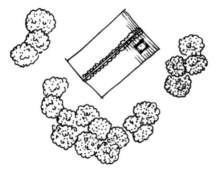

Fig. 40 **Group trees around buildings in clumps rather than straight rows to integrate them into the surroundings.**

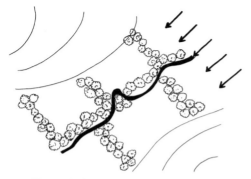

Fig. 41 **Plant shelter across valleys to stop wind funnelling.**

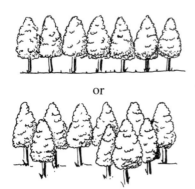

or

Fig. 42 **If a single row of shelter is used add extra trees at random.**

Fig. 43 **Avoid abrupt changes to the skyline.**

down with stones, sawdust or grass clippings. Keep the mulch away from the tree stem or it may rot and allow disease in.

Watering

Trees need moisture, especially while getting established. Obviously forestry trees have to take their chances, but the amenity trees around the homestead can be looked after. Keep a check on the soil. In dry weather mulched trees will last longer than those unmulched. Deciduous trees will show moisture stress by beginning to get autumn colours. By the time a tree wilts or shows obvious signs of dryness a lot of damage has been done so it's best to check the soil regularly through a dry spell.

Landscaping

Landscaping, like fashion, goes through many fads and you may not particularly like what 'rules' are in vogue just now. But if you are going to the expense of buying trees and the trouble of planting and protecting them then it is wise to have some overall plan. (See Figs. 36–45.) There are landscape consultants around who may be able to advise you. The patterns they like may give you ideas worth considering.

At the turn of the century, when the countryside was being 'developed' by settlers and pioneers, many brought the species and landscape ideas they were familiar with. But New Zealand has features and attractions of its own. Generally a very formal planting pattern conflicts with the wild, natural, Godzone qualities. You may like formal patterns: straight, neat shelter belts; tidy woodlots with trees in nice, straight rows; imposing lanes of poplars; but consider whether your property is really suitable. Certainly around Cambridge, avenues of poplars and other introduced deciduous trees have become a feature of the landscape and it works. But if I tried to impose the same ideas up in Hokianga it would look totally out of place. So you decide — formal or natural?

If you want to go for formal then it has to be done right. Your shelter belts must be even. The proportions must be right, too. The size of the woodlot must match the landscape. If you want to enclose a space with shelter belts they need to be close enough together so the space between them feels right. Simplicity is the main key in formal plantings. Keep to one species in your rows and woodlots, keep spacings even and make sure the overall effect is tidy.

But few landscapes suit a formal pattern. Most can be made more interesting with more natural, softer planting patterns. Sometimes this is difficult in a farming situation as fencing is easier in nice, straight lines. Electric fencing is a great help here. Not only is it cheaper, but the wire tension does not have to be so great, so you can put posts further out of line and it is relatively easy to run a hot wire out and around odd trees.

To achieve a natural planting effect some of the guidelines are:

- Follow the landscape rather than the fence-lines. For instance, plant gullies with tongues of trees extending slightly up the hillsides.
- Avoid straight lines. The straightness of shelter belts can be broken by planting clumps at the

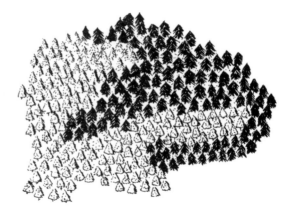

Fig. 44 **Merge blocks of different timber species**.

ends and letting a few individual trees extend well into the paddock. Or instead of planting one belt at an end of a paddock, plant several big clumps of trees at random throughout it.

- Don't plant trees out as individuals. Plant them in clumps and vary the spacing between them.

Trees make a landscape more attractive, reduce erosion, provide shade for stock and eventually...timber.

Fig. 45 **Merge forestry trees into different species and increase the tree spacing near the boundary to make a gradual transition to grassland**.

- Avoid dramatic contrasts. If using more than one species in a group then make the changes subtle. If varying species in a group keep the stronger, darker trees in the centre.
- Mix species in the woodlot, easing more into a second, lighter species near the boundary with the grassland. Then randomly dot some outside the woodlot fence, thus bringing the forest out into the paddock. Increase the spacing of trees near the woodlot edge.
- If planting two types of timber trees, don't make definite demarcations between the two blocks.
- Avoid regular patterns. Don't plant your forest trees in rows up the hill away from you. Instead plant around the contour of the hill. Then you will not have your eye caught by a regular pattern or the irritation of seeing where the planters did not quite get the rows right.
- Avoid alternating species all along a shelter belt. Make sure the two species are not in too great a contrast to each other.
- Avoid running shelter belts up and over ridges or having woodlots start and stop on the top of a hill. The boundary between earth and sky is an important landscape feature and shouldn't be radically altered.
- Trees around buildings should form a backdrop not a definite row. You don't have to screen out the building completely, just a glimpse of it through the trees can make it more interesting.
- Tie all your plantings in together. Run clumps of trees between belts and woodlots to tie them together and give some unity to the landscape.

Two-tier farming — plant up to 100 stems a hectare without reducing grass growth.

- Emphasise natural features of the landscape. Plant lush green species along valley floors and water courses to emphasise the lushness of the valley. Keep drier looking plants like pines and eucalypts for drier, hotter sites.

Microclimate factors to consider:

- Straight dense shelter belts can cause the wind to accelerate if they are not square on to it. Air speed will also accelerate through any gap in the belt.
- Very dense planting can reduce air flow so that pockets of frost on valley floors or on flat areas may take longer to disperse.
- Orientate shelter belts north–south to maximise the sun on each side of the belt.
- The north side of hills or tree plantations is the warmest. Make the most of these sites, putting your sun-loving trees there.
- Shelter belts need to run across valleys to stop wind and cold air funnelling down them.

57

Tree Common name	Latin name	Uses Erosion Control	Shelter	Shade	Fodder	Bees	Timber	Distribution	Description	Comments
Beech	Nothofagus			*		N	*	Taupo to Te Anau	Ht to 30 m.	Usually grows in uniform stands.
Five finger	Pseudopanax arboreus			*		N W		All NZ	Ht to 8 m. Large five lobed leaves. Creamy purple flowers.	
Kamahi	Weinmannia racemosa and W. silvicola					N Sp/Au		All NZ	Ht to 25 m. Racemes of white flowers in profusion.	Two closely related species.
Karaka	Corynocarpus laevigatus	*		*		N Sp		Coastal	Ht to 15 m. Trunk to 60 cm. Big dark leaves. Orange fruit 4 cm long.	Germinates readily.
Kauri	Agathis australis			*			*	Mostly in NI	Ht to 30 m. Straight trunk with little taper. Slow growing.	Doesn't like frosts or wind.
Kowhai	Sophora tetraptera & S. microphylla			*		NP W/Sp		All NZ	Feathery leaves and drooping yellow flowers.	NI and SI kowhais; select for your site.
Kohuhu	Pittosporum tenuifolium	*	*			NP Sp		All NZ	Ht to 9 m. Pale leaves. Red/black flowers.	Hardy and quick growing.
Lacebark or Ribbonwood	Hoherias	*				N Au		All NZ depending on species.	Ht to 6–11 m. Clusters of white flowers.	Includes five species.
Mahoe or Whiteywood	Melicytus ramiflorus					NP Su		All NZ	Ht to 10 m. Whitish bark. Yellow/white flowers, purple berries.	Can stand wind but may become mis-shapen.
Manatu or Ribbonwood	Plagianthus betulinus	*		*				All NZ to 450 m	Ht to 15 m. Trunk 1 m diameter. Bushy when young. Adult leaves 7.5 x 5 cm	Largest native deciduous.
Native fuchsia	Fuchsia excorticata					N Sp		All NZ	Ht to 14 m. Trunk 60–80 cm. Pink/purple flowers, black berries.	World's largest fuchsia. Berries are edible.

Tree Common name	Latin name	Uses Erosion Control	Shelter	Shade	Fodder	Bees	Timber	Distribution	Description	Comments
Ngaio	Myoporum raetum	*						Nth of Otago often coastal	Ht to 10 m. Trunk 30 cm. Fleshy narrow leaves. White flowers, purple berries.	A spreading branching habit.
Pohutukawa	Metrosideros excelsa	*		*		N Su	*	From Nelson north, often coastal	Ht to 20 m. Usually spreading branches. Red flowers.	Called the NZ Xmas tree for its bright Dec. show.
Quintinia	Quintinia serrata					N Sp		Taranaki northwards	Ht to 9 m. Panicles of star shaped flowers. Pale, blotchy leaves.	Open branching.
Rangiora	Brachyglottis repanda	*						Kaikoura northwards	Ht to 7 m. Large leathery leaves, furry underside. Panicles of tiny white flowers.	Leaves have medicinal use as poultices.
Rewarewa or NZ honeysuckle	Knightsia excelsia					N Sp	*	NI and Marlborough	Ht to 30 m. Tall narrow form. Leathery woody leaves 10–15 x 4 cm.	Wood is not durable used outside.
Rimu	Dacrydium cupressinum			*			*	All NZ	Ht to 40 m. Beautiful tree, feathery needle-like foliage.	Very slow growing, hardy but dislikes wind.
Totara	Podocarpus totara			*			*	All NZ	Ht to 30 m. Small prickly leaves, red wood and bark.	Hardy and fairly quick growing.
Wineberry or Makomako	Aristotelia serrata	*		*		N Sp		All NZ to 1050 m	Ht to 10 m. Trunk 30 cm. Serrated leaves. Pink/cream flowers, red/black berries.	One of first trees to occur naturally on slip sites.

Key: N — Nectar source, P — Pollen source, Au — Autumn, Sp — Spring, Su — Summer, W — Winter.

Table 10. **Native trees and their uses.**

Common name	Latin name	Uses Erosion Control	Shelter	Shade	Fodder	Bees	Timber	Firewood	Description	Comments
Alders	Aldrus e.g. A. rubra, A. incana A. glutinosa.	*	*			NP W	*	*	30 species. Deciduous.	Generally hardy. Can be pruned. Leguminous. Don't use in very windy areas.
Ash	Fraxinus			*			*		Ht to 30 m. Wide spreading branches. Deciduous.	Some species have different coloured autumn foliage.
Arizona cypress	Cupressus arizonica		*						Ht to 15 m. Attractive blue-green foliage. Evergreen.	Can stand wide range of conditions.
Bead tree	Melia			*					Ht to 12 m. Lilac flowers and yellow fruit. Semi-deciduous.	Doesn't like less than -8°C. Berries are poisonous.
Bean tree	Catalpa			*					Ht to 15 m. Large heart shaped leaves, white flowers, long beans.	
Birches	Betula			*		P Su	*	*	Attractive golden autumn foliage. Deciduous.	Hardy and can stand cold but may be mis-shapen in severe wind. Several types.
Beech				*			*		Deciduous. Different species have different autumn colours.	Generally hardy.
Chestnut	Castanea			*					Ht 20–25 m. Large many-lobed leaves. Deciduous.	Dislikes wet sites, Otherwise hardy.
Douglas fir	Pseudotsuga menziesii		*	*			*		Ht to 100 m. Evergreen.	Hardy. Doesn't mind cold but takes twice as long as a pine to reach millable size.
Elm	Ulmus			*			*		Ht to 40 m. Deciduous.	

Tree Common name	Latin name	Uses Erosion Control	Shelter	Shade	Fodder	Bees	Timber	Firewood	Description	Comments
Eucalypt or gum tree	Eucalyptus		*	*		N Su/Au	*	*	Huge variety within 600 different species. Evergreen.	Check with your nursery for right species for your situation.
Fir	Abies		*	*			*	*	Ht 30–60 m. Evergreen conifers.	Hardy. Likes 1000 to 2000 mm rainfall and cold winters.
Hickory	Carya		*	*	*		*		Luxuriant foliage. Deciduous.	Produces edible nuts.
Honey locust	Gleditsia triacanthos		*	*	*		*		Deciduous. Produces edible bean pods 40 cm long.	Leguminous. Timber is ground durable. Space 10 to 12 m apart on pasture.
Japanese cedar	Cryptomeria japonica		*				*		Evergreen. Prickly short needle like foliage. Low branching.	Doesn't mind clay or frosts. Some species change colour to bronze in autumn.
Juniper	Juniperus communis		*						Ht 7–10 m. Low branching. Evergreen.	Needs trimming to stay tidy.
Larch	Larix		*	*			*		Deciduous conifer. Ht to 30 m.	Prefers cold climate. Timber is moderately ground durable.
Lawson cypress	Chaemaecyparis lawsoniana		*				*		Ht to 60 m. Evergreen.	Very hardy and resistant to windthrow but is subject to canker.
Leyland cypress	Cupressocyparis Leylandii		*						Evergreen with pretty feathery foliage.	Very hardy, can withstand cold.
Lime tree	Tilia		*		N Su				Ht to 30 m. A stately tree with masses of flowers. Deciduous.	Check which species are suitable for bees, some are fatal to them.

Table 11. **Exotic trees and their uses.**

Tree Common name	Latin name	Uses Erosion Control	Shelter	Shade	Fodder	Bees	Timber	Firewood	Description	Comments
Macrocarpa	Cupressus macrocarpa		*				*	*	Ht to 30m. Some have buttressed trunks. Use elite trees for timber.	Timber doesn't need treating. Has been connected with abortion in cows.
Mexican cypress	Cupressus lusitanica		*						Ht to 30 m. Evergreen.	Very hardy but dislikes salt winds.
Oak	Quercus			*	*		*		Attractive deciduous trees. Several varieties with different autumn colours.	Slow growing. Stock will enjoy acorns.
Pencil cedar	Juniperus virginiana		*				*		Ht to 25 m. Narrow columnar form. Evergreen.	Frost hardy. Doesn't mind clay soils.
Pepper tree	Schinus			*					Ht to 15 m. Similar form to weeping willow.	Quick growing. Doesn't like cold.
Pine	Pinus e.g. P. radiata, P. nigra, P. ponderosa	*	*	*			*	*	Ht 30–50 m. Needle foliage. Evergreen.	Should be millable in 25 years. Most common forestry tree.
Poplar	Populus e.g. P. alba, P. pyramidalis, P. deltoides	*	*	*	*		*		All deciduous. Many varieties, and forms, mostly tall narrow form.	Easy to grow from poles. Check for a species resistant to rust. Wood used for veneers.
Redwood	Sequoia		*	*			*		Ht to 110 m. Evergreen conifers.	World's tallest trees. Very long lived. 50–80 yr rotation for timber.
Robinia or Black locust	Robinia pseudoacacia					NP Sp			Ht to 20 m. Deciduous. White fragrant flowers.	Dislikes wet. Can sucker and spread. Leguminous.

Tree		Uses							Description	Comments
Common name	Latin name	Erosion Control	Shelter	Shade	Fodder	Bees	Timber	Firewood		
Sheoak	Casuarina		*				*		Ht to 15–25 m. Evergreen with fine needle-like leaves.	Avoid if you are running fibre animals as needles will contaminate the fleeces.
Sycamore	Acer pseudoplatanus			*		N Sp			Ht to 30 m. Deciduous. Similar appearance to Plane trees.	Large and quick growing.
Walnut	Juglans			*	*		*		Ht to 15–35 m. Deciduous.	Slow growing. Edible nuts.
Wattle	Acacias e.g. A. dealbata, A. baileyana			*		N W	*	*	900 species. Variety of forms and heights and uses.	Generally quick growing and hardy though some don't like cold. Check with nursery.
Western red cedar	Thuja plicata		*	*			*		Ht to 55 m. Evergreen.	Prefers over 1000 mm rain. Timber is light and easy to work.
Willow	Salix e.g. S. viminalis, S. cinerea	*	*	*			*	*	About 300 species. Deciduous. Generally pale green narrow leaves.	Grow from cuttings. Can be pruned. Check with nursery to get right species for your purpose.

Key: N — Nectar source, P — Pollen source, Au — Autumn, Sp — Spring, Su — Summer, W — Winter.

Table 11. Exotic trees and their uses.

7. Weeds

Most properties have some weeds. A small plot of blackberry vines supplying fruit for jam is fine, but once it starts creeping on to good pasture land it is time to think about control. Control is the key word with weeds. Eradication is much harder, even the herbicide companies nowadays only talk about control. With a well-planned programme you might well wipe a weed out, but don't expect to do it all in one year or you are likely to be disappointed.

How you go about weed control will depend to some extent on your philosophy and to some extent on your bank balance. You may be totally against sprays and chemicals, or you may just be looking for the quickest, easiest way out of the problem regardless of the consequences. Whatever your school of thought, try to consider the options with an open mind to get the best for your situation.

I don't like plastering chemicals around the place and avoid them if at all possible but I believe they do have their place. Some are of low toxicity with a short half-life and do little long-term damage and can be invaluable help. But it is silly to get the spray gun out to clean up a handful of plants which could be grubbed out in the time it takes to find the gun, mix the chemical and clean up afterwards.

Natural controls — the three Gs

Goats
These are a great aid to weed control. They chew weeds out, fertilise the ground and produce meat, milk or fibre at the same time. Goats love to browse on weeds, but if you are farming for their fibre or milk production be sure not to stress them.

There is no need to push them hard, just graze them as normal and keep bringing them back to the weedy paddocks. They will continue to nibble away at the problem and eventually wipe it out. Push them hard and you might get rid of the weed sooner but you'll end up with problems in your goats. (See Chapter 10.)

Grazing
Cattle, when mob-stocked can stomp and chew out rushes; sheep will chew out Californian thistles or Scotch thistles down to ground level. The secret of successful mob-stocking for weed control is to hold a lot of animals on a small area for a short time, perhaps a day, or half a day, before shifting them onto another small plot. That way they eat everything in sight but get enough fresh food each day so they do not starve or sicken. Bring the mob back to the weeds every few weeks. Continually chewing off its green growth will eventually kill most of them.

Grubbing
This might sound like hard work, but it removes weeds for good. Once you have ripped the roots out that plant is dead. Of course it is not feasible for a large infestation (unless there are lots of you), but where you have just a handful of plants creeping in it is the cheapest form of control. I made a rule to grub out five blackberry plants a day on my place and as a result cleared up a considerable area in a few months. What's more it stayed clear. If grubbing, make sure you get as much root as possible.

Biological controls
DSIR and MAF have done a lot of work on natural insect pests of weeds. So we now have ragwort

Weed	Spray to use	How to apply	When	Discussion
Blackberry	Escort	35 gm/100 litres	Nov–May or whenever cane is in leaf	Don't spray bare canes, and don't graze sprayed ground for 3 days.
Broom	2,4,5-T	1 in 300	When in flush of new growth	No longer being made, so hard to get hold of.
	Tordon 50D	1 in 200	When in flush of new growth	Tordon is residual — may affect clovers for up to 2 years.
Californian thistles	MCPA	Per instructions	When plants are small, spray	Cultivate first, then spray regrowth.
Gorse	2,4,5-T	1 in 300	When in flush of new growth	Don't burn gorse, spray green growing plants.
	Tordon Brushkiller	1 in 400	When in flush of new growth	Don't burn gorse, spray green growing plants.
	Tordon crystals	Sprinkle in drip zone round plant	Before gentle rain	Expensive way to do it but good for a few plants.
	Escort	Per instructions		Expensive.
	Roundup	Use with additive Pulse		Expensive.
Rushes	Roundup	Wipe on or spray	In growing period	Gives good kill; burn later to clean up debris.
	Paraquat	Per instructions	In growing period	Very toxic.
Sedge	Roundup	Wipe on or spray	In growing period	Works well, but don't miss any plants as they are very invasive.
Tobacco weed	Tordon	Spray plants to 1.2 m high	In growing period	Cut large plants over and paint stem with one part Tordon and 20 parts diesel.
	Weedazol 4L	Spray plants to 1.2 m high	In growing period	
Thistles (Scotch)	2,4-D	Spray	Whenever a problem	Try grubbing or grazing them out first.
(Nodding)	Tordon 50D	1 in 200 for spot treatment	Whenever a problem	For a few plants.
	2,4-D	2–3 litres/ha	Seedling stage July–Sept	Spot treat with Tordon in following years.

Table 12. **Weed control.**

flea beetles, Scotch thistle weevils, a moth that preys on alligator weed and a mite that attacks gorse. These controls are unlikely to wipe a weed out, but can keep them in check.

Chemical controls

If using chemicals, do so carefully, following the instructions. Avoid getting chemical in contact with your skin and don't breathe any of the vapour. Wear long sleeves and trousers, breathe through an air filter and wash those clothes at the end of each spraying session.

Always spray on a calm day or early in the morning when the air is still. Keep the spray nozzle close to the weeds, don't spray around in the air. Keep the sprayer pressure as low as possible and use nozzle shields to get better control over the direction of the spray drift. Pick fine weather. Sprays vary in how they are affected by rain but be sure the spray will at least get a good chance to dry on the plant and be absorbed. So watch the forecast and stop work if rain is likely later in the day.

Part 3: The animals

8. Stock sense

To farm stock well you need to develop some stock sense. The well experienced farmer can wander through a flock of sheep or a herd of cattle and just 'know' when something is not right: usually from picking up on some behaviour or stance that is not normal. So it is important to observe your animals, get to know what is normal and then you will be able to pick up any changes. Catch problems early this way and you have a much greater chance of curing them.

Spend time with your stock. A good dairy farmer will wander quietly around the herd once it is grazing and pick up signs of cows coming in heat, or cows with sore feet or whatever that might not be noticed in the hurly-burly of milking. Likewise on a smallfarm you will see troubles much easier when animals are relaxed out in the paddock than jammed up and nervous in the yards. Treat animals with firmness and kindness. Above all 'stay cool' and give out calm 'vibes', not anger or frustration. Animals sense bad vibes very quickly.

Work *with* the animals' natures and instincts, not *against* them. For instance, sheep are flock animals, so work them in flocks. So, if one gets through a fence, run a few more out with it then bring them all back together instead of trying to drive that one on its own. Single sheep go into a panic and charge off in any direction. Work them in groups of at least four and they will be calmer and easier to manipulate.

Cattle are also herd animals. Even if you don't have space for many animals, just two will be company for each other. But if you decide to put one in the freezer then you'd better dispatch the second at the same time, or get a replacement companion quickly.

When moving stock, always take them quietly. Bunch them up first then move towards the bunch slowly. You will find animals tolerate you at a certain distance; any closer and they feel threatened and have to move back to restore that social distance. Go slowly until you work out just how much pressure you need to apply to get them to move, and apply it gradually. If you go too fast they are likely to scatter and stampede off in all directions. Once they start to move, ease the pressure off. They will still want to move away from you, but this way will not be in a panic, and you will have time to guide them to the left or right.

If trying to turn an animal, you need to find its 'point of balance', an imaginary spot usually just behind their shoulder blade. When you move to the front of that point they move back and vice versa. Work on the point of balance of the leaders, get them going where you want, the rest will follow. If working on your own extend your influence by carrying a long stick or a plastic electric fence rod which is very visible.

Dogs can be a wonderful help at shifting stock. But I don't believe it is fair to use a working dog on a smallfarm unless you are shifting stock daily. Dogs are bred with the instinct to work. If they don't get regular use they become frustrated and try to muster the chooks, the cats, the kids, the traffic. And then when you do want them to do a job they are so excited about it they are no help at all.

If your fence layout is good, and if you work your animals quietly, then moving stock is easy enough without a dog. There are times when a bit of a bark is indispensable. But your poodle or chihuahua will do. I have a small, scruffy terrier with no instinct for herding sheep whatsoever. But she knows what sit, stay and speak up all mean and is all the dog I'll ever need.

If you are running goats, pigs, or horses then learning to work with their nature takes a different form. Most will sell their soul for food. Goats far prefer to be lead to a new paddock than chased. If they discover that you dish out goat pellets from time to time they will soon learn to come when called. And who wants to spend all day chasing the horse around the paddock if it will come galloping up eagerly for treats?

Pigs obviously can take a bit of handling to shift — but there is no need to make life difficult. Just run a trail of food where you want them to go, or lead them into a fresh pen or paddock with their slops bucket.

9. Sheep

I have started the livestock section with a chapter on sheep for a good reason. I believe they are the best way for a smallfarmer to start if he or she is a beginner in the livestock keeping business. They are small enough for you not to have to be an All Black forward to handle them (though it sometimes would help), and need only a limited amount of regular care. It's cheaper to find out from a few sheep that you cannot handle livestock than from more expensive animals, such as goats or cattle.

But sheep are also worth keeping for their own sake. A good sheep will produce about 5 kg of wool a year. The same animal can produce one or two lambs which in six months should be ready for the table or freezer. If you want your land to look like the proverbial model smallfarm with lovely, clean, rolling green pasture, then small stock like sheep are the way to go. They graze pasture much closer and more evenly than bigger stock, and their small hooves soon smooth out any irregularities and tramp in dung and fertiliser.

However, sheep do require regular care and maintenance. It is not much in terms of time, but it is essential. And to provide even that little bit of care you need proper facilities. Fences must be good; either seven wire and batten, netting, or nine wires strained tight. You need some sort of yarding set-up, which the sheep will enter willingly, where you can catch them for individual attention. (See the yard suggestions in Chapter 2.) Some people just don't like sheep and if you are an intolerant type, the chances are you won't either.

Once you come to know your animals you will recognise individuals in the flock and understand some of their social hierarchy and behaviour. Prepare yourself for some frustrations, but as you learn about sheep they will be learning about your property and what you expect of them and it should get easier. Meanwhile, you will be gaining valuable stock handling experience and hopefully getting good returns in the way of meat and wool.

Breeds

All our New Zealand sheep breeds produce both meat and wool, but they vary greatly in the quantity, quality and type of both that they grow. As well, some breeds are better suited to particular climates than others. The following selection should cover most situations and they are breeds which are generally available.

Wool breeds
Merinos
These are normally run extensively (few stock per hectare). They weigh 35–45 kg and produce 3.5–5 kg of very fine, 18–25 micron wool. They have distinctive curling horns, white face and pink nose and can stand severe cold.

Halfbred
These are the result of crossing some English breed such as Romney or Leicester (nowadays Coopworths may be used) with the Merino, still with the aim of producing fine wool, but also of getting a lamb carcass that is worth killing. Like the purebred Merino, the Halfbred is usually farmed extensively on high country stations, but I know of some coloured halfbreds kept by smallfarmers for their lovely spinning wool. Halfbreds can vary a lot in looks, some throwing

to the Merino and others to the Romney. They weigh 40–50 kg and produce 4–5 kg of 25–31 micron wool.

Corriedale

Sometimes Corriedales are called the 'inbred halfbred'. They were developed last century by crossing longwool breeds like the Lincoln or Leicester with Merinos and interbreeding the progeny. They are mainly run on high country sheep stations. They weigh 45–55 kg and clip 4.5–6 kg of relatively fine (28–33 micron) wool.

Lincolns

These are distinctive for their long, heavy fleece which hangs in ringlets. In the pioneer days they were the most popular breed as they seemed to do well in heavily timbered areas and their coarse strong wool (39–41 microns) resisted snagging. They are fairly large sheep, weighing 55–65 kg and producing 5–7 kg of lustrous wool a year.

Meat breeds

If you are not interested in home spinning and only want sheep to put lamb or mutton in the freezer then you may prefer a meat breed.

Dorset

There are polled and horned Dorsets. Dorsets are known for their very white wool and skins which are often valued for fashion leather garments. They usually have pink noses and white feet. I had a Dorset ram at one stage, and vowed he was the ugliest thing on four feet. But he did produce big, beautiful meaty lambs that never went overfat, and he was so docile to handle at shearing even though he grew to an enormous size that I was quite endeared to him eventually. Dorsets normally only clip about 3 kg of wool but it is very white and about 27–32 microns. Dorsets are also valued for their extended breeding season which has made them useful in trials on out-of-season lambing.

Hampshire Down

This breed thrives on lowland pasture. The mature sheep is a big animal weighing 55–65 kg and the young stock gain weight rapidly. The Hampshire

Merino rams.

Corriedale rams.

Lincoln ewes and lambs.

Dorset horn ram.

Polled Dorset ram.

Hampshire Down ram.

Southdown ram.

Black-faced Suffolks.

Down is predominantly white but has a dark face and legs. Their wool is fine, 26–30 microns, but they clip only 2–3 kg a year.

Southdowns

These are an early-maturing, chunky, compact sheep. They have lost favour slightly as a result of the drive for leaner meat, but are still used over other breeds to produce early lambs for slaughter. The Southdown-Romney cross lamb can grow to 13–15 kg in 12–15 weeks. They produce only 2–2.5 kg of wool which is very bulky (high volume for its weight) and quite fine (23–28 microns).

Suffolk

These handsome, black-faced and black-legged sheep are popular with smallfarmers because of their distinctive looks and big, lean carcass. They are a hardy sheep, weighing 55–60 kg when mature and clipping 2.5–3 kg of 30–35 micron wool. The meat is valued for its high ratio of meat to fat.

South Suffolk

This relatively new breed (first registered in 1958) combines the quick maturity of the Southdown with the high ratio of meat to fat of the Suffolk. They normally weigh 50–60 kg when mature and have dark brown face, ears and legs. They only clip 2–3 kg of wool of 28–32 microns.

Dual purpose breeds

If you want both meat for the freezer or saleable lambs and a bit of pocket money from your wool clip then go for one of the dual purpose breeds.

Romney

In the 1960s more than 75 per cent of the national flock were Romneys. But since then the Perendale and Coopworth have so gained in popularity that the purebred Romney has dropped to about 50 per cent of the national flock. One reason for this was that too many breeders over-emphasised selection for wool and ignored easy care traits. But from about 1970 many breeders began selecting for a more active, hardy type of Romney with clear legs and face which required little shepherding. (See Fig. 46.)

South Suffolk ram.

Fig. 46 **Clear-faced and woolly-faced sheep**.

A good Romney should produce 5–6 kg of relatively coarse 33–37 micron wool. A mature sheep will weigh 45–55 kg. The carcass is good for butchering but not as early maturing as some of the meat breeds.

Romney ram.

Coopworth

These were first registered in 1968 and were developed by crossing the Border Leicester and Romney. Now there are more than 11 million Coopworths in New Zealand. Their popularity stems from their easy care characteristics, heavy fleece weight — 4.5–6 kg of 35–38 micron wool — and a very high lambing percentage, twins and triplets being the norm rather than the exception. The Coopworth fleece is white, quite lustrous and excellent for spinning.

Coopworth ewes.

Perendale

Developed by crossing Cheviots and Romneys. The Perendale is a small, active sheep which is a great help for hill country farmers if stock have to be moved some distance. But it is a nuisance when you want a sheep to sit still on the shearing board for a few minutes while you get the wool off it. They are hardy, easy care sheep. They clip

Perendale ewe.

72

Cheviot ram.

3.5-5 kg of wool of about 31–35 microns. The wool is bulky and is usually of good colour.

Cheviots

These are one of the parent breeds of the Perendale. They are a hardy sheep but only produce a light fleece of 2–3 kg of 28–33 microns. However, the wool is valued for its high bulk and resilience (the bounce back factor in a carpet). They are a small compact sheep weighing 40–50 kg with white face and legs, both free of wool.

Coloured sheep

These are not a breed as such. Black or coloured sheep can normally be found in most breeds. Often when driving past farmland at lambing time you may notice one little black lamb amongst hundreds of white ones. This is a genetic throwback. If you are wishing to breed up coloured stock, many farmers will consider selling these freak coloured lambs at reasonable prices. But remember, their genetic make-up means when they come to lamb themselves they are still likely to throw white off-spring. On the other hand buying coloured sheep which have been selected for colour over several generations should ensure black progeny.

Management

How you manage your sheep will depend largely on the class of your land and how quickly your pasture can recover after grazing. I have known smallfarms where up to 30 sheep/ha were run successfully, but on my own rough Northland

block which is subject to dry summers and wet winters, I have balanced out at only about 8/ha. When deciding your stocking rate consider what the neighbours can run through the year, then whether your block is as fertile as theirs and as well subdivided. The more paddocks you have the more control you will have over what the stock eat and when, so you can make sure no feed is wasted. It is the grass you can grow rather than the area of your farm which will decide how many stock you can feed.

Remember with a small block you do not have the leeway of a bigger farm, so that come spring, if you started with 20 sheep and half of them produce twins and the rest singles, by summer you will have 50 mouths looking for food. That is a radical increase and if your place dries out then things can get awfully tight awfully fast.

Generally, the more heavily stocked you are the more care you have to give a flock, the more subdivision into small paddocks you need and the more susceptible you are to trouble if Mother Nature does a dirty on you with a drought or harsh winter.

Also, consider what you got those sheep for. If you want nice fat lamb for the freezer, you are more likely to get it with fewer animals on the place. If you have too many you could easily end up with a heap of scrawny lambs you don't want to kill for yourself and no one else wants either.

Grazing management

In the old days farmers used to put sheep out on the hills and leave them undisturbed in the same paddock until they had to be brought in for shearing or whatever. This was called set-stocking and sheep numbers had to be set so that the sheep all got enough to eat by grazing the grass off as it grew.

But now farmers recognise the value of rotational grazing, involving closer subdivision, tighter stocking and shifting sheep regularly to new paddocks. The idea is to have sufficient paddocks to shift stock regularly and thus allow grazed pasture time to recover before it is grazed again. (See Chapter 4.) How long this takes will vary according to your location and the season. In spring in Northland, 20 days might be long enough for the grass to get back to a good grazeable length, in winter further down country it might be 100 days. The rule is, the slower the growth, the slower the rotation.

How effectively you can slow the rotation down depends to some extent on how many paddocks you have. If your farm is divided into four paddocks and you decide the sheep must stay in each one a fortnight, you may find that in winter the sheep have chewed it out in a week or less, and therefore have to starve the rest of the fortnight. But you can slow the rotation down without starving the sheep by break fencing. This is easiest to achieve with temporary electric fences (flexinet is ideal) which you move each day, controlling exactly how much of a break they get.

Good winter management is the key to good farming. If your stock are fed well during the winter the rest of the year will largely take care of itself. During winter your sheep should be in lamb, and while you do not want them to get fat, you do want them well fed, especially in the last couple of months of their pregnancy when the lamb embryo will be growing rapidly. You need to be able to feed them well without hammering the pasture because this must be able to come away well in spring. Once the ewes have lambed their appetites will suddenly double.

Getting just the right balance during winter is important. If you underfeed, your sheep run the risk of sleepy sickness and some of the metabolic diseases. (See 'Problems', page 90.) If you overfeed, you run the risk of lambing and bearing troubles. It is also important to synchronise lambing with the start of the spring grass growth so there is plenty of feed for ewes with lambs at foot, so they can milk well and give the lambs a good start. A ewe produces 70 per cent of her milk in the first five weeks after lambing and to do that she needs good spring pasture.

You can tie weaning in with your pasture situation. Normally farmers consider weaning at about 12 weeks, though if lambs have been grazing out in the paddocks with their mothers their rumens will have matured enough to do without milk if necessary from the time they are 8 weeks old. So weaning times can be flexible.

Try to anticipate whether you are likely to run short of feed later in the season. If you think you could, for instance if it looks like being a really dry summer, then wean early. The ewes can rough it while you give the best feed available to the lambs. But if feed has already run out then delay weaning. Keep the ewes on the best feed available so they can continue feeding the lambs well. Alternatively take the lambs off the mothers and sell them as stores for someone else to finish.

Once you have weaned lambs and if you intend to finish them to prime weights then they get top feed priority. To have them gaining weight to the best of their ability the scientists say shift them on to fresh pasture before they have grazed a paddock down below 3–5 cm in length. If you work it right you will get the lambs prime before April and away for slaughter, and then your ewes can go back to top feed priority before they go to the ram. At tupping time you want your ewes gaining in weight. (See 'Breeding', page 75.)

After mating you are back to the winter cycle. Try to hold the condition of the ewes for the first month of their pregnancy then after that you can push them a bit harder on a bit of clean up work. But in the last two months of pregnancy they must go back onto good feed as the lamb embryo will be making big demands on them. If you want to get all scientific about it and have a set of scales, Table 13 gives some target weights to aim for at different stages. Note that there will be variation between sheep breeds and hill or lowland situations.

Time	Age	Target weight
Birth	0 days	5 kg
Weaning	90 days	20 kg
	240 days	35 kg
Mating	575 days	55 kg

Table 13. **Target weights for sheep.**

Drenching regime

The need for worm control will vary according to your location, the stock you are running, how many and the season. Wet climates tend to be worse for parasite problems than dry or frosty areas. Check with your vet on the need for drenching locally. (See 'Internal parasites', page 86.)

What drench to use

There are three main families of drenches. The first is based on the Thibendazole molecule and includes Nemafax, Panacur, Rintal, Synanthic, Systamex, Thibenzole, Telmin RLT and Valbazen. The second is based on Levamisole and includes Anthelpor, Citarin 1, Exhelm E, Nilverm, Nilzan, Ripercol and Riporon. The third and newest group is based on Avermectin, for instance Ivomec, which may also control some external parasites on some animals.

They should all work, but parasites can develop an immunity to a particular drench family. To avoid this, change drench type every year.

How to drench

For a few animals you may not want the expense of a calibrated drenching gun, so an old injection syringe with millilitres marked on will do fine. Just suck up the required amount of drench according to the manufacturer's instructions, insert the syringe in the side of the mouth (not the front where the teeth are or you will end up with a crushed syringe), tilt the animal's head slightly and squeeze the liquid in. Remove the syringe and hold the mouth closed for a few seconds until it has swallowed. Using a gun the technique is basically the same, but don't tilt the head back too far or squirt the fluid too far back down the throat or it may go into the lungs. This can have dire consequences.

Shearing times

When and how often you shear also depends on sheep type, climate and the market you are aiming for. Fine-woolled sheep run in the South Island are usually shorn once a year in winter. Blades or snow combs are used which leave about 1 cm of wool on as protection against the climate. One of the advantages of winter shearing is it produces a stronger fibre. This is because any wool break which occurs will have grown out to the end of the fibre. With summer shearing wool breaks will be half-way along the fibre. (See Fig. 47.) Wool breaks occur when the sheep is stressed, through cold, for example, and lack of feed in winter.

In the north shearing six monthly is recommended because the warm, moist climate leads to pink fleeces which start to rot and break down, particularly along the back of the sheep. Shearing in May and November works well. After the May shear sheep have time to grow a bit of wool before the worst of winter and do not have enough weight of fleece to get cast if they get wet through while heavy in lamb. Shearing again in November removes the main clip before the heat of summer and danger of fly strike. Another option is eight monthly shearing; for instance, February, October, June, February and so on. This produces a slightly longer staple but the change in shearing times can get confusing for both you and your sheep.

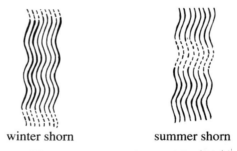

winter shorn   summer shorn

Fig. 47 **Wool staples showing position of wool break**.

Foot care

Sheep with sore feet do not graze well and if they don't graze they won't put on meat or wool. Problems usually show up in winter when damp gets in between the toes or under any excess horn. At the May shear trim up any that are overlong and treat any footrot cases. (See 'Problems', page 89, and Fig. 48.)

Breeding

On a smallfarm you need to consider whether it is worth your while breeding your own sheep or whether it would be simpler to buy in lambs to finish for home killing. There is more work involved in lambing your own flock, but if you

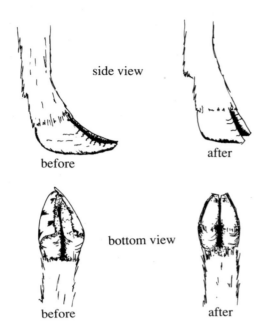

side view

before

after

bottom view

before

after

Fig. 48 Trimming feet for sheep or goats.

have the time then it can be satisfying and spring isn't spring without lambs gambolling amongst the daffodils!

Selecting a ram

You may want ewes that produce a good wool clip and earn you money, but still want meaty lambs for the freezer. If so, either stick to a dual purpose breed or use a meat ram over wool or dual purpose ewes. By crossbreeding this way the progeny benefit from hybrid vigour. This is a recognised phenomenon of genetics which means first cross animals perform better than either purebred parent.

On the other hand you may like to dabble in stud stock. In which case you need to stick to purebred animals. You will need to change your ram every second year or he will be mating with his own daughters, or every year if you plan to mate sheep as hoggets.

Breeding programme

Gestation is normally 145 to 150 days, so work out when you want the lambs born and thus when to put the ram out. In the north August 1 is a good

lambing date (ram goes out March 1) as the worst of winter is past and lambs are able to make the most of spring grass growth. In the deep south you might want to delay until October 1, so don't put the ram out until May 1.

When the ram goes out the ewes should be gaining in condition if you want maximum lambs born. Put lean ewes onto good feed a couple of weeks before tupping so they begin gaining weight. This will put them at the peak of fertility and increase your rate of twins and even triplets.

But a word of warning. Do you want heaps of multiple births? Remember what I said earlier about the lack of flexibility on a smallfarm. If you are on good summer country, fine, go for multiple births. But I always ended up cursing them on my rough Northland block as with its dry summer they always took much longer to get to a killable size than singles.

Tupping

Ewes normally cycle every 16 to 20 days and their heat, or oestrous period, when they are receptive to the ram, can last from 6 to 16 hours. They will continue to cycle for about three months — it varies between breeds — but leaving the ram out for two cycles should be enough. That way he should get a second go at any ewe he missed first time around. If you leave the ram out for a third cycle it will mean lambing is spread out over an irritatingly long period.

The ram

A ram is capable of mating 100 or more ewes in a breeding season so he will be grossly under-utilised if you only have a couple of dozen sheep. If you want a quality animal it may be worth buying him in partnership with a few neighbours. Work out beforehand how you will share him and who is going to graze him for the rest of the year.

Rams deserve good care. Some smallfarmers run their ram with their flocks all year round which is fine except it means you get lambs any time from June to September. I like to know when to expect lambs and get them all within a few weeks of each other so that shearing, drenching and docking do not drag on and on as more tail-enders appear. But it is sometimes difficult on a small block to juggle just one animal so he is out of the way of the ewes. A compromise is to let him run with the main mob from tupping time through the winter and lambing up until the lambs are weaned at about eight weeks. Then it pays to pull him out and run him with last year's wethers or with the horse for the next four or five months until it is tupping time again. But give him some other sheep (rams or wethers) for company. Aim to get him in peak condition by six weeks before tupping to ensure he is at maximum fertility when he goes to the ewes.

Care of pregnant ewes

Smallfarmers often make the mistake of killing their pregnant ewes with kindness. Don't overfeed them or they will be susceptible to lambing difficulties and bearing trouble. Don't underfeed them or they may suffer from metabolic diseases. Don't suddenly change their diet, for example by putting them on lush feed just before lambing, as this too will lead to bearing trouble.

Do vaccinate ewes (see 'Problems', page 92) as this will give some initial protection to the new born lambs. Don't stress pregnant sheep when handling them. Use only mustering and yarding techniques they are used to.

Lambing kit

Before lambing assemble the following gear: a shepherd's crook or other means of catching a sheep and restraining her; long-acting antibiotics (these have limited shelf life, so last year's leftovers will not do); disinfectant soap; lubricant gel (pure soap flakes like Lux will do); raddle or ear-marker to mark ewes you had to assist so you can cull them later; an energy source for exhausted sheep (either a drench of glucose or dextrose solution or one of the proprietary products like Ketol); and finally, trim your fingernails short!

Lambing time

Nowadays most breeds have been selected for easy care characteristics. This means they should manage their own lambing perfectly capably without your interference. But if you want to know when Beatrice, Maggie or Priscilla have had their babies then take a quiet stroll around the flock in the early morning and evening. Start your walks several weeks before lambing so the ewes are used to seeing you. Don't take the family dog and don't be in too big a rush to try out your new lambing kit. Remember, disturb the sheep as little as possible. The sheep that need watching most are the two-tooths, because they are lambing for the first time. Also, sheep which have twins can sometimes forget where they left one of them, or run off with their second-born and forget all about the first.

When to lend a hand

Mother Nature normally gets it right. The lamb is presented front feet and head first and plops out within 30 minutes or so. But occasionally things go awry. If you want an easy care flock you must be prepared to accept a few losses as the non-easy care animals cull themselves. But most of us aren't that tough and prefer to save an animal if it is within our powers.

A ewe needs help if:
- Only the lamb's head is visible.
- Only the tail or one leg is visible.
- If the water bag has burst and there has been no progress for the last half hour.
- If lambing has been going on for the last hour and a half without success.

If you are going to help, be as clean as you can. Wash your hands and arms and the back area round the vulva of the ewe with a non-irritant disinfectant soap. You may need some lubricant to enable you to get your hand inside the ewe. Above all, be gentle. You first need to ascertain the lamb's position. If it is any other than normal presentations (A and B in Fig. 49) then you need to gently push the lamb back in to the uterus until, with your hand inside, you can correct the head or leg positions. Then the ewe will probably go on to lamb successfully by herself. But stay on hand in case she is very tired and still needs help.

Remember if you have to turn any legs, cup the feet first in your hand so that the hooves do not damage the uterus lining. If the head is bent backwards you may have trouble keeping it forward while pulling on the front feet. A soft cord or necktie can be looped around behind the head just under the ears. If that slips off, put it back behind the ears and pass it through the mouth as well.

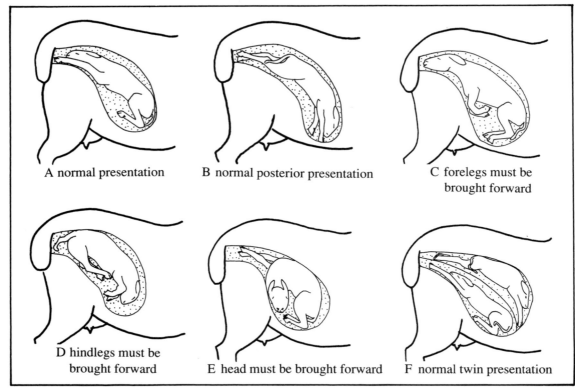

A normal presentation   B normal posterior presentation   C forelegs must be brought forward

D hindlegs must be brought forward   E head must be brought forward   F normal twin presentation

Fig. 49 **Lambing positions**.

Fig. 50 **Securing lamb's head with soft rope**.

(See Fig. 50.) Don't tie it around the neck or you will throttle the lamb.

If you have had to help a ewe she runs the risk of metritis (infection of the uterus) so it pays to give her a shot of a suitable long-acting antibiotic. If the lamb inside is dead the uterus may be dry, making lambing difficult, so you need to introduce copious lubrication. Warm soapy water will do. But if in doubt contact your vet.

Ring womb is another condition for the vet if you think the sheep is worth his or her visit. In this, the ewe's cervix does not dilate to let the lamb through. You can try to initiate dilation by pushing a couple of fingers up into the cervix and working them back and forth and up and down to try to make the gap bigger (90 mm will be enough). If this doesn't work, and you don't want to pay for a caesarian (very expensive), the only other option is to kill the ewe. You then have two minutes to cut the lamb out, and raise it as an orphan.

But don't be put off by these gruesome details. Most ewes manage admirably all on their lonesome.

Care of the lambed flock

Most farmers set-stock ewes and lambs. That means opening up several paddocks and leaving them at peace for the first few weeks of the lambs' life. Certainly it is a good idea to disturb lambs and their mothers as little as possible. But remember, once a ewe has lambed she will be eating for two so she needs good, clean feed.

Culling for age

How long you keep your ewes will depend largely on how heavily stocked you are. By the time a working sheep is about 5 years old her teeth start to wear out (sooner if she has been on rough poor feed). Sheep with bad teeth cannot eat and feed as efficiently as younger stock so they lose condition quicker and are dragged down further by the demands of their own lamb. So until false teeth become a reality for sheep it pays to keep turning your flock over so none are more than 5–6 years old.

Aging

You can tell a sheep's age by its teeth. As a lamb it has eight milk teeth in its lower jaw until it is a hogget (a year old). At one-and-a-half years it starts to get its first pair of adult teeth so is called a two-tooth. It will still have small milk teeth to the side. The following year it gets a second set, thus becoming a four-tooth, and in its third year a third set making it a six-tooth. By its fourth year it is said to have a full mouth of eight teeth. After that the teeth gradually slant forward, spread, wear down and break off.

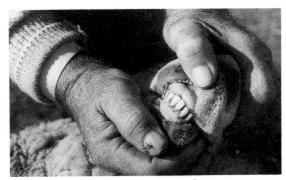

Age a sheep by looking at its teeth.

Orphan lambs

These are the delight of any children around the smallfarm and the bane of any adults. You may find a lost lamb and no ewe willing or able to take care of it. First priority is to get a feed of colostrum into the lamb. This is the rich milk ewes produce immediately after lambing. It contains antibodies to ensure the lamb gets a reasonable start to life. If the mother has no milk, is dead, or there is no sign of her, then try to get a feed of colostrum from another recently lambed ewe.

Mothering on

If you don't want to be plagued with all the hassle of feeding a pet lamb then it will pay to try to mother the orphan to another ewe, either one that has lost its own lamb or a strong ewe which could feed another mouth.

Put the ewe in a small pen and if possible restrain her head so she cannot bunt the orphan. Hold the lamb to the teat and see it gets a good feed. Then leave them together, with her still restrained, to get used to each other. Normally once a lamb has had a feed and that ewe's milk has passed through its system the ewe will identify with the lamb's smell and accept it. This may take 24 hours. Other tricks are to spray both the ewe's nose and the lamb's back end with some strong-smelling substance. If the ewe has lost a lamb you can try skinning it and putting the skin on the orphan like a coat — it might just fool the ewe.

Chances are that when you first find your orphan lambs they will be pitiful little things that have been abandoned in the worst possible weather and are not strong enough to be mothered up. So you become mother. An infra-red lamp suspended 120 cm above the lamb is one good way to warm them through. A warm bath, a thorough drying and a good possie next to the wood stove is just as effective.

Then get some food into it. If a lamb is strong enough to feed, it's strong enough to be put onto a ewe, but if you want to hand rear it (don't say I didn't warn you) then bottle feed. If it is too weak to suck you will have to use the stomach tube. This is simply a plastic funnel with a long, soft rubber hose. The object is to feed the hose into the lamb's mouth right down into the stomach and pour the feed directly to where it is needed. Sit the lamb on your lap and put the end of the hose in the side of its mouth. No force is needed. Just gently feed the hose on down. If the lamb shows any sign of distress you might have taken a wrong turning and gone into the lungs. Withdraw the tube and try again. Once it is all in, the lamb should show no discomfort and may chew on the tube. Slowly pour in the required feed amount. It must be warmed to blood heat. Then pull the tube out and leave the lamb to digest its dinner.

Feeding

Initially ensure a lamb gets a feed of colostrum. If ewe's milk is not available either use cow's colostrum, or mix up a pint of milk, a beaten egg, a teaspoon of cod liver oil and tablespoon of glucose. Feed about 50 ml/kg of lamb, warmed to blood heat, every four hours the first day and three times a day thereafter. From four to five days feed the lamb 500–750 ml/day; six to 12 days, 750–1000 ml/day; 13 days on, 1.5–2 litres/day.

From a week on young lambs will begin to nibble at grass and hay. Ensure this is available so they will be used to it when you come to wean them.

Docking and inoculation

Docking is best done while the lambs are still very small. Some shepherds catch newborn lambs and dock them in the paddock but this runs the risk of scaring the ewe away. An alternative is to muster pockets of ewes and lambs and attend to all those at once. To dock, the easiest way for a new chum to farming is to use an elastrator and rubber rings. Put the tail ring on about 3 cm from the base of the tail, leaving just enough to cover the vulva in ewe lambs and the anus in ram lambs. To castrate with rings, set the lamb on its backside. Feel for both testicles, making sure they are both down in the scrotal sac and not retracted into the belly. Put the ring on at the base of the sac but without catching the teats. (See Fig. 51.) It's preferable to have a second person holding the lamb.

Some argue that tailing and castrating with a knife is better for the stock though it is more gruesome for the operator. If using a knife make sure it is very sharp. Take the tail off with a clean swipe. To castrate, make a cut near the end of the scrotal sac, squeeze both the testicles through, cut the seminal cord and throw the testicles away. (The old timers used to bite them out.)

Next inoculate lambs if you didn't do the ewes when they were pregnant (See 'Problems', page 92.) To inoculate, pull up a wrinkle of skin on the side of the neck, and slip the needle in under this

(be careful not to go right through the fold and inoculate yourself on the other side!). Slowly squeeze the dose in. Remove the needle and give the spot a rub to disperse the fluid.

Then earmark the poor little tyke. This enables you to prove it is yours if it escapes and, if you want to, is a way of keeping a record of who the mother was and when it was born. A simple system of earmarking lambs, which will tell you at a glance what you are looking at, is to use a different colour tag each year, inserting the tag in the left ear for ewe lambs and right for rams (R for R). This has worked well for me with just a handful of sheep, but if you have more you may like to do it officially, and get MAF to allocate you an earmark and register it. As well as the ownership earmark you can clip the ears to tell what year a sheep was born. The standard system uses one to two clips in different positions for each year. (See Fig. 52.)

Fig. 51 **Castrating ram lambs. Two testicles are below the ring and two teats above it.**

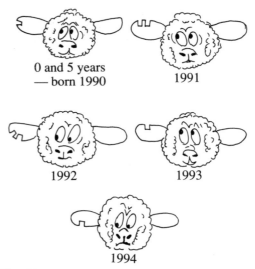

0 and 5 years
— born 1990

1991

1992

1993

1994

Fig. 52 **Age marks for sheep.**

80

Weaning

Both hand-reared and ewe-raised lambs can be weaned from 6 weeks on. But if you have plenty of feed for your ewes the lambs will do better if left on them up to 12 weeks old. Weaning is simply a case of separating lambs from their milk source, be it ewe or you. Either put the lambs down the other end of the farm, out of sight and sound of the ewes, or keep them side by side if your fences are up to it. Often the two groups settle down quicker if close by. Once weaned, lambs should get top grazing priority as you want them growing at maximum rate for the freezer. Remember to keep them clear of worms with regular 3–4 weekly drenches.

Shearing

This can be fun for the smallfarmer or it can be a real nuisance. If you see it in the latter category I would recommend you get in an outside shearer. There is normally someone in the district who can take the wool off a small mob for a small fee. If you foresee shearing as being fun and are tolerant, understanding, patient and thoughtful, have a go yourself. There are shearing courses available around the country, some run by the agricultural training schools such as Telford and Bulls. The Wool Board also conducts classes around the country. Or you could work with a shearer for a while and he may pass on some of his superior knowledge and skills to you. Failing even that, try following my instructions. (See Fig. 53.)

Technique

First catch your sheep. Come at it from behind, put an arm under its neck, lift its front feet high off the ground, walk it backwards onto the shearing board, then with a knee in its back tip it off its hind feet onto its backside. Getting the sheep at the right angle is crucial to stop warfare on the shearing board. The sheep should be on its backside leaning slightly backwards, with its shoulders propped between your knees. If the sheep is too far forward it will get its legs underneath it and be off. If it is too far back it will be uncomfortable and kick like fury.

Shearing sequence

A. Start with your handpiece at the brisket (that narrow bony ridge between the forelegs). Shear down each side of the brisket then grab the right foreleg and pull it slightly upwards to take the wrinkles out of the belly. Make one blow down the right side of the belly then three or four across it. Go carefully if it is a wether so as not to cut its pizzle off and go carefully at the bottom of the belly so you don't chop the teats off. (It's better to have wool on the teats than teats in the wool!)

B. Open up along the top of the right hind leg, with a blow away from you. Then return the handpiece along the inside of the same leg, continue smoothly around the crutch and out the inside of the left hind leg.

C. Make a couple of blows down towards the tail then swivel the sheep slightly so all its legs are pointing towards your right. Put a fist in the crease above the left hind leg. Finish shearing around the tail, clear that hind leg by bringing the handpiece back up it and push it on round towards the backbone as far as you can, so clearing that whole hind quarter.

D. Clip the top knot off and any cheek wool. If you are just doing a belly crutch pre-lambing, then stop here.

E. Move the sheep forward slightly (keep your right leg behind its backside and left leg around by its back). Hold the sheep's muzzle up and away from you. Start at the brisket and bring the handpiece up the side of the neck coming out just below its right ear. Keep the head stretched back so the skin is tight and the handpiece can flow over it.

F. Make several blows up the left side of the animal's neck to clear it, gradually swivelling the sheep so it is more on its back. Make one or two blows over the left foreleg, just enough to clear the bump at the front of the shoulder, then pull that foreleg up and clear the shoulder blade with downward strokes.

G. The sheep should now be lying on its back. Put your right leg between its hind legs. Stretch the left foreleg up parallel with the neck and hold both it and the head, keeping the animal stretched around your left leg with its legs pointing slightly behind you. Now shear in blows along the side from where you had cleared the belly wool. Work your way around the side (always going from tail to head). Keep rolling the animal towards you slightly until your last long blow should be over the backbone.

H. Bring your right leg forward and holding the head, usually by the right ear at this stage, run the handpiece down the right side of the neck. Step backwards pulling the animal's head with you.

I. Now all its legs are facing to your left and it is sitting on its backside again and its head has flopped through between your legs.

J. Shear over the right shoulder and along the top of the foreleg. Then pull that foreleg upwards stretching the belly folds and the flap under that leg tight. Clear under that leg.

K. On the last side keep the sheep in a curve out from you so that its head, behind your knees, and tail, are close to you and the belly is pushed away. This keeps the skin tight and holds the sheep still. Make repeated blows from the backbone across the last side to where the belly wool was removed.

L. Once you have reached the hind leg, let the sheep slump the other way so its head is in front of your knees again and its backside slightly out from your feet. Again push your fist into the crease above the hind leg (this keeps the leg straight), and continue your blows from the backbone now going out over and along the length of the hind leg. Let the sheep slump further and further so you can reach around the hindquarter and make the last blow down the back end of that hind leg.

M. Let her go.

Hints

- Whatever part you are shearing, keep it stretched so that the skin surface is tight.
- Don't make double cuts. If you have left a bit much on in places, leave it there for next time.
- Don't lose your cool. If a sheep is kicking chances are you aren't holding it right. Don't take it out on the sheep — it won't be any easier to hold next time.

Shearing gear

Machines

These are pretty expensive if you only have a few head to shear. It is a good idea to go shares with other smallfarmers. If you are going to buy a plant you can choose a portable (some of these are electric, others petrol so can be used at the back of the farm), or a wall mounted machine. Portables are lighter, and usually have flexible drives instead of the angle elbows used on permanent machines. Portables are cheaper new, and sufficient for most small farming needs.

Handpieces

Handpieces are expensive new and buying one secondhand is full of traps for the unwary. Buy off someone you can trust, or get someone who knows about them to check it out first.

Combs and cutters

If you are buying yourself a handpiece and machine, shout yourself some new combs and cutters. Because new gear is thicker than old, as it hasn't been worn down with repeated sharpenings, it can be a bit harder to push through a fleece, though a beginner shearer is unlikely to notice.

If buying secondhand combs and cutters, check the combs still have some of the oil groove (a semi-circular groove about 1 cm wide on the cutting face of the comb which allows the oil to lubricate the comb evenly). Also check it has all its teeth and no rust or imperfections.

Grinding gear

Get a shearer to show you how. It has to be done on a shearing grinder and on shearing emery paper.

Setting up a handpiece

Again get a shearer to show you how. Basically the comb is put on first by unscrewing the two broad screws at the back of the handpiece, then sliding the comb into place under them so the sharp shiny side faces the handpiece claws. The comb must be positioned so it is square on to the handpiece and its prong far enough out so that once the cutters are put on, the tip of the cutter is a

Fig. 53 **Shearing sequence**.

good centimetre or so from the tip of the comb. This ensures the prongs of the comb can push folds of skin out of the way before the cutting tips come along.

Tighten up the screws holding the comb in place. Turn the handpiece over, loosen off the tension knob and slip a cutter onto the claws, shiny edge down.The claws have two small pins protruding which slot into corresponding holes on the back face of the cutter. Tighten the tension knob. Getting tension right is important. Too loose and it won't cut the wool; too tight and the gear will overheat. It should be firm. Test it by putting your thumb nail in the gear cogs at the handpiece elbow and turning them slightly. You should be able to make the cutter slide back and forth.

Sorting wool

To get the best return, wool needs to be sorted. Do this as it comes off the sheep. Shear your sheep in groups according to their age, for example lambs or ewes. Also separate them if they are of a different wool type.

For a small mob you will probably only need to divide the wool into two classes: fleece wool, and bellies and pieces. If you have a bigger mob or are pooling wool with neighbours then you can divide the bellies and pieces into crutchings (from the back end), bellies, leg pieces and top knots (the short hairy pieces from the top of the head and cheeks). If you don't have enough wool to fill a couple of fadges (wool packs) then put it all in one fadge with some newspaper between each class or type of wool so it can easily be sorted out at the wool store.

Selling

There are many small independent wool buyers around who buy up small lots. For the smallfarmer this is often the best way to go, but some of the buyers will play on your ignorance and not give fair returns. Keep an eye on the papers and see what wool of your type and class is fetching at auction. Allow private buyers a decent cut (remember they have to sort and rebale all those oddments) and see if the price offered is within cooee of your calculations. If not, try another buyer. They generally pay cash on the day.

The alternative is to go direct to the auction system, usually through a stock firm. You will get the going rate for bin wool this way, but it may be a while before you get paid.

Butchering

Killing

Work with an experienced farmer or butcher the first time you want to kill your own mutton. If you have any doubt about your ability to quickly and efficiently slit an animal's throat, or bend its neck back and break it, then shoot it first. The price of a bullet is not much when the alternative may be an animal dying miserably and slowly.

If you are a good shot you may be able to drop the target animal while it is grazing peacefully in the paddock. Otherwise hold it in the yards and put a bullet in the back of the skull into the brain. Slit the throat quickly so it can bleed out thoroughly while the heart is still pumping. If you push the knife point right to the neck vertebrae and cut some of the tendons around them it is easy to snap the head back at the same time. This will make it easier to remove the head later.

Skinning

To start, run a sharp knife around each leg just above the first joint and cut the skin in a line up the inside of each foreleg to the brisket, and up the back of each hind leg to the anus. Skin out the legs by grabbing the wool, pulling up on the skin and forcing your fingers in behind it. Use the knife as little as possible and cut against the skin rather than the carcass to avoid damaging the meat.

With the carcass still on the ground grasp the skin with one hand and punch under it with the other breaking it away from the flesh. Work from each leg in towards the belly as far as you can go. Cut a slit between the back leg tendon and the bone, insert the gambrel. This is a metal bar which has rope tied in the middle and a hook on each end. You can make a wooden one easily enough using a piece of 50 mm x 50 mm about 450 mm long. Cut grooves 30 mm wide about 50 mm from the end of the stick. Push the stick into the slit made in each hind leg, tie your rope to each end of the gambrel and hoist it up to a comfortable working height from some suitable tree or rafter.

Next slit the skin down the belly. Pull the skin clear of the belly on each side and punch in under the skin towards the back and upwards to clear each hindquarter. Eventually the skin will only be attached at the head and tail. Cut around the anus letting it fall back into the carcass. Some people tie a string around it to stop any contents spilling out. Pull the skin off the tail. Pull the hide down and off if you have already removed the head, or cut it as close around the ears as possible. Remove the head. If you want to use the skin refer to Appendix C for some curing methods.

Dressing

Next job is to clean the animal. Start by sawing through the brisket, then open the abdomen up by cutting down the belly. Once you have started the slit up near the pelvis, put a finger into the opening and protect the point of your knife to stop it piercing the gut. Cut down to where you sawed through the brisket. Let the paunch and guts roll out. Pull down the loosened rectum. Take the bladder out carefully and then pull all the insides out into a large container. (A wheelbarrow is good as then you can take it all straight away for burying.) Save the liver and heart at this stage. Pull out the kidneys, which are usually encased in a knob of fat next to the backbone.

Butchers vary in opinion about washing the carcass. If you have done a clean butchering job on it, don't bother. The sooner it dries and hardens the safer it will be from fly strike. If you do wash it, use clean cold water and dry it off thoroughly.

Now hang the carcass in a cool dry place. Wrap it in cotton stockinet if you are worried about flies. Leave it hanging for at least 24 hours. Mutton cut up too soon has a strong, fresh fatty taste, whereas aged mutton just tastes good.

Cutting up

Use a meat saw to cut down the backbone (work from the belly side) and sever the carcass in two. Lift each half off the gambrel and place on a suitable table. Cut off the hindquarters. These can be left as one big roast or cut in two for small

families by cutting across the leg on a diagonal and sawing through the bone to give a hindquarter roast and a leg roast. (See Fig. 54.)

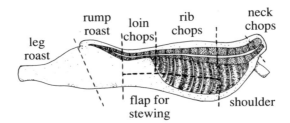

Fig. 54 **Butchering mutton**.

Cut off the shoulder. Note the shoulder blade extends well back along the animal's side so don't start your cut too close to the foreleg. The shoulder can be roasted whole or boned out for stew and curries. Now flip the ribcage over and cleave a line along the ribs so that you have about 12–15 cm of rib attached to the backbone. The excess chopped off is the flap and can be rolled and stuffed, stewed, or cooked and fed to the dogs. Stand up the line of ribs on the backbone, use a knife to cut down between each rib then use a chopper, aim carefully and chop through the backbone with one clean, sure swipe. Sever the chops off one by one. (See Fig. 55.) Bag and freeze the meat. Note that big joints of mutton are fine in the freezer for up to 12 months, but smaller cuts like chops are best used within six months.

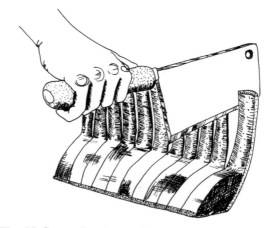

Fig. 55 **Sever the chops off one by one**.

Mutton and dogs

Beware the risk of hydatids if you are killing sheep at home and have dogs. Keep the dogs away from the kill area, burn, bury (deeply) or boil (for an hour) any offal. If you want to feed dogs mutton then boil it thoroughly or freeze it for a few days beforehand. Always examine the offal of any animal you slaughter to check it is a healthy carcass. Look for liver damage, lung damage or cysts in the flesh.

Problems

Internal parasites

All being well and with good management you may avoid other disease problems but you won't avoid worms. They come in a variety of forms. There are lungworms which destroy lung tissue; stomach worms which damage the stomach lining and upset the digestive process so the nutrients in the food eaten cannot be absorbed efficiently; liver flukes which bore into the liver tissue; cestodes which make their homes almost anywhere in the sheep's body — some suck blood, stealing oxygen and protein out of it; others rob nutrients from the gut contents. Sheep infected with worms may eat a fifth less than they would normally, and at the same time are less able to get the goodness from what they do eat.

Scouring is often a symptom. Normally sheep excrete pebbles but if the sheep are wormy they will have diarrhoea and dirty, daggy backsides. Sheep infected with lungworms will cough and snort a lot. Fat and protein deposition are reduced in wormy stock so it is harder for them to put on weight. The damage to their insides even affects how much calcium and phosphorus they can get out of their food so bone growth may be reduced. This leaves wormy young stock looking stunted, skinny, dirty and often potbellied.

Even when worms are present in fewer numbers so the symptoms are not so obvious, they still take their toll on a sheep's wellbeing, reducing its wool production or keeping it that little bit thinner than it should be considering the feed it is on. Fortunately sheep do develop a degree of immunity to most worms as they get older. That doesn't mean

you can forget about worms in your old girls but you don't have to worry about treating them quite as often.

The life cycle of most worms involves a parasitic stage when it is in the host animal. While there it matures and lays eggs, which one way or another get passed through the animal and out with the dung onto the pasture. A female Barber's Pole worm is normally in egg production by the time it is 18 days old, and she can lay up to 5000 eggs a day. So it doesn't take many worms to put millions of eggs onto the pasture. The eggs hatch out into little larvae and hang about waiting for another sheep to come along and munch them up. Precisely what they do from there depends on the type of worm involved. But once inside the animal they will all develop to adults and start adding their own eggs to the growing pile outside. From the farmer's point of view the significant points of the life cycle are that larvae can exist on pasture for months under the right conditions and that the huge number of eggs produced mean that the worm population can build up very rapidly.

Unfortunately there is no simple recipe for control. There are so many variables, where you are, what the weather has been like, what season you are in, what your pasture is like, what sort of stock you are running, how many, how you manage them. The best idea is to talk to your local vet as he or she will understand what works best in your area and under your conditions.

Because the larvae can survive so long it is not practical to think of spelling pastures until they have all died. However, you can clean paddocks up by taking a crop off them, or grazing a different class of stock on them to vacuum up the larvae. (Most of the cattle worms stick to cattle and sheep worms to sheep.) This works best if your cattle need about as much grazing as your sheep, say a ratio of 50 sheep to 10 cows.

If you are only running sheep, remember it is the young stock that are the most susceptible, so put them on fresh ground and use the old ewes to clean up behind them. If you incorporate these management ideas with drenching, you should avoid losses from worms. The following programme should give your stock adequate protection. With experience and advice from your veterinarian you may be able to cut out some of the treatments.

Drench programme

Drench ewes and the ram before tupping. This helps the ewes gain weight and may improve lambing percentages. You may drench ewes again at docking time so they do not infect the pasture for the young lambs. In warm, wet, spring conditions lambs may need drenching before they are weaned. If you shear your ewes in November that is a good time to grab the lambs. From then on drench lambs every three to four weeks until about January.

That sort of regular programme will help reduce the pasture population of worm larvae before autumn when conditions would encourage a build up. Try to combine drenching with moving lambs onto fresh pasture, preferably to areas made safe by grazing with older stock or cattle. You may also use tactical drenches. These take into account changes in weather which might suit parasites. For instance, if during summer there is a sudden burst of wet humid weather, then it may pay to drench stock 15–20 days later so that the larvae they pick up in the wet don't get a chance to mature and reinfect the pasture. (See 'Drenching regime', page 74.)

External parasites

Ticks

These are small crawlies with a complex life cycle (see Fig. 56) that results in them looking for a host animal three times in their life. Almost any animal will do and once latched on they suck up their fill, drop off and leave behind a really itchy bite. Ticks

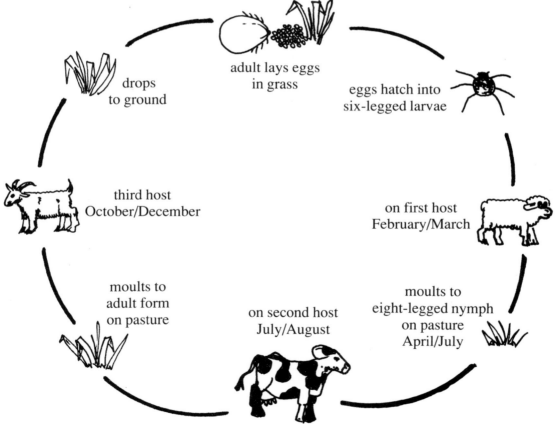

drops
to ground

adult lays eggs
in grass

eggs hatch into
six-legged larvae

third host
October/December

on first host
February/March

moults to
adult form
on pasture

moults to
eight-legged nymph
on pasture
April/July

on second host
July/August

Fig. 56 **Tick life cycle.**

are mainly a North Island problem, where there is long, rank grass or rushes. On good, healthy stock they are not a danger, but enough of them sucking off one animal may leave it anaemic, weak and susceptible to other ills.

Because ticks are hopping on and off stock at different times of the year they can be hard to control. If you can get all of them at one or other of the times when they are on stock then you have some hope of wiping out the population. Do this by dipping either in February/March, when the ticks are tiny larvae the size of a pin head, or in July/August when they are eight-legged nymphs, or in November/December when they attach as adults before laying eggs. You can dip stock at one of these times and return them to the infected pasture and redip in one to three weeks, mopping up all the ticks around. If they are a problem on lambs, whizz the ewes through the paddocks just before the lambs then dip the ewes if they need it.

Lice and keds
By law, farmers must dip sheep against lice and keds at least once every 12 months. There are two types of lice: one chews up skin debris and isn't much trouble, the other is a bloodsucker. It is a longer shape than the short, round, chewing-lice. A heavy burden of sucking-lice will drag a sheep down, leaving it anaemic, skinny and with a moth-eaten looking fleece and damaged pelt. Fortunately lice spend all their life on the sheep so are easier to control by dipping than ticks.

There are many ways of dipping. If you have access to a plunge dip or shower, fine, but be sure you know exactly how much water the plunge dip or shower tank holds so that you can mix the dip to the maker's instructions.

There are also pour-on dips. These are in concentrated form and a measured dose is dribbled along the animal's back. From there it is absorbed into the bloodstream and circulates to the skin so is effective against all the crawlies on the animal at that time. Pour-ons are usually used on sheep with short wool, and may be put on just after shearing. But plunge or shower dipping should be left until at least three weeks after shearing to allow any cuts to heal. If you are planning on slaughtering

dipped sheep, check the dip instructions first as some have a withholding period before meat from the dipped animals is safe for eating.

Prolapse or bearings
Around lambing time fat sheep get lazier and lazier, and might not bother to get up and empty their bladders as often as they would if they were on their feet working for a feed. When straining to empty out, the fat sheep are at risk of forcing out their insides. It is usually just the vagina, which hangs outside like a great red sausage, but sometimes they force the whole uterus out as well. The longer a bearing ewe is left the worse she gets, as the pressure of the bearing on the bladder makes her continue to strain trying to urinate.

If by the time you find her the bearing is dirty, badly torn or bruised, you have a limited chance of saving her and dog tucker is probably the best option. But if you find her soon after she has pushed the bearing out, lie her on her side with her back end higher than her head. Thoroughly wash your hands and the bearing in warm water with a dollop of Dettol in it, then gently ease the bearing back into place inside the ewe. Hold it there until it is warm and circulation restored and let the ewe urinate.

You can prevent the bearing from being pushed out again by tying strands of her fleece (if she has long wool) across her vulva. Or you can put in a couple of stitches using a thick soft thread to close up her vulva. If it is near lambing time be sure the thread is soft enough for the ewe to push the lamb through and break or else you will have to watch her for signs of lambing and cut the stitches. Give the ewe a shot of penicillin. Mark her, and once she has raised her lamb to weaning cull her, as she could prolapse again next year, or pass the likelihood of doing it on to her offspring.

Correcting a prolapsed uterus is much the same as for a bearing but use your fist to push the uterus right back into the animal. But prevention is the best cure. Don't let your ewes get overfat before lambing. Don't give them a sudden change to lush green feed, save it until they have actually lambed. While they are pregnant make sure they have to get some exercise, so that they urinate regularly.

Foot problems

Regular foot trimming should keep any feet troubles to a minimum, but at times when the ground is wet, the yards muddy, the paddocks a bog and sheep overcrowded you could come across footrot or foot scald.

Scald is the more common. The space between the toes fills up with mud and stinking rotten material and the skin looks inflamed or scalded. There may be a little bit of the side hoof lifting away but it is not as bad as true footrot where in severe cases the whole horn may slough off. However, scald can lead to feet abscesses which are hard to treat.

Footrot is transferred by animals walking over infected ground. So if you bring in new stock keep them separate from your own flock until you have checked them for footrot. Or if you take sheep to showgrounds or saleyards, quarantine them for a while back home in case they have picked up the bacteria. The bugs responsible are only viable for about ten days on the open ground, so if you can identify and cull or treat the carrier animals you only need to spell ground for a couple of weeks before it is safe for the rest of the flock.

To treat either condition trim the hoof wall flush with the pad, remove *all* rotten material and loose horn (see Fig. 48), and get the animal to stand in a footbath with either a 10 per cent zinc sulphate or copper sulphate solution, or a 5–10 per cent formalin solution. From the bath move the stock to dry ground or wooden gratings until their feet have dried. Repeat the bathing once a week until the rot has cleared up.

Blowfly strike

This is the result of flies laying their eggs on sheep. The eggs hatch into maggots and literally eat the animal alive. It is an awful mess to have to clean up so prevention is the best cure. Flies are usually only attracted by dirt or smells, so sheep which have scoured from worm infections, or which have rubbed against dirty banks to itch at lice or ticks are at risk. Keep sheep clean by controlling parasites and crutch (shear the back end of) any daggy or dirty sheep.

In some areas fly strike is a common problem even on clean, well-tended animals. If this is the case in your area then try to time your annual dip against lice and keds (required by law every 12 months) with the fly strike season (usually summer) and use a dip that repels flies.

A fly-blown animal will be obvious either from the big, raw patches on it, or patches of black, evil-smelling wool. Maggoty sheep tend to wriggle their tails and turn to look or bite at the area that is blown. Your job is to shear a wide margin around it to make sure you get all the fly eggs, flick off all the maggots, and smear the attacked area with a fly strike treatment. If you don't have one on hand, ordinary machine oil works well and is soothing on the wound, but make sure you get all the maggots, and eggs off. If the skin is badly broken a penicillin injection won't go amiss to guard the sheep against infection.

Facial eczema

Facial eczema (FE) is caused by the toxin sporidesmin, which affects the animal's liver function. The damaged liver is unable to fulfil one of its normal tasks — removing a phylloerythrin from the blood. The result is the skin becomes sensitive to light and itchy. The toxin is exuded by a fungus which grows on decaying plant matter, such as that found at the bottom of a pasture sward, under warm, humid conditions. It is the animal's frantic scratching that causes the skin to flake and bits to fall off. Even if an animal shows no external signs of FE it may, because of the liver damage, pack up later, perhaps in winter when feed is short or when it is heavily in lamb.

There is little hope of treating affected animals. Prevention is the only answer. First understand under what conditions spores flourish. Typically FE occurs in late summer. Perhaps the season has been dry, there is a lot of dead grass around. Suddenly there is heavy rain and the fungus rockets away. The spore numbers build up rapidly and paddocks may turn dangerous or hot, two or three days after rain.

Because every farm and even every paddock is different the only way to be certain how hot a pasture is, is by spore counting. For this you will need a little microscope, and some guidelines on spore counting from your local MAF or vet. Usually light sandy soils are worse than heavy soils. Low fertility ground growing the poorer grasses, such as browntop, yorkshire fog and dogstail are safer than rye pastures. Clover and kikuyu are safer than rye grass. Paddocks facing south or east are safer than northern slopes. Paddocks on ridge tops open to the breeze are safer than sheltered humid valleys. Long grass is safer than short, as spore numbers rise near the base of the grass sward.

If conditions suit an FE outbreak on your farm then graze safe paddocks first, or stand stock off the grass and feed out hay or silage, though the resulting overcrowding may be fraught with problems of its own. Fortunately as quickly as spore counts rise, the danger passes. Three-day-old spores are much less toxic than new ones. If the rain continues then some of the toxin will be leached out. But look out once the rain stops and humidity rises again.

If you are in a known FE risk area then gear up for summer by putting fertiliser on in spring to encourage summer clover growth. Also cut down grazing pressure by selling surplus stock early. The only alternative is to spray pasture with a suitable fungicide. However, this is expensive and may not protect against a severe FE outbreak.

Staggers

This is a general term and is often applied to two quite separate conditions. The first is rye grass staggers and is caused by sheep grazing certain types of rye grass which contain a fungus that produces a toxin. The toxin causes muscle tremors in the animal so that it walks with a high stepping gait, may fall over sideways or, if excited, throw itself over backwards.

Generally the fungus is only active from December to April and is more usually limited to February and March. The condition is seldom fatal on its own, but as the stock affected blunder around they can damage themselves through getting tangled in fences or falling into drains and the like. The trouble is that if you try to shift them you may induce more attacks. If you can, move the sheep onto an alternative pasture type, such as clover or lucerne, and leave them to recover.

The other type of staggers is sometimes known as grass tetany . (See the following section.)

Metabolic or deficiency diseases

These are basically caused by the animals being unable to absorb enough of a particular element from feed to match the demands being placed on them, so they have to draw from their own body resources. Usually deficiency diseases only occur in ewes heavily in lamb or freshly lambed, or old stock.

Milk fever

This is caused by a blood calcium deficiency. Affected sheep may move with a stilted gait, show some muscle tremor and will go down and into a coma and die within about four to six hours.

Grass tetany

This is caused by a deficiency of magnesium in the bloodstream. Animals stagger and collapse, and may throw their heads back and paddle with their legs. It often occurs at the same time as a calcium deficiency.

Ketosis

This is also known as pregnancy toxaemia or sleepy sickness. It is caused by a shortage of glucose and excess of ketones in the bloodstream. Again it is mainly a problem of pregnant ewes, especially at times of feed shortage or in bad weather. The sheep turn dopey, may appear blind and will refuse food and water.

Treatment

Each condition can be treated by getting the required element into the sheep as fast as possible. This is usually done by injection, though if you detect a glucose deficiency soon enough you may drench the ewe with 100–125 g of glycerine (as long as the ewe can still swallow adequately).

The trick with calcium and magnesium deficiencies is determining just which element is missing as dosing with magnesium when that is not the problem can do more harm than good. The safest bet is to treat the sheep with a calcium solution first (calcium borogluconate). There are several concoctions available for use with dairy cows. About one-fifth of the dose suggested for a cow will serve for a ewe. If calcium was the culprit she should respond to the injection in about 10–15 minutes. If there is no change then treat with magnesium. An injection of 12 g of Epsom salts dissolved in pure water will do. If you have more than one sheep affected with any of these conditions you should check with your vet as to the best way of treating them.

Prevention

Fortunately just good sound management should avoid all these deficiency problems. Don't let sheep get overfat in their late pregnancy. Don't graze them too hard when they are heavily in lamb. Don't suddenly stop their feed. When mustering or yarding them work quietly with a minimum of dog barking or chasing around the paddocks. And drench to be sure worms aren't affecting their uptake of calcium or magnesium.

Pneumonia

There are numerous bugs, viruses, fungi and other conditions identified as causing pneumonia in sheep. Lung damage from pneumonia and pleurisy is one of the most common reasons for downgrading of lamb carcasses at the freezing works. Pneumonia is not necessarily a cold climate disease, though sheep shorn in winter and exposed to bad weather are susceptible to it. But by far the more common incidence of pneumonia occurs in the North Island in the late summer months from January through to March. Many of the bugs involved live all the time in the sheep's respiratory tract and cause no problems. But when the animal is stressed, or exposed to dry, dusty, yard conditions, hot, humid weather, and overcrowding, the bugs can explode into a severe infection.

Farmers can also cause pneumonia by poor drenching or dipping technique which makes the sheep inhale dip or drench fluid.

Symptoms

Generally the sheep will be depressed, off its food and may have a snotty nose and weepy eyes. They may have a cough and a high temperature.

Treatment

Keep the affected animal warm and dry and treat with a suitable antibiotic as recommended by your vet. Most importantly though, prevent the outbreak of pneumonia by providing good shelter for sheep in severe winter conditions, especially once they have been shorn. Ensure they have good feed during cold periods. In the north, do jobs which require yarding before the worst of the dry, dusty months. Drench sheep carefully so that you don't force fluid into their lungs. If you are on a regular drenching programme, after the early January drench leave the lambs for 6–8 weeks until the worst viral pneumonia period is over. Make sure lambs have plenty of shade and water at this time.

Clostridial diseases

There are a number of these but the most important with sheep are pulpy kidney and tetanus. Less common but still important are blackleg, malignant oedema and black disease. The thing to realise about clostridia germs is that they are already out there on your farm now (though just which variety will vary from region to region). Generally the clostridia can survive in the soil for a long time. They may even be present in your flock's gut or muscle tissue and not causing any harm.

Clostridia don't like oxygen and prefer anaerobic conditions. So when something happens to an animal to reduce the amount of oxygen in its gut contents or muscle tissue, the clostridia bacteria multiply rapidly. As they multiply they create the conditions they like best and so go on multiplying even further. The build-up is dramatic. But it is not the bacteria themselves which kill your stock but the toxins they produce. When the bacteria are only present in small numbers the animal can cope with the small amount of toxin, but as the bacteria multiply the animal's ability to make its own anti-toxin is swamped.

Pulpy kidney

This tends to affect young lambs 4–14 weeks old and always seems to hit the best animals. The bacteria responsible live in the gut, normally without doing any harm. But if the feed changes and the passage of feed through the gut is slowed down (for instance, if the lamb goes onto lush feed with not enough roughage) then the bacteria flourish. The more bacteria, the more toxin; the lamb will eventually go into convulsions, fall into a coma and die.

Blackleg

This shows up on bruised or wounded muscle as an ugly, dark-coloured swelling which spreads rapidly from the injury site.

Malignant oedema

This is rarer than blackleg but the symptoms can be similar.

Black disease

This affects sheep whose livers have been damaged by liver fluke.

Tetanus

This is also mainly a problem in lambs. It attacks them if they have been wounded or bruised. Often docking injuries invite an attack, particularly if rubber rings are used. These create an area of dead tissue ideal for the tetanus bacteria to live in. Also called lockjaw, tetanus sends sheep into spasms until they go down and end up lying stretched out as stiff as a board.

Control

By the time you realise you have an outbreak of one of the above diseases it is generally too late to treat it, though the incidence of pulpy kidney can be reduced by shifting lambs onto rougher feed. Prevention is the best cure, using vaccination. Find

A coloured ewe and twins.

out from your vet which clostridial diseases are present in your area. The best and cheapest control is to vaccinate ewes about two weeks before lambing, then they can pass that protection on to their lambs, which then won't need further treatment. However, if there is a risk of an outbreak, for instance hoggets going onto very rich clover, then you can re-vaccinate after weaning.

If you didn't vaccinate the ewes before lambing then protect lambs at docking time against pulpy kidney and with tetanus anti-serum. Note that tetanus anti-serum is not the same as tetanus vaccine. Vaccine is made from killed bacteria and stimulates an animal's own immune system to make anti-serum. But it takes about a fortnight for animals to respond to the vaccine, and for lambs which are being injured at docking that may be too late, so use the anti-serum instead. Lambs will not need vaccinating again until a couple of weeks before they are due to lamb themselves.

10. Goats

If you like animals in general you will end up loving goats. They are natural clowns, affectionate and communicative, and seem to genuinely enjoy human company. I would rate goats as intelligent as dogs. But goats are more individualistic, and while they know full well what you want of them, they can calculate much better than a dog what is in it for them. Dogs don't seem to worry about such things.

Goats can be productive pets, too. Good milking goats or fibre-producing goats will bring in much better returns than conventional farming stock, but it might cost you more to get set up in the first place. Besides milk and fibre, goats can provide good meat for the freezer. Their skins can also be tanned for rugs or making into waistcoats, bags and the like.

Goats can be run complementarily to sheep or cattle. They like to browse on weeds a lot of the time and will leave much of the good rye grass and clover for your other stock. They can be a great help in clearing your land if it is rough or scrub covered. Good quality animals will need good quality feed and treatment, but if you are starting with rough ground and rough animals then breeding up to purebred status can go hand in hand with the land being cleared and improved.

Goats seldom have to be worked with dogs. They quickly learn to go into new paddocks if you call them and if they need handling they are not much bigger than a sheep — though a wild one might be a bit stroppier. If you only have a few girls and need to find a boyfriend for them, they love a ride in the car as much as any dog. I got six girls in the back of a VW beetle once. They thought it quite a lark. I wasn't convinced, especially when I came to clean the car out later!

This milking herd was given covers for the winter months so they could carry on grazing through the rain and not have to run for shelter.

Now let me give a few warnings. Their intelligence, which is so charming at first, can be a trial. Goats can calculate . . . how to jump from that stump on to that log and to that post and over there into the orchard, the neighbour's orchard or the back garden . . . and having got there they can be extraordinarily destructive. Being browsers rather than grazers goats think everything is worth a nibble — so fencing, fencing and more fencing is what goat keeping is all about.

Fortunately goats hate electric fences. A few well placed hot wires can goat-proof an otherwise doubtful fence quite cheaply. But realise the goats will know when the power has gone off long before you do.

High-class goats, be they for milk or fibre, can

be fragile. If you are on rough land, okay, goats might still be the best farming option, but start with hardier ferals or animals in the early stages of being bred up.

Goats need regular feet trimming and treatment against scald and footrot. They are also highly susceptible to internal parasites and don't seem to develop an immunity to them the way sheep do, so drenching is a continuing task, especially in warm, moist climates.

If you are milking goats then they are as big a tie as any dairy cow, and need a regular routine of being milked and shifted to fresh pasture at the same times every day. If you are running fibre goats you will need shearing facilities and shelter for after shearing. If you keep enough does to warrant a buck, then he is a definite drawback. Billy goats do smell, especially in the rut.

Breeds

There are dairy goats for milk and fibre goats for fleeces. Either will provide some meat if you kill surplus young stock for the freezer, but there are also specialised meat breeds if the carcass is all you are after.

Dairy goats

Saanen

A large-boned, white-haired animal with erect ears. They can milk exceptionally well on good grazing. The world record holder produced 2120 kg of milk in a season, but production between 500 and 1000 kg is more usual. The milk has 3.5–4 per cent milkfat.

Saanen.

Anglo-Nubians.

Two future milkers; above a Saanen, below a British Alpine.

Breed	NZ commercial herds kg/day	World record production litres/season
Saanen	1–3.4	3422
Toggenburg	1.5–3	2608
British Alpine	1.3–2	2189
Anglo-Nubian	0.6–1.2	2065

Table 14. **Milking goat yields.**

Toggenburg.

Cashmere-bearing ferals.

Angoras.

Anglo-Nubian

This breed comes in all colours and mixtures of colours, sometimes spotted, pied or marbled. They have long, drooping ears and roman noses. The Anglo-Nubian's milk is richer than the Saanen's, about 5 per cent milkfat, but they produce less volume.

British Alpine

A handsomely marked goat, black with a white belly and legs, and a white strip down each side of its face. The Alpines can grow almost as big as the Saanens but don't produce quite the same volume of milk. Its milk is 3.5–4 per cent milkfat.

Toggenburg

It has similar markings to the British Alpine but is brown or tan rather than black. Its milk is 3.7–3.8 per cent milkfat.

Fibre goats

Cashmere

Most goats grow a layer of fine cashmere down (14–18 microns) during the winter. Feral goats can serve as foundation stock for a cashmere flock and you can select for the qualities that are worth more. The alternative is to use a first-cross Angora buck or G4 (the progeny from an Angora goat, crossbred with a feral) over your cashmere flock. But don't use just any G4. Pick one with very fine fibre and a big difference between the diameter of down and guard hairs or you will end up with just crossbred mohair and not cashmere at all.

Angora

These are the cute little goats with lovely, soft long ringlets and floppy ears, handsome, curling horns and handsome prices. The mohair (which comes from the term muhayyar, meaning 'choice' or 'select', which the Arab traders originally applied to the fibre), is not a hair at all but a wool ranging from 26–40 microns. It grows all-year round so can be shorn twice a year. Mohair is a strong, soft fibre with high lustre or sparkle. Only white goats are acceptable though black and ginger goats are known.

Cashgora

These are basically first-cross animals (Angora x feral) in an Angora breeding programme. They produce fibre that is part way between cashmere and mohair and is about 18–24 microns in diameter with low lustre. Cashgora is finding its own market and some farmers have opted to stick to first-cross animals rather than continue breeding up to mohair.

Note that fibre diameter on cashgora and mohair animals increases with age by up to 10 microns, but the fibre from an old cashmere goat may only be 1–2 microns coarser than when it was young.

Meat goats

You can get good meat from surplus fibre or dairy goats if they are killed between 3–6 months of age. If you are running goats extensively then you can improve returns for meat to the export trade by selecting meatier, quicker-growing goats, or running a meat breed buck (such as the Kiko or the Boer) out with the ferals.

Management

Just because goats have four legs and go baaa don't make the mistake of thinking they can be run just like sheep. They are quite different in their grazing and social habits. Goats are natural browsers while sheep are grazers. In their natural state goats spend about 30 per cent of their time feeding. Of that only 34 per cent is grazing, the rest is browsing when they pick and choose. Goats like to be fussy if given the chance. They don't like to eat feed that has been nuzzled by another goat or that has been spoiled in any way. If the feed quality declines sheep will eat more to make up for it but goats will eat less and lose weight. If you want to run sheep and goats together they will only be in competition for pasture about a third of the time. For the rest of the time the goats will prefer to pick at weeds and scrub. Unfortunately their grazing habits mean that they are not as well adapted to intensive farming as sheep, and so are more susceptible to some of the problems associated with it, particularly worms.

There are also differences between types of goats and the feed they need. A scruffy little feral goat used to running about in the scrub and bush can do fine in that environment, but try putting a high-class milking goat in the same situation and you run the risk of losing her. High producing goats need high producing land to match, though they, too, like a chance to browse and need a bit of roughage. So give them hay or cut titbits off the roadside to supplement grazing.

The cashmere goat likes to be run extensively with a lot of country to range and browse over. She grows a winter coat of cashmere every year anyway and putting her onto rich feed is unlikely to alter how much down she grows.

But this is not true of the Angora. High quality goats capable of growing heavy fleeces do need good pasture to produce to their full potential. But they still like a bit of browse too, so give the mohair goats a run in the bush and work in the scrub and weeds for a couple of months after shearing when their coats are short. But then bring them back to good clean country for the rest of the year to keep their fleeces free of vegetation.

Some farmers push goats hard to clean up weeds, but you don't really need to. Sure, if they have nothing else to eat they might demolish the gorse a bit quicker but you'll end up with skinny sick goats. Give them regular paddock changes and keep bringing them back to the weeds — they will eat it out soon enough.

Grazing regime

How you manage your goats will depend on many variables. There are no simple rules, so I can only make suggestions.

Let's start with milking goats. Research has shown they produce best if they are only made to eat 30–35 per cent of the grass on offer before being let into a fresh paddock. I told you they were fussy, but that needn't be a problem; just get set up right for it. Subdivide your farm so it's like a regular little dairy farm with enough paddocks to give about a three-week rotation. For this you would need 21 paddocks of equal size. If that means too much fencing, make fewer permanent paddocks, but break fence the goats with temporary electric fences. If they are given a fresh shift each day they are less likely to pick up worms and they shouldn't turn up their noses at any of the feed on offer. There will be lots of grass left behind but it needn't be wasted. Bring in another class of stock, and make them do the clean up work. Weaner cattle are ideal. There will be enough grass left for them to fatten well.

With fibre goats, you don't have to pump the grass in to quite the same degree though of course the same rules will apply about their fussiness. The feral-based cashmere goats are happiest run extensively. If you are running sheep and goats, let the goats graze ahead of the sheep and don't force the goats to graze paddocks down hard. Parasites are transferable between the two species, but sheep do develop some immunity to them as they age. Goats don't.

Whatever the type of goat, remember they do like variety in their diet. Besides hay and weeds, goats learn to love feed concentrates — pellets, grain or dairy ration. If dairy goats get used to the idea they will get treats at milking they are much happier about coming to the shed on time. Likewise, fibre goats fed titbits will tame up quickly and learn to be called to new paddocks rather than need mustering.

If feed is getting short, and you are scared to move them on too soon in case you use up all the paddocks before they have time to regrow, then you can slow the rotation down by holding them behind an electric fence. This controls exactly how much fresh ground they get each day. If they start to lose condition give them a bigger break or feed a supplement. Generally you can run about three cashmere goats where you would run two sheep, about one Angora doe per sheep, but milking goats might need one and a half times as much as a sheep would.

Shelter

Goats do not like getting wet. Their coats are easily penetrated by rain and they have no grease in the coat or fat layer under the skin to protect them against the cold, so once wet they are susceptible to cold and pneumonia. If you want your goats to survive on cleared land then you have to provide shelter. Something like a cut-down version of a bus shelter on skids is fine. It can be moved to each paddock with the goats. Alternatively build a little house in each paddock. Make the doorway big enough so dominant goats do not stop other goats from getting in. Or you can provide individual covers for goats for after shearing or in very cold, wet periods.

Fencing

The goat's intelligence, nimbleness and natural curiosity combine to make it very hard to keep at home. Goats can jump and climb. Some of mine preferred to sleep in an old tree hut 4 m above the ground. Unfortunately it is pretty hard to do anything about jumping goats. Nothing short of a ball and chain will keep them in and they can teach all their buddies how to get out, so it is best to cull your jumpers. But most goats can be kept in with strategically-placed hot wires. Strengthen conventional fences with an outrigger around the top (if they are climbers), or around the bottom (if they are diggers and pushers). If you are putting in new fences then five wire electric will hold them but *don't* turn the power off. Goats seem able to tell when the current isn't passing through an electric fence and they will have a go at it.

For goats that climb, make sure there are no objects leaning against the fences, or even fence post stays, which they can climb up and jump out from. If bringing in wild stock, put them into your most secure paddock to start with, preferably somewhere near the homestead so they can get used to you coming and going without feeling directly threatened. Once they have quietened down a bit start feeding out titbits to tame them.

Harvesting goat milk

Goat milk is more easily digested than cow milk as the fat globules are finer and more easily assimilated. It is particularly rich in antibodies and when fresh has a lower bacteria count than cow's milk. Goat milk is prescribed for people with dyspepsia, peptic ulcers and pyloric stenosis. It is also preferable for people with liver disfunction, jaundice and biliary problems; for children with a liability to fat intolerance and eczema; and pregnant women troubled with vomiting.

Many variables influence a milking goat's production, ranging from her genetic background to how old she is, how she is fed, how healthy, how milked and so on.

Milk production varies throughout the season (normally considered as 305 days long, allowing two months of drying off and rest time before a goat kids again) and from season to season. Goats normally peak in their fourth or fifth year and milk production is normally highest in about the second month of lactation. (See Fig. 57.)

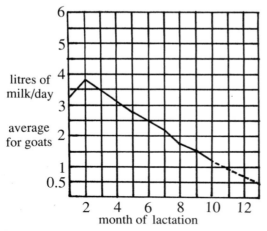

Fig. 57 **Milk production**

How to milk

For best results goats need to be milked twice a day and as near 12 hours apart as possible and always at the same times. Goat milk should taste as good and no different from cow's milk. Off-flavours only develop if your hygiene is not up to scratch. So to start with pick a clean, dry, milking site and use a stainless steel milking bowl. (Plastic tends to absorb odours which can be passed into the milk.) Keep your goat's udder clipped of long hair and wash the teats before milking with plenty of clean running water. Don't use an udder cloth as this can spread infection between goats.

Hand milking

Goats seem to vary as much in udder shape, size and layout as they do in personality, but generally the hand-milking principles are as follows (see also Fig. 58):

- Make a ring around the teat near the base of the udder with thumb and first finger, and squeeze firmly to prevent milk being forced back into the udder.
- Then gently and firmly apply pressure to the rest of the teat with first, second and third fingers in that order so the milk is forced down the teat and out.

- Strip the first couple of squirts of milk into a stripping cup to check for blood clots or signs of any infections. Alternatively, just squirt them to waste as they contain a high bacteria count.
- Release your squeeze on the top of the teat to allow it to fill up again and repeat the process until you can get no more. Then you can nudge the udder upwards as kids do to encourage the doe to let down any more milk.
- When you think she is milked out, strip the last bit, running the thumb and first finger down the length of teat and squeezing out the last milk.
- *Don't* pull the udder or teats
- *Don't* squeeze the udder, only squeeze the teats or you may damage udder tissue.
- *Don't* rub your fingers up and down the teat, except once or twice at the end for stripping out, or you may irritate the teat skin.

Sounds easy? It is, once you get the knack. If in doubt, or if you have a goat with an awkwardly-shaped udder, or if she is a first kidder, or if you are just plain nervous, then ask an experienced goat keeper to show you how. A milking stand is not a silly idea. It enables you to get the goat up to a comfortable height to work on, and if you incorporate a head bail and give her some nuts or dairy ration to keep her happy she will stay in position while you milk. (See Fig. 59.)

Milk uses

Goat milk can be used for anything that cow's milk can. (See Appendix A.) But because it develops off-flavours easily it needs to be treated carefully. Chill it to 7°C within three hours of milking. Take care the goat doesn't eat any strong-smelling plant, as this may taint the milk, and do not leave the billy goat running with the does. Take each doe to him as she comes in heat, then after mating return her to the flock. If you have to give antibiotics to a goat for any reason, withhold her milk for at least four days.

Marketing

The dairy goat industry has been through considerable ups and downs, a boom and a bust; but a few small-scale milk marketing systems have sur-

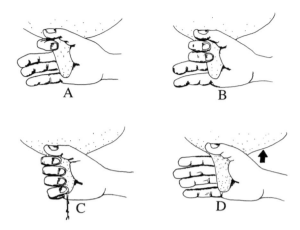

Fig. 58 **Hand milking a goat**.

Fig. 59 **Milking stand for a goat**.

vived. The main one is the Dairy Goat Co-op based in Hamilton, which collects chilled milk from about 60 suppliers for processing into milk powder. For northerners, the Puhoi Valley Cheese Co also collects from outside suppliers, subject of course to demand for their product.

Going commercial

If you want to run goats commercially then you are looking at milking at least 150 animals for a reasonable living and considerable capital expense to get set up initially, so don't enter into the venture without doing your homework first. The

hygiene requirements and some shed designs are available from MAF but more importantly, you will need to seek out a reliable market for your milk. How you process it will depend on your buyer's requirements: whether they want it chilled or frozen and how often it will be collected.

Marketing fibre

Most goat fibre used to be sold through a cooperative company, but with the changes in fortunes in the fibre industry this has been overtaken by private companies. Probably 50 per cent of fibre produced in New Zealand goes through Mohair Fibres Ltd, which offers growers a choice of direct payment or a pool payout. With direct payment the grower accepts the current price for fibre and is paid immediately. Alternatively, their fibre can be pooled with that from other growers and they receive the actual returns from buyers (less charges, of course). Payout may take eight to ten weeks and the pools are held monthly.

See Appendix B for contact addresses.

Harvesting cashmere

This is the down which a goat grows over the late summer and autumn to give it extra warmth in winter. The down is a short fibre close to the skin, growing underneath the coarse, kempy layer of guard hairs. At the end of winter the goat moults and that down fibre falls out, leaving it with just a coarse coat of guard hairs.

Timing of shearing is important as the down must be clipped between the end of June, when the fibre has stopped growing, and before September, when the goat begins to moult. It is a matter of sneaking it in after the worst of the winter weather but far enough in front of kidding to avoid overstressing the does and risking abortions.

After shearing, cashmere goats continue to moult, in contrast to sheep which will just go on growing wool from the stubble you left them with. Goats lose even that stubble, so they *must* be given good feed and shelter after shearing.

Cashmere goats are only shorn once a year. To be worth marketing the down must be at least 30 mm long. Don't bother shearing goats if the down is shorter, and leave parts of the goat where it is below this length.

About a week before shearing, draft your white goats from coloured animals to avoid any contamination of the white fleeces with coloured fibre. Clean the shearing shed thoroughly, including vacuuming the board. Plan to shear the goats in order of colour; white first, then grey, then brown. Clean the board thoroughly between each colour. If you are familiar with sheep shearing techniques (see Chapter 9) then you may apply the same to your goats. But if some have no cashmere on their bellies, only kemp, it may be easier to shear the animal standing up.

Put its head in a suitable restraint or have someone else hold it for you while you sweep the handpiece along the length of the animal, from the tail to the shoulder, on the first side. After a few blows down the shoulder on side two, finish off with a few strokes from shoulder to tail. (See Fig. 60.) If there is some fibre on the belly or neck, lift a foreleg and sweep the handpiece over the brisket and up the neck.

Normal sheep shearing gear is fine for cashmere goats, though it is best to use a half-worn comb. Set the handpiece with not too much lead between comb and cutters and use a lighter tension than you would on sheep. Put a drop of oil on the cutters every second or third goat to stop the gear heating up.

Skirt out any areas of the fleece that have excessive amounts of kemp, vegetable contamination, dags, pizzle stain or shed stain (this is the green stain caused by goats being penned too tightly before they have had a chance to empty out). Also pull out any raddle marks' and short fibre (less than 30 mm).

Preparing cashmere for sale

Next bag the fibre so it is easy for the warehouse to pull each fleece out to class it individually. Make sure fleeces of different colours are put in separate containers. Use either a jute wool fadge, or paper kleensac. *Don't* use synthetic fadges, as the fibres are hard to detect if they get into the fleece. *Don't* use plastic bags, which make the fibre sweat. Put the fleeces carefully side by side until they form a complete bottom layer, then put down a clean sheet of newspaper and put another

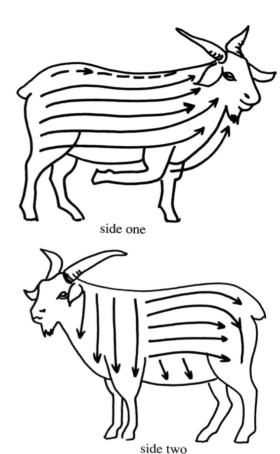

side one

side two

Fig. 60 **Blows for shearing a goat standing.**

layer of fleeces on it, side by side. Don't wrap the fleeces individually and don't stir up the layers. Just put each fleece in carefully so it can be separated easily at the warehouse.

Harvesting mohair

Mohair grows all year round so can be shorn twice a year. Time of shearing will vary. In the north, shearing in July and February fits in with fibre growth patterns, while further south the spring shear is better delayed until September (kidding is likely to be delayed also). Depending on the quality of your goats, they should grow fibre all over so are shorn with the same technique as sheep but with a few subtle differences. (See Figs. 53 and 61.)

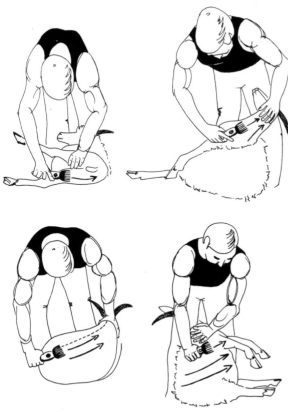

Fig. 61 **Shearing goats**.

Shearing technique

- Shear against the lie of the fibre as much as possible or else the comb may slide over the top and not cut it off close to the skin.
- Only remove the belly if the fibre there is good enough quality to make it worthwhile.
- On the long blow shear well over the backbone so that the last side will be as small as possible.
- If you can, slow your shearing plant down to between 2000 and 2400 rpm.
- Use a lighter tension.
- Use a 17 or 20-tooth comb.
- As goats don't have grease in their coat use extra lubrication. A good mix is 50/50 of clean oil with a friction-reducing additive like Wynns.
- On the last side angle your blows from the backbone to come slightly upwards.

Preparing mohair for sale

As the fleece comes off the goat, skirt out any stains, dags, raddle marks or vegetable contamination, and pull out any kempy areas such as the backline and around the top of the rump near the tail. Also skirt out any short fleece (under 90 mm).

As with cashmere the fleeces are going to be classed individually so lay them side by side in a wool fadge (use jute bags, not synthetic). Then put down a sheet of newspaper and repeat the process putting down another layer of fleeces carefully, side by side. If you are producing less than 20 kg use a big *paper* rubbish bag and put a small bit of newspaper between each fleece. Don't wrap the fleeces individually, just mark where each division comes.

Cashgora

This fibre can be prepared in the same way as mohair.

Marketing fibre

At present most New Zealand goat fibre is sold through the goat fibre warehouse in Hall Lane, Pukekohe. Once there, the fibre is classed and pooled with other fibres of similar type. The warehouse keeps a watch on quality, ensuring lines are properly classed so overseas buyers can be confident about the product they are bidding on.

The warehouse runs four pools a year for mohair, closing March 1, May 1, September 1 and November 1. Only two pools are held for cashmere, closing on September 1 and November 1. Producers are usually paid about ten weeks after the pools close. The warehouse charges a levy for classing, pooling, marketing and research. It also organises fibre preparation and fibre classing courses. (See Appendix B for contact addresses.)

To ensure your fibre doesn't get lost, label it clearly to go to the Mohair Cashmere Warehouse in Hall Lane, Pukekohe. On the outside of the consignment indicate whether it is mohair, cashmere or cashgora and if there is any coloured fibre Also put your own name and address, and your MOPANZ or CAPRONZ membership number if applicable.

Harvesting meat

Goat meat, or chevron, is a useful by-product of running goats for fibre or milk. It is also becoming an important export commodity. Chevron tastes virtually identical to mutton but is leaner (which doesn't mean tougher). If you are milking goats you will curse the number of buck kids you get. However, these can be killed at a few days old and dressed out and jointed like a rabbit. Or you may rear those kids on, castrate the bucks and butcher them at 3–6 months old.

It is a good idea to starve goats at least overnight before slaughter. Butchering and dressing is the same as for sheep (see Chapter 9), but I recommend shooting goats before bleeding them. Just feed the kid a handful of pellets in a bucket and while it is preoccupied put a bullet into the brain.

To cure a goat skin try one of the recipes in Appendix C.

Breeding

Female goats reach puberty between 4–6 months of age and young bucks are potent by about 3 months. However most farmers will not mate stock until they are at least a year old. You have to decide whether you want to quickly build flock numbers up or want young does to finish their own growing before breeding them. The drain of producing and feeding a kid will affect a young doe's own growth and a doe kidded young is more likely to have kidding trouble than a full grown animal.

Generally, if you want a milking goat to grow to her full milking potential, don't mate her until 19–20 months old. So if she was born in spring, mate her in her second autumn. But if you are breeding up fibre goats, and want to reduce the time between generations, then mate well-grown does in their first autumn, at least until you have crossed back to quality goats enough times to have pure stock. Then you can slow the breeding down.

A buck may be potent at 3 months old but shouldn't be worked until 6 months or a year. A mature buck can mate up to 100 does in an eight or nine week season but if you want to use a young buck don't expect him to serve more than 30.

Selecting a buck

In choosing a buck remember he is more than half your flock. If he has bad traits, those traits will come out in most of your replacement offspring. The following are the main features to look out for.

Milking goats

Check that the buck is healthy, well-grown with a strong, straight back, good feet and the ability and inclination to perform his stud duties. His sisters and dam will give the best indication of what sort of milking ability he can pass on to his offspring.

If you want to improve your flock then you need a buck whose offspring will be better producers than your own does so look at the production figures of the sisters and dam and apply the same general rules you would to buying a doe. They should have a good straight back with only a slight slope to the tail. The udder should be firmly attached to the body (a very long udder is easily damaged and difficult to milk). Avoid any stock that are cow hocked (this is where the hocks are too close together and bruise the udder).

Mohair goats

There are two approaches to mohair farming. One is the straight commercial approach where your aim is simply to grow as much good fibre as you can. In that case you want a sound flock with good fleeces and production, and need not be worried about their pedigrees, horn shapes and some of the other criteria stud goats are judged by. Select your buck primarily on his fibre production, but also take into account health, strength, feet and his willingness to work as a stud animal. Pick a goat with good colour. The fleece must be white, not yellowish or ginger. He should have mohair over the entire body apart from the ears, eyes, nose and legs (clear below the hocks and knees). The mohair should be even quality all over the animal and an even length. Avoid animals with any coarse kempy fibres (these usually show around the withers and tail). A heavy clip is also desirable as you will be paid for fleece on weight, but at the same time returns are better for finer fibre so stick to bucks with a fine micron count (anything over 38 microns is getting coarse).

The other approach to mohair farming is to farm stud stock. For this your breeding up programme needs to be carefully planned and recorded. It will pay to join the Mohair Producers Association to get all the latest information on registering goats.

You can upgrade to purebred Angora status starting with any sort of goat as a foundation animal and putting it to a purebred buck or a G1 buck (that is only one generation off purebred). The doe offspring will be first-cross or G4. Put them back to a purebred Angora buck and their offspring will be G3 or three-quarters Angora. Continue the breeding back to purebred stock and the fifth and any subsequent cross can be considered purebred and registered. But of course the better the bucks used on the way the better the quality of the eventual purebreds.

Keep records of each generation: what the doe is, what she was mated to and what she produced. If you bought goats from someone who never kept records, or get part-way through breeding up for commercial production and decide to register your flock eventually, then apply to MOPANZ for the flock to be inspected and the goats given a grade. Then you can breed up from that grade to purebred status.

Cashmere goats

It is the very fine down which attracts premium prices, so while shearing take a note of animals which show a good length of down, and a high yield (a lot of down and little guard hair). Both down and guard hair should be white and the down worth the most is less than 16.5 microns diameter. Select the best bucks with these criteria. If you are unsure which is the best animal send the fleece off for testing. The Mohair Cashmere Warehouse, a private testing house like Wharepuna Fibre Testing at Kirwee in Canterbury, or the Whatawhata Research Centre near Hamilton, all offer testing facilities for fleeces.

Meat goats

If you are breeding goats for meat, select a buck on his carcass weight and weight of kids weaned. Also go for bucks which produce hardy and early maturing kids.

Alternatives to buying a buck

If you have only a dozen or so goats it is not worth the expense or trouble of finding and keeping a buck which you may have to change every year or two, if you can use the stud services of some flock down the road.

The other option is AI (artificial insemination). It means you don't have to take your goats anywhere, you just have to determine when they are in season and organise a date with a straw of semen. It is a good choice if you are trying to improve your flock as you can use semen from some of the country's top quality bucks.

Heat detection

The main breeding season is from December to July, though April and May are the best months to mate does. During this season the does will cycle every 19 to 21 days. Angora goats tend to be more seasonal than Saanens, while some ferals will breed all year around. Goats are on heat for anything from three hours to three days and if you know your goats the signs should be fairly obvious.

Signs of heat

- She will wag her tail a lot.
- She will ride other goats.
- She makes a lot of noise calling for a mate.
- Her vulva will be slightly swollen and show a mucous discharge.

Teaser bucks

Another way to detect heat in goats is to use a vasectomised teaser buck. He will sniff out the ones in heat and if in a marker harness will leave a raddle mark on their rumps. You will need a vet to perform the vasectomy. Any buck will do, but don't use him for at least six weeks after the vasectomy operation.

Synchronising heats

Instead of waiting for the does to come on heat, you can control their season with hormones. This is helpful if you want to AI all the goats at once and get mating and kidding over in a concentrated period, or if you want to get into embryo transfers (see following). To synchronise does artificially you will need your vet's help. The does are given daily treatments of progesterone either by injection or using CIDRs (controlled internal drug releasers) which are put into the goat's vagina for 18 days. Once the treatment is stopped the goat will usually come into season and be ready to go to AI 50–55 hours later. She may also be given a superovulation drug to produce more kids.

To some extent you can synchronise does naturally. Keep them apart from the buck all year, then at mating time run a vasectomised teaser buck with them for three weeks. His presence will start the does cycling and as they are all introduced to him at the same time, they should start cycling in a fairly short time. Conception rates are usually best in the does' second or third cycle, so leave the teaser in and don't start your AI or let the proper buck out for 21 days. If mating naturally make sure you have enough bucks to cover all the does that might be coming in season on the same few days.

Artificial insemination

There are two methods of AI. In the first the semen is put into the uterus via the goat's vagina and cervix. This needs to be done by a qualified technician (though farmers can train to do it). The goat is held with its rear end up in the air by one person while the technician inserts the semen using an inseminating gun or pipette.

The second technique is by laparoscopy and has to be done by a qualified vet. For this the goat is anaesthetised and the semen put into the uterus by pushing a fine laparoscope through into the belly, locating the uterus and depositing the semen inside.

There are arguments for and against both techniques. Conception rates for cervical AI are about 50–60 per cent and for laparscopy about 60–70 per cent. Actual kidding rates will probably be higher because of the numbers of twins born.

Embryo transfer

If you have a flock of poor-quality does and want to breed up quickly to good ones, you can use embryo transfer techniques. This is expensive. You arrange to get embryos out of someone else's top quality goats and put them into yours which will then carry them to full term and kid out top grade goats.

The procedure involves synchronising the heats of both the donor goats (the good ones) and the recipient goats (your scrubbers). The donor goats are superovulated as well so they produce lots of fertilised embryos. The donors are operated on and the embryos removed about five days after they were mated. The recipients are also opened up and the embryos popped into their uterus. The recipient will now carry the good embryo to full term. The donor goat will come back into heat and can be remated and go on to have her own kid naturally.

Care of pregnant does

Pregnant does need good care. If stressed at all they may abort. During the first three months of pregnancy they only require maintenance rations but nearer full term (gestation is about 150 days) they will be wanting half as much feed again. Make sure they have plenty of good shelter over winter and are clear of internal parasites. With fibre goats you are shearing before kidding. Take especial care of the shorn does for at least three weeks after shearing. Run them back into the shed or barn if the weather is cold, or put covers on them. Feeding out some concentrates will also help give them extra energy for staying warm.

Kidding

Goats normally cope with kidding admirably on their own. Twins rather than singles are the norm, especially if the does are well grown and in good condition. Any problems are most likely in first kidders, which may have a large single instead of twins.

When to help

Normally kidding should only take about half an hour and it may be quicker. If the doe has been seriously straining for half an hour without progress then she needs help. The first job is to check the position of the kid. Smear your hand with a suitable lubricant (Pure Lux soap flakes will do — leave your hands soapy), and gently push your hand into the goat's vagina. Don't fight her contractions but wait until she has relaxed and feel for the position of the kid's head. (See Fig. 49.) If the head or a leg is turned back push the kid slightly back into the womb until you can turn the head or bring the leg forward. Cup the hoof to prevent it damaging the uterus. A breech birth is okay. That is when the hind legs come first and is the usual position for the second in a set of twins. Once the kid is in the right position the goat should manage on her own. Don't pull on anything until you are sure the kid is in the right position to dive out of the womb. If you need to help, pass a cord around the back of the kid's head behind the ears so you are pulling on the head and forelegs together. Keep an eye on the goat; she may have more than one kid to get out, and if you had to help her she could need a course of antibiotics to avoid the risk of metritis, or a uterus infection. Once the kid is out, wipe the mucus away from its nose and mouth and leave the doe to clean and mother it.

The goat should pass the afterbirth about an hour after kidding. If it is not out by 12 hours you may need a vet's help. Sometimes a warm drench of molasses and water, as well as massaging the abdomen can help her to clean. Don't pull on the afterbirth or you could cause internal bleeding. Does with retained foetal membranes are susceptible to metritis so check with your vet on a suitable course of antibiotics.

Cashmere goats are normally left to bring up their kids in a near natural situation. If your cashmere goats are still pretty wild it is important that they are disturbed as little as possible around kidding time.

Mohair goats should be able to rear their babies, but bear in mind they are not necessarily good milkers and if they have twins or more may not feed those kids very well. If necessary hand rear some of the kids to take the strain off the doe.

With milking goats you want the does' milk for yourself or for sale. If you only want doe kids as replacement stock and don't want the bucks for meat, now is the time to knock them on the head. You may decide to let the kids run with their mother for the first few days of their life. During this time she will be producing colostrum which is no use to you but vital for the kids to get a good start in life. Or you may decide to take the kids away at birth and hand feed them colostrum milked from the does.

Hand rearing

All kids must get a feed of colostrum in order to acquire immunity to local diseases and infections. If unable to get colostrum from the kid's own mother, milk some from another freshly-kidded doe. At worst try and get some cow colostrum. There is no substitute for colostrum. It contains large immunoproteins which the kids can only absorb through their gut wall in their first 12 hours of life. But if you just cannot get any, mix one pint of milk, one tablespoon of glucose, one beaten egg, a teaspoon of cod liver oil and feed 120–125 ml at blood heat, four times a day for a couple of days.

You can either regulate how much feed kids get or have them on an ad lib system where they can help themselves at any time. They drink more on ad lib but grow to greater weights earlier. If you plan to regulate their feed, little and often is best. That means at least four or five feeds (and one of them in the middle of the night) for the first few days, say at 7 am, 11 am, 3 pm, 7 pm and 10 pm.

Kids start to nibble grass from a few days old and will show interest in hay and starter feed concentrate rations. Make plenty of hard feed

Age (days)	Feed type	Amount/feed (ml)	Feeds/day
Birth	Colostrum	110	immediately
0–4	Colostrum	120	5
4–10	Goat's milk	300–400	4
10–21	Goat's milk	500	3
21–56	Goat's milk	600	3

Table 15. **Regulating feed for kids**.

available and you can begin to decrease milk amounts and frequency of feeds from about eight weeks on. Weaning weight is a better guide than age, aim for 15 kg for doe kids and 16 kg for bucks.

Castration

All unwanted male animals not intended to be kept as sires should be castrated; the earlier the better. About 3–5 days old is best, and they should all be done by no later than 27 days old (remember a young buck is potent from 12 weeks old). See castration in lambs.

Polling

If you are running mohair or cashmere goats you will not be worried about horns — in fact the shape and size of them is an important feature in pedigree mohair circles, and they can be a useful handle to grab hold of when dealing with individual goats. But for milking goats, horns can be a hassle and cause udder damage.

Some animals are naturally polled. The polled gene is easy to introduce and if you use a polled buck over horned stock at least half the offspring should be polled. Unfortunately polledness is connected to infertility so it is not possible to breed pure polled stock.

For kids born with horns it is best to dehorn does by a week old and bucks by 3 days old. There is no nice way to disbud a goat. The best technique is the disbudding iron. (See Fig. 62.) You can make one yourself from a large old soldering iron by grinding the end flat so it is about the size of a five cent piece. For disbudding heat it dull red, then apply it squarely to the horn bud for about 10 seconds. Too long and you will cook its tiny brain; not long enough and the horn will regrow. Buck

Fig. 62 **Disbudding iron made from old soldering iron with tip ground down.**

Fig. 63 **Apply disbudding iron squarely to horn buds.**

kids may need a couple of seconds longer than does. (See Fig. 63.) Reheat the iron and apply it to the second bud. Put some soothing antiseptic cream on the spots, give the kid a feed and let it go.

Dehorning paste is less traumatic from your point of view — no animal screaming, no blood, and it is quick and easy. But it is not necessarily the nicest way for the goats. A heavy downpour after the paste is applied could have caustic running down a kid's face and into the eyes. Also you don't know how much is left on the horn bud to do the job. If you do opt for paste, smear vaseline around the bud and keep kids isolated so they don't rub the paste onto each other.

Another method is to use calf dehorners which physically bite the bud out — lots of blood and pretty upsetting for all concerned. Also it's hard to tell just how deep the dehorners need to bite and it is easy to go crooked so the kid ends up growing scurs.

If you want to dehorn older goats, they must be given a local anaesthetic and the job should be done by a vet.

Earmarking

All goats are considered feral or wild in the eyes of the law unless they have a registered 'goat' earmark. Register your mark with MAF so that both you and the world at large know the animal belongs to you. Valuable animals have been rustled, and as plastic or metal tags can be removed, tattoos are the only permanent proof of ownership (though I've even heard of goats around with short ears!).

With mohair goats all purebred animals must be tattooed with the herd flock number in the goat's left ear, and your own number to identify the animal in your herd in its right ear. If your animals are not purebred you can use plastic tags. Use a blue tag for a foundation goat, yellow for G4, green for G3, purple for G2, red for G1 and white for purebred stock. To attach the tag find the sinew running down the ear and the line where the ear folds over, and put the tag just behind the sinew and to the tip side of the foldline. With Saanens put the tag mid-way between the ridges running the length of the ear and halfway along the ear.

Problems

In their natural state goats are fairly hardy animals. But when we come along and farm them all that changes. For a start we breed them up so highly that while they might produce copious quantities of milk or mohair they lose a lot of that feral resilience. Then we fence them so they cannot move on to clean range and are forced to eat just one type of grass and on areas they may have grazed heavily before. They may be on soft lowland country so they cannot keep their feet in trim and chances are all the bush and natural shelter was chopped down long ago. So it is up to us to correct the imbalances that farming forces on them. As mentioned earlier, you must provide shelter, especially for shorn goats and newborn kids which are very susceptible to exposure and pneumonia.

Health care

Feet

Regular foot trimming is essential as farmed goats cannot wear their feet down naturally and overlong toes are a haven for scald. Foot care should start from the time a goatling is about 8 weeks old, then every 6–12 weeks the feet should be checked and trimmed. The cleft between the toes is quite deep

in a goat, so it is more prone to infection than in sheep. Treatment is similar. (See 'Foot problems in sheep', page 89.)

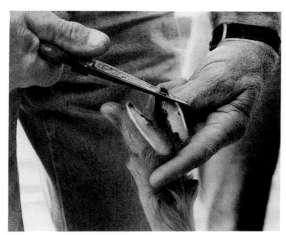

Goat feet should be trimmed every six weeks.

Worms

Goats do not develop an immunity to worms like sheep. (See 'Internal parasites' in sheep, page 86, and 'Drenching regime', page 74.) That means they need protection from weaning right through their lives. Also goats metabolise drench faster than sheep so it is less effective. But at the same time they are more susceptible to anthelmintic shock if incorrectly drenched. Research has shown that goats develop resistant strains of worms if drenched just with benzimidazole and levamisole-based drenches at sheep dose rates.

Levamisoles were also connected with some goat deaths in the early days of goat farming, but studies have shown this was due to anaphylactic shock and only occurred in goats with no drenching history. So drench is safe to use so long as the goat has been drenched regularly since it was a kid. If not, stick to benzimidazoles or avermectins. However, the latter should not be used on lactating goats as residues can be detected in the milk. But dairy goat farmers can use an avermectin drench at drying off and again 28 days before the goats kid, then change back to levamisole. Give two drenches, a day apart, every 21–28 days, or else benzimidazole at double the dose recommended for sheep. During peak worm periods you may have to drench fortnightly to keep burdens down in intensively farmed stock. (See also 'Management', page 96.)

Normally goats are clean animals that excrete hard little pebbles. If what they do turns liquid or sloppy and stains their hind legs then they are not well and worms are the most likely cause. However in extensively run goats Barbers Pole worm will be the main problem and it causes anaemia rather than scouring. So watch your goats and realise that keeping worm burdens down is an ongoing process.

Clostridial diseases

Goats are highly susceptible to clostridial diseases especially tetanus. The best idea is to vaccinate all does a couple of weeks before they kid. This will pass a temporary immunity (about three months) on to the new-born kids through the colostrum and this will give them time to build up their own immunities. They won't need treating themselves until they in turn are about to kid.

If you didn't get around to vaccinating does before kidding, inject the new kids as soon as possible, and again at six to eight weeks old. Any goat not on a regular vaccination programme will need to be protected with tetanus anti-toxin if she is ever wounded or requires any sort of surgery. (See 'Clostridial Diseases' in the sheep chapter, page 91.)

Caprine Arthritic Encephalitis (CAE)

CAE is a viral disease which leaves kids up to 5 months old lame, weak and even paralysed in the hind legs. It may cause their death and can damage the nervous system. It is usually passed on through suckling colostrum from infected does. In adult goats it can cause arthritis and pneumonia.

Various sectors of the goat industry and MAF have set up an accreditation scheme to help reduce the spread of the disease. Getting your flock accredited can take time and money, but stock certified free of CAE command a premium at sales. If you want to join the scheme, first apply to MAF and fill in the appropriate form, then get your local vet to carry out pre-accreditation tests (this involves taking a blood sample from all goats over 12 months of age). If those tests are clear then

MAF will do an accreditation test between six and 12 months later.

If the first tests showed up some reactors then those goats will probably have to be killed as it is considered unethical to sell reactor goats. If both tests were clear then MAF will register the flock as CAE free. To maintain your accreditation status, the flock has to be retested every year for two years and every third year after that. There are also stringent rules covering introduction of new goats to your flock and taking goats to saleyards or showgrounds. In spite of the strictness of the scheme it is gaining acceptance in milking and mohair circles.

Coccidiosis

This is mainly a problem in young kids from 1–4 weeks old. It causes a stomach upset and leads to dark, watery scouring which may be blood-stained. If untreated it can kill the kid. The coccidiosis organisms live in the animal's gut lining and are passed out in the dung and may then be re-ingested or eaten by another goat host. Prevent outbreaks with good hygiene. Ordinary household ammonia is an effective disinfectant for scrubbing out kids' quarters. Treat affected kids with a coccidiostat from your vet. If you are worried about an outbreak occurring you can medicate kids' drinking water.

Facial eczema

Facial eczema is usually not a problem in goats as their browsing habits keep them above the dangerous, spore-infected levels of the grass sward. But if you are in a high risk area and have valuable animals take care not to graze them hard and consider spraying some pasture with fungicide to make it safe. (See also 'Facial eczema in sheep', page 89.)

Lice and ticks

Treat as you would for sheep. If you have only a few animals you may use a louse powder containing rotenone or malathion. Or if you have just one pet goat a dog flea collar will do the trick.

Liver fluke

This is another internal parasite. The mature fluke

is about 25 mm long and 8 mm wide with a leaf-like shape. It lives in the bile duct of the host's liver and eggs from the adult pass through the animal and out onto the pasture. These will hatch in wet conditions. A particular type of freshwater snail acts as the intermediate host. In spring and early summer the young fluke lives in the snail body for a couple of months. It leaves as a free-swimming, microscopic form which stock take in when drinking water or grazing weeds in swampy ground. The fluke passes down into the intestine and from there spends up to 13 weeks burrowing through to the liver. Enough flukes in a host will kill it. The damage they cause in the liver also creates conditions suitable for black disease, one of the clostridial diseases.

If you are in a fluke area, protect by drenching with a flukicide at least once, in April or May, and if it is a regular problem you may have to give three drenches between March and June. Prevent the spread of flukes by destroying the habitat of the intermediate host by draining swamps and bogs, and stopping goats from grazing wet areas.

Mastitis

Mastitis is common in goats with large pendulous udders which are difficult to milk out properly. Symptoms and treatment are similar to those for dairy cows.

Milk fever (hypocalcaemia)

This normally occurs in high-producing milking goats, particularly after their third or fourth kidding. The goat may be producing so much milk she depletes her own body's calcium reserves, and as all muscles need calcium to function, the goat may go down and become bloated and die if not treated. Milk fever can occur any time during the lactation, but is more common just after kidding.

To prevent bloating sit and prop the animal up on its chest before seeking help. Treatment usually consists of an immediate injection of about 20 ml of calcium borogluconate (check with your vet) or about a fifth of a dose of any of the calcium preparations available to treat milk fever in cows.

Avoid the risk of milk fever by not giving too high a protein diet just before or after kidding. Stop milking any affected animal for 24 hours, just

ease milk her if her udder is very full then gradually increase the amount taken over the next few days to avoid a relapse.

Pneumonia

The risk of pneumonia in goats is similar to sheep. Take care to avoid exposure in cold weather and overcrowding or stress in dry, dusty conditions. Treat cases as for sheep.

Poisoning

Goats love to nibble at most things, whether they are good for them or not. There are many poisonous plants (see Appendix D) which goats are bound to chew given the chance. So long as the goat is browsing and has a full gut and just takes a taste of something toxic she will probably be all right. The danger comes if she is held in a yard and forced to eat whatever is nearest. For many plants there is no treatment, but if you can identify the plant responsible, contact your vet. He or she may know of an antidote, or you can try this old-fashioned general poison antidote administered as a drench: mix 2 parts powdered charcoal (burnt toast scrapings will do), 2 parts magnesium oxide (milk of magnesia) and 1 part tannic acid (tea).

Watch out for urea poisoning. Some stock licks and animal feeds contain urea which seems to have a cumulative toxic effect on goats and can kill them. The antidote is an immediate injection of vitamins A, D and E. Eating too much kikuyu grass can also cause colic if the grass is very lush. Treat with one dessertspoon of baking or washing soda in a cup of water given as a drench.

Pregnancy toxaemia (Hypoglycaemia)

This is also known as pregnancy sickness or ketosis. Symptoms and causes are similar to those in sheep.

Give the goat an immediate injection of 100 ml of 50 per cent glucose solution. If she is still able to swallow you can drench her with 100 g of glycerine. Keep her out of the sun and make sure she drinks plenty of water. Drench her with 600–1200 ml of water a day if you have to. Note that hypoglycaemia and hypocalcaemia often occur together so prepare to treat the goat with calcium as well if needed. (See 'Milk fever', page 90.)

11. Cattle

Keep a dairy cow and you can fill up the milk jug, put cream on your porridge or make your own butter and cheese. You can rear a calf or two on the excess milk and sell them later for cash or carry them on for beef for the freezer. Even if you are a vegetarian you can raise nice little dairy heifers on your cow and sell them later to pay for your lentils and soya beans.

The alternative is beef or dry stock (not milking animals). Keep your own beef breeding cows or just buy in weaners at 6 months old and rear them to 18 months or 2 years for your own freezer or for sale. On about 1.5 ha my parents regularly buy in two weaners, carry them for a year, put one in the freezer and sell the second which earns enough to buy in two more weaners.

Beef animals are generally less work than dairy animals. If your land is a bit rough or you don't want the hassle of milking twice a day, go for beef cattle.

However, cattle are big animals, with cows weighing up to 860 kg and bulls to 1135 kg, depending on the breed. That is not much of a problem if they are quiet, hand-reared stock but if wild-eyed and wary you will need good yards and even a crush or head bail.

Dairy cows are a terrible tie. To maintain good production they need to be milked regularly night and morning and as near as possible at the same times each day. So you went to a party last night, you've got a hangover and the last thing you want to look at is a bucketful of rich creamy milk; but the cow is outside the bedroom window bellowing to have the pressure taken off her udder, and you have to do it.

Cows eat more than sheep or goats. One cow may eat as much as five to seven sheep, and if you run a lot of cows you can say bye-bye to the farm looking like a golf course. Cattle pug paddocks badly in the wet and graze unevenly, leaving the paddocks looking a bit moth-eaten unless you are prepared to top (mow the tops off) rank patches in summer and harrow to spread dung evenly.

Breeds

Consider carefully what you want in a cow. There are many breeds and types, with arguments for and against all of them. Do you want meat, milk or both? If you want milk do you want calves that are worth putting in the freezer or more dairy replacements? Temperament is also important on a smallfarm. If you are learning about milking cows then you want a quiet girl who can end up a family pet. Even if you opt for beef, you want stock quiet enough to stay inside your fences and safe enough to ask the kids to go out and shift to a fresh paddock.

Of course it is as dangerous to generalise about cows as it is about people, but most farmers will have definite ideas on the merits of different breeds. There will be exceptions to the rules but just as you wouldn't buy a cocker spaniel if you wanted a guard dog, we don't want you buying a Brahman for a milking cow! The following is a list of the more commonly available breeds, I apologise to any cattle breeders whose breed I have omitted.

Ayrshire.

Friesian.

Jersey.

Shorthorn.

Dairy breeds

Ayrshire

An attractive medium-sized cow, normally weighing 410–500 kg and standing about 125 cm high. They have bold red and white spotted markings and average 3.8–4 per cent milkfat. The breed originated in Scotland but has a reputation for being a bit bad tempered and flighty.

Friesian

A big-framed dairy cow, weighing 560–680 kg and standing up to 136 cm high. They have distinctive pied black and white markings though generally have a white tail swish and lower legs. The Friesian produces a greater volume of milk than the Jersey, so is popular on town milk supply farms where it is litres of milk rather than kilograms of milkfat which count for payment. Friesian milk is about 3–3.5 per cent milkfat. The calves are popular as dairy beef and bull beef, especially if a beef breed bull was used. Hereford/Friesian crosses command good prices at weaner sales.

Jersey

A relatively small cow, weighing 320–440 kg and standing only 122 cm high. Their size and docile nature make them easy to handle and perfect for a family house cow and pet. But not Jersey bulls. They are recognised as one of the most unpredictable and dangerous of bull breeds. Jerseys are normally fawn with black muzzle and tail swish but the colours range from dun to dark brown and even black. They give a lower volume of milk than Friesians but at 5 per cent the proportion of milkfat is higher, so the milk is ideal for butter or cheese making. The meat tends to have yellow fat which makes them unpopular for eating, but by crossing with a beef breed bull you can produce a small but acceptable carcass with meat that scores highly on taste test panels.

Jersey/Friesian crossbred

This cow is not a recognised breed, but it is now earning a good reputation and place in the dairy industry. Because of hybrid vigour it is often able to outproduce both parent breeds. These cows tend

111

to be dark coloured, often black or very dark brown all over.

Shorthorn

A dual-purpose breed kept for both meat and milk. These cows tend to be red, red and white or roan with a flesh-coloured nose. They produce milk with about 4 per cent milkfat. They are one of the oldest established breeds of cattle and were first registered in 1822. They were popular with pioneers but have largely been superseded by straight beef and dairy animals.

Beef breeds

Traditionally beef farmers have run English breeds like the Angus or Hereford. But now those from the Continental countries, the so-called 'exotic' breeds are playing an increasingly important role, particularly in crossbreeding programmes where farmers have learnt to take advantage of hybrid vigour. Some beef breeds do better on poor land; others may grow bigger carcasses quicker; others may be more efficient at converting whatever grass they do eat into beef. Again I have had to generalise in the following descriptions and there will be animals that don't follow the norm. But whatever breed you eventually opt for, there are some rules which apply to most cattle and you should consider before buying.

- The quieter the animal the easier it will be to keep it fenced in and the more of its energy will go into growing meat instead of charging around.
- Runts tend to stay runts so always go for well-grown, big-framed animals. Even if you are pushed for cash, buy fewer but still buy good animals. Somebody very wise once said something about silk purses and sows' ears and they were right. Whatever the reason for some animal not doing as well as its herd mates, it is not going to change just because you have bought it.

Angus

Usually black, these are compact, low-set animals, and naturally hornless or polled. They are early maturing but smaller than other breeds. Cows weigh 540–680 kg and bulls to 900 kg. They dress

Angus bull.

Hereford bull.

Charolais — cow and calf.

Limousin heifers.

Murray Grey bull.

Devon bull.

Santa Gertrudis — cow and calf.

Simmental bull.

out well, though, and have good quality, well-marbled flesh. They can be nervous and wild but will quieten down with regular shifting or feeding out. They are good doers suited to rough country and climates. They originated in North East Scotland and were first imported to New Zealand in 1863. By the late 1950s there were more Angus here than Herefords and Shorthorns put together.

Hereford

These were originally bred as both beef and draft animals in Herefordshire, England. They are red with white faces, manes, dewlaps and feet and underbelly. They are early maturing and good doers. Cows weigh 680–770 kg, bulls up to 860 kg. The first importation was in 1868 and polled Herefords were accepted in 1928. They are often crossed with Friesians to get good dairy beef.

Charolais

These are massive, cream-coloured, horned cattle from France. They were originally developed as draft animals but are now valued for cross-breeding with English beef breeds to get large meaty offspring. However they can be susceptible to calving trouble in spite of their size. They are a newcomer to New Zealand with the first semen imports in 1966 and actual cattle not coming in until 1980.

Limousin

Another recent introduction from France, these animals are a light red colour. They have a good growth rate and high meat yield.

Murray Grey

These were developed in Australia from a small herd of Shorthorn and Angus crossbreds. They are a compact, well-muscled animal and range in colour from a dusty brown to grey. They were first imported in 1971.

Red Devon

Compact, well-muscled, medium-sized beef animals which tend to be good doers and very efficient converters of grass to meat. They are known for a docile temperament and range in colour from rich red to liver.

Santa Gertrudis

Developed from crossing Brahmans with beef
Shorthorns, these are big, early-maturing animals
with the cows weighing 680–815 kg and bulls up
to 1135 kg. They are normally a cherry red colour.
They thrive in hot climates but tend to be active
and nervous.

Simmental

Originally a Swiss breed from the Simm Valley,
the first imports to New Zealand were from
England in 1972. These are big animals, usually
red or orange and white in colour. They are good
milkers and valued for cross-breeding with other
beef breeds.

Grazing management

How much your cows eat will vary through the
year. Winter is the key time. Get your stock
through winter well and if they are breeding cows
they will then calve successfully, come into milk
well making the most of the spring feed and come
back into season to be remated quickly. Let those
same cows get too skinny over winter and they
will produce small calves, take longer to cycle
again for remating and may fail to get in calf at all.

From the chapter on pasture principles we know
we can grow the most grass if the pastures are kept
between 5–15 cm long. This is easiest to control
by rotationally grazing the stock, giving them
regular shifts to fresh ground. Don't expect them
to graze below 5 cm. A cow grazes by wrapping
its tongue around the feed so needs a reasonable
length to get a grip on it. Aim to shift them about
once a week or more frequently so they will
always be on good, fresh, quality feed. If you do
not have enough permanent fencing then break
fence paddocks with one or two hot temporary
wires. Try to give square breaks rather than long
skinny ones which they will pug up. Back fence
(put an electric fence behind them) to prevent
overgrazing, thus allowing pasture to start recover-
ing as soon as they are shifted on.

In winter it may take 30–60 days before the
grass is long enough for the cows to come back

and regraze a site; in spring, 14–20 days may be
enough. Just watch the grass growth and the cows'
condition. You do not want beef cows to lose more
than ten per cent of their live-weight through
winter and you want dairy cows in good condition,
but not fat. Once they have calved their energy and
the grass they eat will go into making milk and
they will not regain condition they have lost.

After calving, cows are eating for two so try to
time calving to coincide with the best spring
growth. If you are aiming to sell the calves as
weaners you will be trying to calve the cows as
early as possible (older calves will be heavier and
get better prices). But if your cows calve before
the spring flush and have to go onto short rations
you run the risk of metabolic problems. Also the
cow may take longer to cycle and get back into
calf for next year. If you do not get good early
spring growth, then delay calving (by delaying
mating) until there is plenty of feed about and keep
those calves and sell them at 18 months.

If you are just buying in weaners to fatten,
ensure they always get plenty of good feed to
reach killable weights quickly. Run them ahead of
sheep or other small stock and time selling them to
fit in with your pasture management needs. For
instance, off-load them before summer if you
always get hit with droughts, or before winter if
feed runs short then and you have other stock that
you want to give priority to.

Breeding

Mating

There is no point keeping and feeding a large bull
all year round just to keep a few cows happy. The
options are: find an obliging neighbour with the
type of bull you want; or go for AI (artificial
insemination). You may find your neighbouring
dairy farmers put their own cows to AI for the first
six weeks or so of the breeding season and only
use their own bull after that to catch any cows that
are late coming in heat. So you may be able to
sneak in the use of their bull before he is required
in the herd.

Artificial insemination

Using AI you don't have the bother of keeping or finding a bull and have the choice of the country's top-producing sires. Chances are the bull down the road is pretty average. He'll do the job all right, but if you have to go through the nine months waiting and then the trauma of calving time why not go through it all for a calf really worth having? This is especially the case if you want a dairy type calf to keep as a replacement milker. AI facilities are available for the smallfarmer, but the technicians are busy people so you need to know just what is required for AI before making a date with a straw of semen. Obviously you need a yard or cowshed where the cow can be confined and, most importantly, the cow you put forward must be in heat.

Heat detection

Some cows are really obvious and let the whole world know they are feeling unfulfilled, but others are shy and may have a 'silent' heat and be past it before you realise. Look for these signs:

• A cow in heat is restless and more aggressive with other cows than usual.

• She may stand close to other cows, sniff their tails, urinate often and early on will try to mount or ride other cows.

• Her vulva may be swollen and she may withhold her milk.

• Once she is in standing oestrus other cows will ride her, leaving signs of mud on her flanks and saliva on her back.

• She will generally let the world know something is lacking with a lot of bellowing and being followed around by other cows.

• There will be clear mucus running from her vulva.

Standing heat, when she will stand to be ridden by other cows or a bull, may last six to 24 hours and ovulation normally occurs about 30 hours later. So if a cow is seen in heat at the evening milking, inseminate her the following day. If she is on heat at the morning milking, inseminate the same day or next day if she is just coming into heat.

Trials have shown that cows are more likely to conceive to AI a couple of heats after calving, that

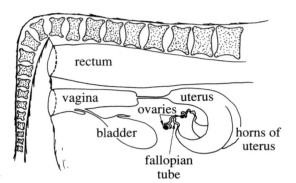

Fig. 64 **Reproductive organs of a cow.**

is, about six weeks later. So unless you are trying to 'bring her forward' to get her in calf early so she will calve earlier the next year, don't mate her for six weeks or so after calving. Once a cow has been inseminated or put to the bull you need to watch her in 18–23 days' time to see if she has come back on heat. If so it means she did not conceive first time and you need to go through the performance again.

Pregnancy detection

If you want to be really sure she is in calf get her 'vetted in-calf'. This is a job for the vet, who inserts an arm into the cow's rectum and from there can palpate the uterus and ovaries and feel for any enlargement or the presence of a placenta. This can be done accurately from 8–10 weeks after mating.

Other techniques used for diagnosing pregnancy include urine and milk tests and ultrasonic testing, but are more expensive.

Heifers

Jersey heifers reach puberty at about 8–10 months; Friesians normally take another month or two. Any time from then on they can conceive if put to the bull while on heat, but a cow that young is nowhere near finished her own growing. The general practice is to not mate them until 15 months. Assuming a heifer is born in August, she can be mated the following November and calved the August after that. If she looks a bit small at 15 months, let her go on growing until she is 30 months, but don't leave it longer than that or she is likely to get too fat and have trouble conceiving.

It can be harder to pick a heifer in heat than an older cow so a lot of farmers prefer to just let the heifer run with a bull and let him do the detective work. Stick to smaller breed bulls to reduce the heifer's risk of calving trouble first time round.

Pregnancy

Care of the pregnant cow

Once you have got your cows in calf you want to keep them that way. You also want to ensure the calf embryo grows satisfactorily and not at the expense of the cow's own body condition. But nor do you want fat cows as overweight cows tend to have more calving trouble and complications after calving. (See 'Problems', page 125.) To avoid this, restrict feed intake in the last four weeks. This does not mean starving the animal. Severely underfeeding the cow will affect her own body condition rather than the calf size and this in turn will affect how well she comes into milk after calving and how soon she comes back in heat for mating for next year's calf. The object is to keep the cow fit and neither too fat nor too thin.

Once a good dairy cow has calved she will put all she eats into milk production. This means that as the season progresses she will get thinner regardless of the feed she is on. Beef cows are different. They can put on weight at the same time as feeding a calf because they don't produce the same copious quantities of milk.

Gestation length

Once you have managed to find a bull or organise AI and all that is behind you, you can sit back and spend the next 282 days or so psyching up for calving. Actual gestation length can vary considerably. A cow mated to a Friesian or Jersey should produce 282 days later, but if put to a Hereford the calf could take 285 days and a Charolais or Simmental 286 days. That will vary, too. If the cow is a first calver she may calve three days before an older cow and if the calf is a heifer it may appear ten days earlier than if it was a bull calf.

Calving

When you wander out to the cow paddock 280 days after the cows were mated and tell them to get on with it, you've got it all wrong. It is actually the calf that decides when to appear. It produces cortisol, a hormone which the cow reacts to by becoming increasingly restless. As well, the birth canal dilates and colostrum comes into the udder. A day or so before calving the ligaments around the cow's pelvis loosen slightly and there will be a noticeable falling away between the hips and the tail bone. The lips of the vulva tend to swell and there may be a mucus discharge.

Calving normally covers four stages:
1. Uneasiness. During this time the cow may strain for up to three hours before the water bag appears. If she strains for longer than this without any sign of the water bag she should be examined to check her cervix is not blocked or the womb twisted.
2. The water bag ruptures.
3. Birth of the calf usually occurs about 1–4 hours after the water bag ruptures.
4. Cleaning of the afterbirth. It may take another four or five hours.

The third stage is the one you are probably most worried about. Normally the head and both front feet of the calf will be presented first as if it is diving out of the womb. (See Fig. 65.) The cow usually lies down until the head and shoulders appear. Then she may rise and the calf will drop to the ground as she does. Some cows stand through the whole performance.

When to help

If there has been no progress for an hour or if the cow seems to have given up it is time to step in. First, examine the cow to work out what position the calf is in. Do this before you pull on anything. Also wash your arm right up to the shoulder in soapy disinfected water. Wash around the cow's vulva and tail, then gently insert your arm into the cow's vagina and feel around the calf to work out its position. As with sheep, goats and horses, the normal presentation is two front feet and muzzle first. If the calf is coming backwards (and that is okay) the two hind feet will be presented first. But if only a head comes up, or only the head and one

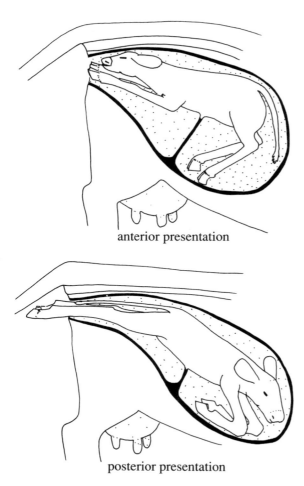

anterior presentation

posterior presentation

Fig. 65 Calving positions.

leg, or only the front legs and no head, or only the tail — then the calf is in the wrong position and you will have to correct it. This is the first principle of assisting at calving — check the calf's position before doing anything else.

A cow should handle a normal presentation herself, unless it is a very big calf in a small cow. Getting the head and shoulders through the pelvis is the hardest part. If you do need to help at this stage try pulling one foreleg slightly in front of the other, but only pull if you are sure both forelegs and the head are presented.

In the early stages of labour, any pull on the calf should be upwards in the direction of the tail. But once the calf is properly in the pelvic cavity, pull

straight back and for the last part (getting the hips and hindquarters through) pull slightly downwards. If getting the back end of the calf through causes any problems grab the whole body of the calf and twist it through 45 degrees so the calf is half turned on its side.

If you need to correct the calf's position only go in between the cow's attempts to strain, and only try to shift the calf when the cow is relaxing. Likewise, once you start pulling, try to pull in conjunction with the contractions. Once your hand is inside the cow the aim is to examine the calf and correct its position all in one go without having to withdraw and reinsert your arm. The more times you put your hand back in the more risk of introducing infection to the uterus.

You may need to slip a rope around the bits of the calf that need shifting as it will be very slippery. Any rope should be strong but reasonably soft and well washed in disinfectant. Use a spliced loop in the end rather than a knot which could damage the inside of the cow or the calf. If the calf's head is bent back you may need to push the whole calf slightly back into the cow to make room in the pelvic passages to bring the head forward. If the head continues to slip back, slip a loop of rope around behind its ears and in the mouth. If you need to bring a leg forward remember to cup the hoof in your hand so it does not damage the uterus lining. If a leg is well back, bend it at the knee, bring it forward bent and as the hock and hoof comes into reach try to straighten it out. If the calf is presented backwards that should be no problem so long as both hind legs appear and labour does not last too long. A long labour may cause the calf to suffocate.

Rearing

Once the calf is born wipe the mucus away from its mouth and nose, then leave it to its mother. With beef cows, calves are normally just run with their mothers until they are about 6 months old. But with dairy cows the objective is usually to keep the milk for the household and the calf may be secondary. If you don't want to rear the calf you can sell it as a bobby for slaughter (usually at

2–4 days old) or sell it to someone else who does want to rear it. Most farmers leave calves on their mothers for the first few days as in that time the cow is producing colostrum which is not wanted in the milk jug and which the calf needs to get a good start in life.

Sharing

With a dairy cow you have the choice of sharing her milk with her baby or handrearing the calf and keeping all the cow's milk for yourself. The advantage of sharemilking her with the calf is you only need to milk once a day and if you want a few days' holiday you can just leave the calf on her. You don't have to panic about finding a relief milker. The disadvantages are you need a good yard to hold the calf and the cow may get fussy about letting her milk down for you. Also the calf is not likely to strip the cow out thoroughly so she will not be encouraged to maintain her top production and could be at risk from mastitis.

The system most commonly used is to let the cow and calf run together during the daylight. Shut the calf away overnight, but leave the cow loose so she can continue to graze and make milk. You milk the cow next morning then let the calf loose for the day.

Handrearing calves

With handrearing you remove the calf, milk the cow out yourself and just feed the calf out of the milk you get. That way you know how much the cow is producing and how much the calf drinks. If you are going to handrear one calf it is not much extra trouble to raise a few more so buy bobbies off your dairyfarmer neighbour. Surplus calves are sold to freezing works and slaughtered for veal, and also for the rennet in their stomachs.

It is hard to select the best calves when you come to a pen full of calves with soulful eyes that you know are doomed for slaughter unless you rescue them. But keep in mind just what you want those calves for. Don't be tempted to just take the prettiest or the poor little ones. If you want calves to be future milkers, stick to heifers with both parents of dairy type (crossbreds are okay so long as each parent was a dairy animal). If you want to raise beef for the freezer (or to sell the calves as

weaners for someone else to fatten and put in the freezer) then go for calves with a beef breed father.

Pick the bigger, alert looking calves with clean, shiny coats and clean, damp noses. Avoid anything that shows signs of scouring. A healthy calf should have soft but firm droppings, neither hard and lumpy, nor watery. Ideally the bobbies should be about 4 days old and either have been on their mothers until then or have been fed colostrum for that time from freshly calved cows. Calves must have had a good feed of colostrum in the first day of their life as cows pass on immunity to local infections and disease through large proteins (globulins) in the first rich milk. But the calf can only absorb these through its gut in its first 12 to 24 hours of life. Without colostrum the calf will be prey to stomach upsets and infection. In their natural state calves suckle infrequently so they can be trained to just a couple of feeds a day without too much stress.

Rearing calves

How you decide to rear them will depend on how many there are and how much trouble you want to go to. If you want to raise more than a dozen I'd suggest you get or make a calfeteria. This is basically just a large vat (a 200 litre drum will do so long as it is clean) with teats positioned around the rim. If you plan to ad lib feed, one teat between half a dozen calves will do, but if you want to

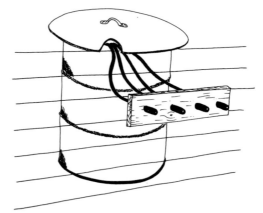

Fig. 66 **Calf feeder with teats 750–850 mm above ground level.**

regulate how much they get and how often, they will need a teat each. The teats connect to plastic hoses which syphon the milk from the vat when the calf sucks (See Fig. 66.) The most commonly-used calf teat needs a 22 mm hole and the hose used is 11 mm outside diameter.

Calves learn to suck on this sort of calfeteria quicker than you can teach them to drink from a bucket. One drawback is that you don't know exactly how much each calf gets, though with just a few calves you can run the hoses into individual buckets. You do need to pull out all the hoses and teats and wash them thoroughly in hot water from time to time. In cool weather a clean up every few days is sufficient but if the milk is turning sour sooner, wash everything after each feed.

If keeping up all that hygiene is likely to be a problem then it might be better to bucket feed your calves. Put the calves on one side of a rail, buckets the other, and allow the calves to stick their necks through individual bails into their own buckets. Buckets are easy to scrub out and you can keep an eye on how much each calf drinks. But you have to teach the brats to drink first!

Teaching a calf to bucket feed

First time round use warm milk (about skin temperature). Back the calf into a corner, hold the bucket firmly in one hand and with the other slip a couple of fingers into the calf's mouth. When it starts sucking on them push his head down into the bucket with your palm over his snout. Just lower his head enough so that when he sucks your fingers he's sucking up a bit of milk too. Then slowly ease your fingers out and hope he keeps sucking milk up. Some calves will pick this up quickly but others take several sessions, especially if they were left on their mother until you collected them. Each feed use your fingers to guide the calves to the milk until they get the hang of where it comes from.

Some calves just won't learn to drink. This is most common in calves left for the first few days on the cow. If you have had a good try at teaching the blighter where the milk comes from, leave it for 12 hours and try again. Chances are if you are ad lib feeding off a calfeteria the calf will have learnt off others in the pen by then. If not it will be hungrier and keener to learn. Another trick is to feed them a bit of Vytrate out of a bottle and teat and once they are sucking enthusiastically transfer them to the milking teat.

How much to feed

There are two approaches to calf feeding. The first is ad lib, that is making milk available to the calves all the time so they just drink whenever they want. Calves do drink more this way but reach weaning weights sooner. It also means less work for you as you just have to top the vat up once a day instead of at every feed. But you still need to clean the vat and hoses out occasionally to avoid stomach upsets. Try adding yoghurt to warm milk overnight, by morning it will all be yoghurt and the beneficial bacteria can help prevent scours.

If you don't want to feed calves so liberally (long term average on ad lib is 6.5–8.5 litres/day) then you have to restrict their feed and regiment feed times. As a general rule calves need about 10 per cent of their body weight in milk daily. Thus a 40 kg calf needs 4 litres a day, at least for the first week. This can be increased by 1–2 litres a week to reach about 9 litres by the time the animal is 6 weeks old. Then gradually reduce its milk intake for two weeks before weaning. As well as milk, calves should have meal (there are calf starter mashes available from your stock agent) from about 10 days on. The meal helps stimulate growth and development of the rumen and if given from an early age means the calf will be well able to digest grass by the time it is weaned. Give meal little and often and remove any stale meal from the box or trough. Keep it where the chooks cannot find it or the calves won't get a look in. Calves should always have access to clean fresh water, even when fed on milk.

Shelter

If you want all that expensive milk the calves are drinking to go into weight gain instead of just keeping them warm, provide good shelter. The optimum is a shed twice as deep as it is wide with an open front facing north so the calves can get into the sun when it shines, but be cosy and draught-free at the back when it is cold. A 100 mm layer of untreated sawdust makes an ideal bed.

Rearing problems

They suck everything in sight. The natural sucking response lasts about 10–15 minutes in a calf. If it has gutsed its dinner in a couple of minutes flat then it will still be wanting to suck on something, be it a penmate's ear, tail or worse. If you can slow down their milk intake so it is harder for them to get their fill then the sucking response will stop once their bellies are full.

Scours

Calves should not scour if they had adequate colostrum in their first 12 hours of life, if they have clean, draught-free shelter and if they get consistent, good-quality feed. Scours is usually a nutritional problem. For instance it may be caused by a change from whole milk to a milk mix, or badly mixed feed, or the calf drinking too fast. On its own this type of scours is not dangerous and in most cases will come right in 24 hours.

If the scouring calf is dopey and lethargic give it plenty of warm Vytrate or similar electrolyte mixture. When a calf is scouring badly, liquids pass through it too rapidly for the stomach lining to absorb so the calf will dehydrate. Adding the right mix of salts and sugars, such as those in Vytrate, alters the chemical nature of the water, making it easier for the gut to absorb. If the calf wants to feed it's usually okay to leave it on milk. You can help it by adding Renco (rennet) to the milk and making it into a junket, thus doing half the digestion for the calf.

It is when nutritional scours don't clear up and lead to bacterial scours that serious trouble starts. This is highly contagious. Calves run a temperature, stop drinking and dehydrate rapidly. Affected calves must be kept warm and dry and separated from the others to stop the infection spreading. If they won't drink even electrolyte mixture you will need to get the vet in. The bacteria causing the scours will need antibiotic treatment and the calf could need a drip feed.

Fostering on

An alternative way to rear calves is to foster several of them on to one cow. The success of this will largely depend on your patience and the foster cow's temperament. Ensure the calves to be fostered are all of the same size, remove the cow's own calf and foster on four or five strangers. Leave the cow unmilked for 12 hours then put her in a confined space and let the hungry calves in for an hour. Repeat this twice a day for several days until she allows the calves to suckle. You can try using some strong smelling odour on the calves and on the cow's nose to confuse her; for example, neatsfoot oil or perfume.

Weaning

Some people like to wean on age, some on weight. Generally the minimums are 6 weeks old or 60 kg. Ideally a Friesian calf weighing 48 kg at birth should reach 80–90 kg by 10 weeks. A crossbred calf weighing 31 kg at birth should reach 72–82 kg at 10 weeks. Of course if you are running beef calves on their mothers then there should be no feeding problems for you so long as the cows are on good feed and milking well. The offspring should reach weaning weights of 170–200 kg at 6 months old.

Weaning is simply separating a calf from its source of milk. With beef calves that just means getting them the other side of the fence to their dams. With handreared calves you can either cut the quantity down or you can maintain the volume but make it steadily weaker until they are just drinking water. After weaning continue feeding meal until the calves are about 12 weeks old and make sure they are on good, clean, leafy pasture.

Castration

While bull beef has a ready market, unless you are geared up for it there are problems running bulls. They fight, ride each other, make holes in the ground, dig and fight along fencelines. Most of the behaviour is due to boredom and frustration and some farmers keep bulls quiet by running a donkey or billy goat with them.

If you are running cows it is best to castrate bull calves not wanted for breeding. Some farmers castrate early, at about 3 weeks, using a rubber ring and elastrator. If using rings, check they are new and not perished at all. If the ring has lost its stretch it may not retract properly, which can cause complications. Take care to get both testicles down into the sac before you let the ring go. This may take a bit of probing with your fingers to pull the testicles down gently but it is worth the trouble. If you miss one you end up with a rig, an animal with one retained testicle which may behave as badly as a bull, and may or may not be potent.

Others like to leave calves a bit longer to let them muscle up and get a bit bully. But if leaving them until later, say 3 months, the best castration method is cut and clamp. Get a vet or someone experienced to show you how. The animal must be well restrained — jamming it up in a pen full of its mates works. An assistant holds the calf's tail up while you make a cut in the lower end of the scrotal sac. The cut must be low down and large enough to drain freely. Some people chop the end of the scrotal sac right off. There is a second skin around each testicle; cut that as well then pull each testicle out, clamp the cord, cut it and remove the testicle. Finally dust the cut off with a suitable antibiotic powder.

Dehorning

Cattle should be dehorned if they are destined for the freezing works as otherwise they may suffer carcass damage and bruising when trucked or yarded. Even for homekill animals dehorning is a good idea. The best method is genetic dehorning. By that I mean breeding naturally polled cattle. If you bring in a polled bull and put him over horned cows, half the offspring should be polled. Those that aren't will still carry the polled gene and if mated to another polled bull 75 per cent of their offspring will be polled.

But if you bought horned calves, the sooner you dehorn the better. With young calves the horns are just buds, little lumps under the skin on the scalp. At this age an electric dehorner, basically like a soldering iron, is best. When you apply the hot iron to the bud it sears the root, preventing it growing. The iron must be applied long enough to really burn the bud but not cook the calf's brains.

If the animals are older you may have to resort to dehorning cutters. These gouge the horn off the scalp. They are very messy, create lots of blood and leave a very distressed animal. And to cap it off you still have to go back and do the other side. Some aspects of farming are gruesome and dehorning is one of them. Avoid it by going for polled stock.

Milking

Your cow has calved successfully and is now walking round with bags of milk dribbling everywhere and you want to know how to get it out. The technique is the same as for goats (see Chapter 10) except of course the cow has four teats, not two.

Ease into milking gradually. If the udder is very full the cow may feel a bit tender, or she may have a sore teat, so start gently. When you think you have milked her out, gently massage the udder, wiping it with a downward motion. This will encourage her to let down more milk which should also be stripped out. These strippings are the richest milk. Don't expect to get the same type of milk or amount during the cow's whole lactation. Table 16 shows how much milk quality varies after calving.

Production also varies. Most cows reach a peak

Time	Total solids %	Protein %	Fat %	Lactose %
Birth	27	14	8	3
12 hours	16	9	13	4
36 hours	14	4	4	5
11 days	13	3	4	5

Table 16. **Variation in milk after calving**.

about the fifth to eighth week. Well fed, good quality cows should maintain that level for another five weeks, before production starts to drop off at about 10 per cent a month.

Drying off

Dry cows off either two months before they are due to calve, to give them a rest before the next season, or when they are not giving enough milk to make milking them worthwhile. If your cow is giving less than 3–4 litres you can dry her off abruptly (simply stop milking her). She will soon stop producing and any milk in her udder at the time will be reabsorbed. If she is producing more than that dry her off over a couple of days. Don't milk her right out the first day, next day miss a milking and on the third day just ease a little bit of milk out that evening to take the pressure off the udder.

Butchering

In most districts there are qualified, home-kill butchers prepared to come out to your property to kill and clean the animal. Usually they will take the carcass back to their base and chill it for the required period. Some may even cut it up and bag it for you.

All you need for a professional home-kill butcher will be a yard where the animal can be confined, and possibly a tree nearby strong enough for the beast to be hauled up in. Some operators will have a hoist on the back of their truck in which case they will need vehicle access. Having clean water available will be a help, and you will be responsible for disposing of the offal, head, offcuts, feet and so on. Make sure you have *lots* of plastic bags and room in the freezer.

Doing it yourself

There is no reason why you cannot do it yourself except it is a *big* and *messy* job. Once you have put a bullet in your beast you have over 400 kg of animal to deal with and while you cannot improve the quality of the meat it is very easy to spoil it. So having given you due warning, if you still want to go ahead I next suggest a home butchery course

such as those held at the agricultural colleges and training houses from time to time. They would be a few days off the farm well spent. Failing all else, follow these directions:

To even hope to do a reasonable job you will need:

- A .22 rifle or bolt stunner.
- A 15 cm skinning knife.
- A 30 cm straight blade knife.
- A meat cleaver.
- A meat saw.
- A water bucket.
- A block and tackle or chain hoist.
- A beef spreader. This is like the gambrel used for sheep but bigger and stronger.
- Cool store facilities, even if this just means arranging with the local butcher to chill the carcass in his cold room.

Slaughtering

First kill your beast. Keep it off feed for 12 hours beforehand but give it plenty of water. Stun it with a rifle or bolt stunner at the intersection of imaginary lines drawn between opposite eyes and horns. (See Fig. 67.) The bullet must pass squarely into the head so don't fire when the beast has its head down or thrown up high.

Once the animal has dropped beware of its legs thrashing around. Hoist the beast off the ground till its head is clear. Stretch the chin so that the throat is tight, then stick a pointed knife through the skin at the breastbone and make a 30 cm long cut up the throat exposing the wind pipe. Then stick the knife back to the breastbone, angle it at about 45° to the animal's back (see Fig. 68) and make a deep cut forwards on one side of the windpipe to cut the main veins and arteries and allow the beast to bleed out. Catch the blood in a bucket.

Insert the spreader in the hind legs by making a slit in between the large tendons just above the hocks. You can aid bleeding by pumping the forelegs up and down a few times.

Skinning

This is the tricky part. Lower the beast back to the ground; hopefully you caught all the blood as it was bleeding out or you will be lowering it into a mess.

Fig. 67 **Stun or shoot the cow at the intersection of the lines shown.**

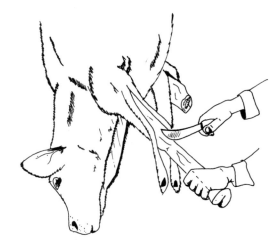

Fig. 69 **Removing the forelegs.**

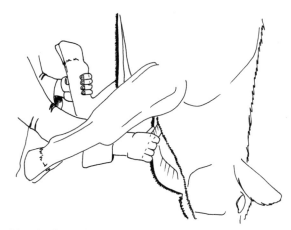

Fig. 68 **Bleeding a beast after slaughtering.**

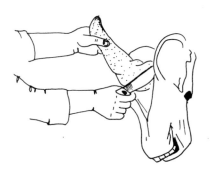

Fig. 70 **Removing the tongue.**

First skin out the forelegs and the head. Cut across the back of the forelegs between the hoof and the dew claws, severing the tendon and releasing the tension in the legs, then split the skin over the back of the forelegs and from that tendon cut to a point 12 cm above the knee. Skin around the knees and shins and remove the forelegs at the square joint. (See Fig. 69.)

Skin the head by cutting just behind the poll and open the hide down to the nostril. Skin across the head and over the right side then over the left side to the jaws. Remove the head by cutting through the neck close to the head just behind the jaws, then disjoint the Atlas joint (the top joint of the vertebral column). Remove the tongue by making a cut just inside each jawbone back to where they meet. (See Fig. 70.) Cut the cartilage at

the tongue's base and pull it out. Remove the cheek meat. If you want the brains, turn the head over and split it with a cleaver.

Now prop the carcass so it is lying chest upwards on its back. Cut the tendons in the hind legs between the sole of the foot and the dew claw, then split the skin from the dew claw to the hock, and another 15 cm further up the leg. Cut around the lowest joint of the hock and remove the lower leg. Next continue the split in the neck over the brisket and just past the last rib. Cut the hide between the two hind legs then join that cut up with the cut from the brisket along the belly. Haul as much skin away from the belly as you can. (See Fig. 71.) Split the skin on the inside of the thighs, starting just behind the udder or scrotum, and cut up the leg to the split you made when you removed the hind shank. Skin the inside of the thighs well round but don't clear the outside yet. Avoid cutting the flesh. Skin the forelegs the same way.

The next part is 'siding' and for this the knife must be very sharp so whisk it up on the steel every so often. Begin by running the knife under the skin from where it has been cut along the abdomen. Grab the already loosened skin and pull it up and out with your left hand, then with your right hand (assuming you are right-handed) place the knife firmly against the hide with the blade facing outward slightly to avoid cutting the flat

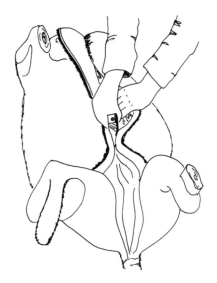

Fig. 71 **Opening the abdomen**.

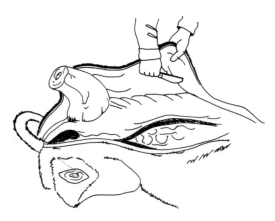

Fig. 72 **Siding**.

muscles over the stomach and side. (See Fig. 72.) Hold the skin as taut as possible. Make sweeping strokes of the knife and continue siding in this fashion until you cannot cut or reach any further down the animal's side. (See Fig. 73.) Use the same method to remove the skin from the shoulders. Leave the thin membrane that lies between the meat and the skin on the carcass as this protects the meat from drying out too fast.

Now you can open up the belly. Start at the ribs and make enough of an opening to get your hand and knife *inside* the belly then push the knife blade upwards to the opening you made between the hind legs. Saw through the breastbone (see Fig. 74) then saw through the pelvic arch. (See Fig. 75.) Hoist the carcass to a comfortable height for working on the rump. Slit the hide along the underside of the tail, cut the tail off near the rump and haul it out of its skin. Next skin out the rump (see Fig. 76) being careful not to stick your knife into the meat or the hide. Remember to leave that membrane on the meat. In some places the hide

Fig. 73 **Completing the siding**.

Fig. 74 **Sawing the breastbone**.

will pull off. Once the rump has been cleared, wipe it and the hocks with a clean cloth that has been dipped in warm water and wrung dry.

To gut the animal start by cutting right around its rectum so it is separated from the rest of the carcass. Pull it up enough to tie a bit of string tightly around it so nothing can fall out, then cut it free from the backbone and let it fall inside. Now pull the beast up higher on the hoist, put a big container between the forelegs and pull the rectum and other guts forward and down so they flop out. (See Fig. 77.) Cut the liver out carefully and remove the gall bladder. Check it for any signs of disease.

Now cut the diaphragm (membrane between the chest cavity and abdomen). Leave about 75 mm of diaphragm attached to the carcass, pull the rest down, loosen the heart and lungs by cutting through the large blood vessel attached to the backbone — heart, lungs and gullet should all come out together.

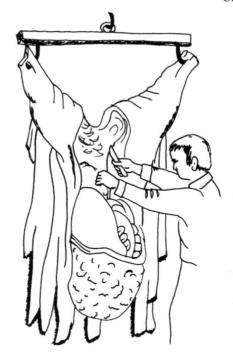

Fig. 77 **Loosening the guts**.

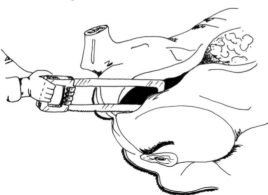

Fig. 75 **Sawing the pelvic arch**.

Fig. 76 **Removing hide from the rump**.

Fig. 78 **Pulling the hide from the back**.

125

Lower the carcass so you can reach the hindquarters and rip the hide off the back. (See Fig. 78.) If it won't rip use a knife the same way you did for siding.

Next split the carcass in two so that air can circulate through it better. Wal Footrot uses a chainsaw but first time I'd recommend a hand saw. Start from the belly side of the beast (see Fig. 79) then once you are over the pelvic arch continue the cut from the back of the animal. (See Fig. 80.) But mark a line with your knife down the centre of the backbone first. Once you get to the neck it is easier to use a cleaver to finish off.

Now wash the carcass in cold water to remove blood and dirt and trim off any ragged pieces of meat.

Chilling the carcass

If the carcass is not chilled properly the meat may suffer from bone taint or green bone which makes it inedible. To avoid this it is vital that the meat is chilled to less than 4°C within 24 hours. That means right through, even the thick cuts like the rump and shoulders.

If a controlled temperature environment is available the carcass can be improved if held at 0°–1°C for 3–5 days before cutting. You do not want the carcass to freeze, but chilling it properly immediately after slaughter cannot be over-emphasised.

Cutting up the carcass

The first job is to quarter it. Count up 12 ribs from the neck, insert the knife blade between the 12th and 13th rib midway between the backbone and flank (marked 1 in Fig. 81) and cut on a line parallel to the ribs to the backbone (2) then cut out towards the flank (3). Leave about 100 mm of flank uncut to hold the forequarter up while you cut through the backbone with a saw.

The forequarter. Insert the knife between the fifth and sixth rib and make a short cut to mark the spot. Cut on a line from 1 through to 4 using a hand meat saw to cut through the rib bones, then cut back to 6 and use the saw again to cut through the backbone. Remove the foreshank by sawing across the line from 4 to 5. Cut the shank free. Then cut through the meat to the ribs along line 4

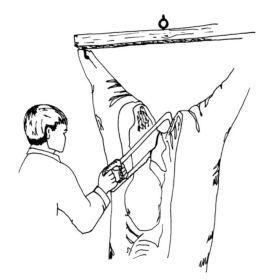

Fig. 79 **Splitting the carcass.**

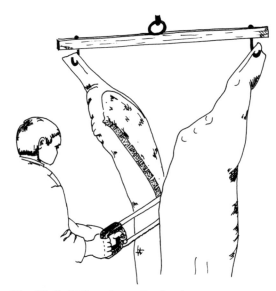

Fig. 80 **Splitting down the back.**

to 5, saw along the ribs on the same line and remove the plate and brisket. Next cut from 8 to 9. Mark the line with a knife first then saw through the neck vertebrae.

Now you can divide the forequarter into usable pieces. The square cut chuck can be divided into pot roasts. Cut the foreshank into several smaller sections for boiling or else bone it right out and

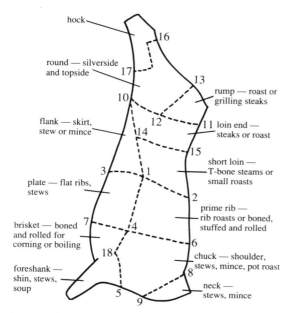

hock

16

round — silverside
and topside

17

13

10

rump — roast or
grilling steaks

flank — skirt,
stew or mince

12

14

11 loin end —
steaks or roast

15

3

1

short loin —
T-bone steams or
small roasts

plate — flat ribs,
stews

2

prime rib —
rib roasts or boned,
stuffed and rolled

brisket — boned
and rolled for
corning or boiling

7

4

18

6

chuck — shoulder,
stews, mince, pot roast

foreshank —
shin, stews,
soup

8

neck —
stews, mince

5

9

Fig. 81 **Cutting up the carcass.**

mince the meat. Divide the prime rib into several standing rib roasts. Divide the breast into brisket and plate or flap by cutting it along line 4 to 7. The brisket is good for corning, the plate can be cut up for short ribs. Bone the neck out for mincing.

The hindquarter. Lay the hindquarter on the table inside up. Remove the flank by cutting from 10 to 1. Remove the kidney knob by cutting under the fat and pulling the knob out. Separate the loin from the round and the rump by finding point 11. This is about half way between the tail and the start of the rise of the pelvic arch or along about four vertebrae. Cut a line from 11 to the point 10 where the flank was removed, this will be 25 mm in front of the pelvic arch. Use a knife to cut through the meaty portion, but saw through the bone. Separate the rump from the round by cutting on line 12 to 13 just behind and parallel to the pelvic arch. Next remove the hind shank (line 16 to 17) by cutting through the meat to the bone on the back of the shank, then turning the knife up and following the bone to the joint line and working the knife between the joint to finish the cut. Now take the loin and divide it into a short loin and loin end by cutting along line 14 to 15. This separation starts at the cartilaginous end of the hip bone. These two cuts

hold the sirloin and the porterhouse steaks. The porterhouse are those with a large portion of the tenderloin muscle. Cut them to the thickness you prefer. You can separate the flank into fat and lean and either grind the lean meat for mince or use it as flank steak but you must first pull the tough white covering off the muscle. Remove the aitch bone from the rump then roll, tie and trim the boneless rump up. The round can be divided into three parts by following the seams between the muscles which will give an inside, outside and heel of round roast. Or cut steaks from the whole length of the round but leave the last 15 cm for mince or stew. Treat the hindshank the same as the foreshank, cutting it into several small sections for boiling or boning it out for mince. Then go and do the same for the other side of the carcass.

Corning

To make your own corned beef prick the meat all over with a needle and rub brown sugar and salt petre into it and let it stand for 24 hours. Then immerse it in a salt brine for 8–10 days. The brine should be salty enough to float a potato in. You can also pickle the tongue by adding parsley, thyme, celery, cloves, a lemon and an onion or two to the brine and soaking the tongue in it for six days.

Problems

If you are running a few beef cattle up the back of the farm and they are well fed and the young stock drenched for worms and vaccinated (see following) then you are unlikely to run into serious disease problems. However the demands made on the high-producing dairy cow mean she is more susceptible to trouble. It pays to understand the difficulties that are most likely to arise and then you are better equipped to avoid them.

Bloat

It is quite usual for a cow to develop a lot of gas in its rumen, but if that gas begins to foam or froth she cannot burp it so it builds up and can kill her. It is usually only a problem if the cow or steer has been eating pasture with clover or lucerne in it. The condition develops rapidly and death can be as soon as 30 minutes after turning the cows onto the feed.

Symptoms
A swelling starts on the left flank high up in front of the hip where there is normally a depression. Gradually the whole belly swells, breathing becomes more rapid and the animal will eventually go down and die, because a nerve reflex action to the pressure build up prevents her from breathing.

Treatment
Prevention is best. Feed hay before cows are allowed onto lush pasture or drench cows at milking time with one of the bloat anti-foaming oils. If you detect bloat early enough you may dose the cow with 50–115 ml of paraffin oil, peanut oil or linseed oil. Walk her about, knead the rumen and stand her facing up hill. If the cow is already lying down you need to act immediately. There is no time now to call the vet, so before such an emergency arises get the vet to show you exactly where to puncture a cow to let the gas escape. Use a sharp, narrow-bladed knife. Plunge it into the distended gut in front of the left hip aiming towards the opposite side front elbow. That should allow the gas to escape, and having averted immediate disaster, you can now go and call the vet to treat the cow against infection and sew her up if necessary.

Brucellosis

Brucellosis is otherwise known as contagious abortion. Cows affected may show no outward signs but will abort calves, usually between the fourth and ninth month. Generally the same cows do not abort the following year but they may be carriers of the disease and pass it on to other stock. There is no treatment so preventing the disease spreading is the only answer. At present this is being done with a nationwide testing programme covering both brucellosis and TB. Any affected animals are destroyed and farmers compensated for them. Testing is compulsory and carried out by MAF. Cows are normally tested under 2 years old

and then retested every three years. Herds that show no reaction to the test are given brucellosis and TB free accreditation.

Tuberculosis

There are three varieties of TB — bovine, avian and human. Cows are normally only affected by the bovine variety. Unfortunately this can spread to humans, usually through drinking milk from an infected cow. The disease can also be picked up by possums and they are often responsible for spreading it around the countryside. Cows affected may show no outward signs so TB is only detected by testing or after slaughter.

To test, cattle are injected with a sterilised form of the bacteria usually into the fold of skin just to the side of the cow's vulva under her tail. The technicians return three days later to see if there has been any reaction or swelling. Reactor cows are retested and if the second test is also positive they have to be destroyed. Approach your local MAF and advise them what cows you have, where they came from and what you are running them for, they will decide when or whether to test them.

Clostridial diseases

The most important of these for cattle are blackleg and malignant oedema, though pulpy kidney, tetanus and black disease do also occur. Each is caused by a different member of the clostridia family of bacteria. (See Clostridial diseases in sheep.)

Older stock may be sensitised to the bacteria (have their immune systems geared up to combat them at the first sign of the bacterial population increasing), but young stock from 1–24 months will not have that protection so you vaccinate. Not all clostridia are in all parts of the country so check with your vet which diseases you need to cover against.

Facial eczema

Calves are the most frequently affected of cattle. They may show a discharge from the eyes or nose, swelling around the eyes or ears and scabs on the nostrils. In dairy cows milk production stops and there may be scabbing and shedding of skin over the teats and inside hind legs. By this time the animal will already have suffered severe liver damage as the eczema is only a secondary part of the disease. (See Facial eczema in sheep for methods of preventing outbreaks.)

Some research has been done into dosing animals with zinc to avoid FE liver damage. The treatment requires zinc oxide to be mixed into a slurry and given daily as a drench. A 340 kg Jersey required 10 g and a 390 kg Friesian about 12 g.

Mastitis

This is a disease of all milking animals and can be serious. Prevent it occurring by keeping the cows' teats soft, and healing any cracks using antiseptic creams or a solution with a glycerine base. Whether you milk by hand or machine, check your technique is not straining or damaging the udder and take care not to spread bacteria from teat to teat or cow to cow.

Symptoms

The milk turns watery or thick and pus-like and may have clots, which range from yellow to blood-coloured. The udder is hot and painful.

Treatment

Your vet will supply a suitable antibiotic treatment, either an injection or teat treatment. Normally only one quarter will be affected and this should always be milked last to avoid spread-ing the infection. Bathe the udder with warm water, carefully massage it to break up the lumps and inflammation, massaging and stripping alternately. Then wash the outside of the affected teat with methylated spirits and insert the antibiotic up into the teat. Hold the end of the teat and 'milk' the material up into the udder. If the cow is given antibiotics by injection, her milk should not be used for human consumption (the withholding period will be stated on the treatment), but if only intra-mammary treatment was given milk from the other quarters is usable.

Metabolic diseases

These include calcium deficiency (milk fever), magnesium deficiency (grass staggers or tetany) and glucose deficiency (ketosis).

Calcium

A deficiency of calcium in the bloodstream usually occurs at or just after calving in high-producing or overfat cows on good pasture. Early on she may appear off her feed and staggery. The condition may be accompanied by bloat or prolapse of the uterus.

Treatment

Sit the cow upright to stop her bloating, and administer calcium borogluconate on your vet's instructions. The cow should get up six to 12 hours after treatment. Don't milk her out that day — just ease the pressure in her udder. Half milk her the following milking and milk her out next time.

Don't let your cow get overfat prior to calving. If you are worried about milk fever and know her calving date the vet can give you an injectable calcium supplement to be given a couple of days before calving.

Magnesium

Magnesium deficiency hits cows that are in high milk production or grazing magnesium deficient pastures. A sudden change in diet, particularly from mature to immature grass, could trigger an outbreak. Time calving so it falls at the time of the main spring flush of feed, not before. Feed cows as much as they want the fortnight or three weeks just

'Big' and 'Trouble', Friesian X Angus calves.

before calving and make sure they get a steady intake once calving has started. Give them the same sized break each day rather than putting them in one paddock and leaving them there for a week so they get lots to start with and little for the last few days.

If you are feeding out hay during winter you can give cows a magnesium supplement such as magnesium oxide, Epsom salts or magnesium chloride. Treat as much hay as you are sure the cows will eat with enough to treat them all (50 g of Causmag/cow/day mixed with molasses and water to a sloppy liquid. Pour it on the edge of the bale so it soaks in well). Once that hay is cleaned up give the cows the rest of their day's rations.

Symptoms
Cows tend to be excited, uneasy and irritable.

Treatment
Once she has a deficiency she is a case for the vet and immediate injections of a suitable supplement.

Glucose
Hypoglycaemia is characterised by lethargy, some staggering and a lowering of milk production. It usually occurs in high-producing animals with a high food and milk turnover. (See Hypoglycaemia in goats.)

Treatment
If you can sort the problem out early enough, give her a glucose solution or a mixture like Ketol orally as a drench. But if she has gone down she will need an injection of glucose solution or cortisone to reverse the ketone production. Prevention boils down to maintaining a good appetite in the cow and giving her adequate feed.

Parasites
Cattle are plagued with everything from lungworms, tapeworms and stomach worms to liver flukes. The most important worm in cattle is Ostertagia. Type I infection is the adult worm which is active in the gut, Type II infection is the infective worm larvae that burrow into the gut lining and lie there in a semi-dormant state for

months before coming out as adult worms. While dormant the larvae are more resistant to drenches and may not cause obvious scouring symptoms in the cow. But they can suddenly break out as a Type I infection and cause severe diarrhoea or even death in a few days.

Control
The incidence of worms and need for control varies (see 'Internal parasites' in sheep, page 86.) Generally parasites are more of a problem in damp weather and it is young stock that are hit hardest.

You can either rely entirely on a drenching programme that kills the worms often enough to stop the build-up of larvae on pasture or drench less and combine it with grazing controls.

By alternating sheep and cattle on a paddock you can use one type of stock to 'vacuum' up a lot of the dangerous infective larvae making the ground safer for the other type of stock. But on a smallfarm it may not be possible to completely swap sheep for cattle and you have to rely on drenching to keep them clean.

The Animal Production Society recommends the following:
- For dairy calves born in spring, drench in January and again in March and three times thereafter at 4–6 week intervals.
- For autumn born dairy calves give them four drenches at 4 week intervals, starting a month after they are put out to pasture.
- For beef calves run extensively (a few grazed over a large range) drench in April–May and again in July–August. As long as they continue to gain weight satisfactorily that is all they will need. But in some areas, and if your paddock layout means those calves cannot go onto safe ground that has been grazed by sheep, then drench them at weaning and three more times at 4–6 week intervals.

Talk to your vet to find out just what parasites are a problem in your area and which drench will cover them all.

How to drench
Most drenches are oral, which means you have to squirt the dose down the beast's throat: easy enough with a handreared dairy calf but not so

easy with a snorting, stroppy beef weaner. If you have access to yards with a head bail that will make the job easier. Alternatively, try putting a rope around the beast's neck, and pull it up hard against your yard rail while someone else squirts the drench in. Or go for an injectible drench. If you pack animals into your crush pen they will be held reasonably still while you shove an injection home.

Ticks and lice

While one little tick or louse will not do much damage, if it brings all its aunts and uncles too it can drag an animal down, make it anaemic and cause considerable hide damage.

Lice usually only attack animals that are down in condition, so keep your stock healthy and well fed and you'll not have lice trouble.

But ticks are more difficult (see ticks in sheep). There are numerous tick sprays and lice powders available. Unless you have the use of an animal shower, probably the easiest method for the smallfarmer is the pour-on. These are just dribbled along the animal's back. They are a concentrated chemical and work their way right through the bloodstream and back to the skin to get all the parasites on the animal at the time. If you don't like the idea of such a concentrated chemical use a spray and put it on where needed with a garden

sprayer. Pay particular attention to the animal's crutch, under the tail, around the udder or scrotum, the brisket and under the neck. With a quiet house-cow you may find it easier to sponge the liquid on. Note, some remedies are not for use on lactating animals and there may be a withholding period before a treated cow can be killed for meat.

Leptospirosis

This disease is also known as red water. It can cause abortion in cows, death in calves and is a very serious and sometimes fatal illness in people. There are several types of the disease. Cattle, man, pigs, horses, sheep, rats and dogs can all be affected by different strains. Grown cattle often show few symptoms (though pregnant cows may abort), but more than 50 per cent of calves will run a temperature, refuse food, pass red urine and die in 24–48 hours. Apparently recovered cattle can pass the disease on through their urine. Pigs can also spread the disease without showing any signs of having it, so if you flush pig pens onto grassland, spell it well before it is grazed. Drain wet, boggy areas of the farm and most importantly vaccinate against the disease.

Calves can be vaccinated by your vet at 3–4 weeks old. Or cows can be vaccinated every year in the last month or two of their pregnancy so they will protect the calves via the colostrum.

12. Horses and donkeys

No smallfarm with children or the young at heart would be complete without some horses or donkeys. They are probably the best way of introducing your children to responsibility, patience, tolerance and self-discipline, to say nothing of lots of good clean fun.

Horses encourage us to push ourselves to our limits and to develop confidence and courage. Their value in child development has been recognised with the growing popularity overseas of horse-based schools where maths, English and computer studies take their place along with pony treks, horse care, jumping and the like. Riding for the Disabled has caught on here, showing again how great these biddable animals are at developing confidence in young people.

If you are worried a horse might be a bit much, try a donkey. Of course the personality is quite different: donkeys tend to be much more individualistic. They are ideal for people who are not sure if they want a horse or a dog. But while the donkey will make a great pet, if you eventually want to ride further, jump higher, go faster — a horse is definitely the way to go.

The smallfarmer can also consider the heavy horses as an alternative to a tractor for hitching up to a trailer or sled or snigging to thinned logs in the woodlot. If you really like horses you can farm them, though the returns probably won't recompense you for the time taken in breeding and training them. Most horse farmers admit it is their hobby, not actually a moneymaker.

But the main argument in favour of keeping a horse is simply that they are nice animals, tolerant and gentle despite their massive size. Once you have a horse you have a real friend who will take you places.

Horses are big animals and they eat a lot (one average horse eats about as much as eight sheep). They can do considerable damage with that bulk and strength if they decide to bite, kick or just stand on you accidentally. And it's a long way down from the top to ground level if you descend in a hurry. Horses require regular attention. To remain well behaved and fit they should be exercised at least two or three times a week, their feet picked out and cleaned as often and if being used on roads they must be shod every six weeks. This is expensive — or, if you do it yourself, hard work.

Generally they are not multipurpose animals. The horse trained to pull a cart is not good for riding and vice versa. And if by getting a donkey you thought you had escaped all the drawbacks — sorry. Donkeys are cute little things. They can learn to pull a cart but it would probably be quicker to go in the car. They will carry panniers of pine cones or groceries, but they won't go anywhere in a hurry if it doesn't suit them and they can be stubborn. A donkey lover might prefer to call it cautious, but whichever you choose it's equally frustrating.

If your child has a donkey and wants to join a pony club, unfortunately the other ponies mightn't think much of that idea and chances are your child and donkey will get sent home early.

Anything to do with horses or donkeys can be expensive. You may find a free-to-a-good-home horse or you may pay through the nose for one with some hifalutin mother or father (each is as likely as the other to end upside down in the creek). It doesn't take long before your horse is wearing more in dollars of saddlery than the animal is worth, and if you want to join in any distant events, shows and the like, you have to get the horse there, which means buying or hiring a float and a car big enough to tow it. Yes, dollars, and lots of them, but if the alternative is motorbikes, surfboards, drugs, parties — then horses for a growing family don't look so bad after all.

Buying a horse

Most of the oldtime, crooked horse dealers are now selling cars, but that doesn't mean buying a horse isn't still fraught with traps for the unwary. Some pony clubs and riding schools will act as agents and find a horse suitable for your situation. First you need to decide just what you want the horse for. Is it a work horse to pull logs out of the bush, a pony for the kids to learn to ride on, something adults can enjoy riding as well, a jumper, a hunter or just a pet to give carrots to occasionally?

If you are serious about wanting a work horse I'd suggest you get in touch with the Heavy Horse Association which holds regular field days. There you can see horses in action and pick up points to look for when choosing a horse as well as handling tips.

If you want a riding horse, well, there is an enormous array of them out there for sale. The ones advertised as repeated ribbon winners can command big prices, but there is no guarantee they will continue to win ribbons with a beginner on their back. At the other extreme there may be some farmer's old stock horse which has never seen a pony club ring in its life. Within each category there will be quiet horses and fired-up ones rearing to go. If the advertisement says 'suitable experienced rider only' it's rearing to go; if it says 'ideal beginner' it is probably so quiet it falls asleep on its feet.

You do want something quiet to start with so you can move around it with confidence and take it places without worrying if it is going to bolt for home. But the trouble with getting one too placid is you and the kids will soon outgrow it and the

Stock horses.

poor old nag, once valued for its calm nature, will be cursed as a great lazybones.

If you have done a little riding and sent the kids to riding school a few times you might be able to start with an 'ideal second horse' so it will suit your family a bit longer. If going on a buying expedition take an experienced horseperson with you and make sure they know what you want from a horse.

Avoid any vices. Make sure the horse is happy to have all its feet picked up and tapped without kicking. Watch it while the owner walks around it. Any signs of ears going back suggest bad temper. You want a horse with a good mouth so you do not have to haul hard on the reins to get it to stop or turn. The animal should be keen and biddable, and step out with only a slight pressure on its sides. If it needs a great wallop with a stick to get it moving, rides could prove more tiring for you than for the horse.

You want a horse with manners. Ask it to move over and push on it lightly — it should move out of your way. Lead it and make sure it lets you do the leading and not the other way around. But most of all you want a horse that is sound in body and limb. Sellers should agree to the horse being checked by a vet for soundness. He or she will pick up breathing defects, faulty limbs or action, disease or injury.

In some areas there are annual horse auctions. These can be a good way to find a horse as there is usually a big selection in the one place. If the auction is run by a stock firm, they usually allow ten days before your money is banked in which time you can have the horse vetted to make sure it is as described at the sale.

If you want a horse for the pony club or hack and hunter ring, they have to be certain heights to qualify: ponies are classed as under 14.2 hands.

Aging a horse

Horses and donkeys can live to about 50 years, though 30 is more usual for a horse and 40 for a donkey. Aging a horse is done by examining its teeth (see Fig. 82), but just as some people show their age more than others so do horses, and you might find a spry 20-year-old that can still give many years of pleasure.

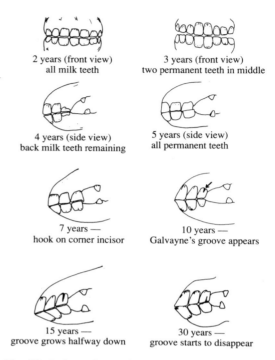

2 years (front view)
all milk teeth

3 years (front view)
two permanent teeth in middle

4 years (side view)
back milk teeth remaining

5 years (side view)
all permanent teeth

7 years —
hook on corner incisor

10 years —
Galvayne's groove appears

15 years —
groove grows halfway down

30 years —
groove starts to disappear

Fig. 82 **Aging a horse by its teeth.**

Breeds

Most horses will have no specific breeding or pedigree. There is nothing wrong with this if it is the right size, shape and temperament for you. Some advertisers will claim the horse is 'half Arab' or 'first cross quarter horse'. That usually means an ordinary mare was put to a reasonable stallion of a particular breed. But don't get too excited about the 'half Arab' bit until you see it, as the other half may be more obvious.

Different breeds of horses do have their different characteristics. The following are the more common breeds found in New Zealand.

Arabs

Usually a small, fine-featured horse with lots of go and spirit. They tend to curve their necks and carry their tails in a graceful arch and have slightly dished faces. They are warm-blooded horses with big, wide-spaced eyes, a fine muzzle and large nostrils. They are famous for their endurance and stamina. They are free moving as riding horses but can take longer to mature than other breeds. They are intelligent, but their spiritedness may make them a bit bouncy for the inexperienced.

Anglo-Arab

This is the offspring of the Arab crossed with the Thoroughbred. It should be a bit bigger than the Arab but with the same stamina and soundness and the Thoroughbred's speed and jumping ability. The Anglo-Arab is usually about 16 hands and rarely exceeds 16.2.

Appaloosa

Easily recognised by its spotted markings, the Appaloosa is a medium-sized horse, similar in build and temperament to the Quarter Horse. It is originally descended from Spanish stock taken to America. The Nez Perce Indians in the region of the Palouse River selected the animals for the spots, speed and endurance. Markings vary from leopard (evenly spotted all over) to a blanket where the horse is predominantly dark brown but has a spotted rump.

Clydesdale

The most common of the heavy working horses in New Zealand, this breed combines great strength and size with a good temperament and gaiety. They stand 17–18 hands high and are usually black, brown or red with white faces and often white feet and feathers.

Quarter Horse

These medium-sized horses are well muscled and able to stop, start and change direction with exceptional agility. They were originally bred in America from a mixture of Spanish stock crossed with some blood imports from England, including a famous Thoroughbred, Janus, who was the grandson of the Godolphin Arabian. Quarter Horses were selected for their fast starting ability and raced over a quarter-mile. Besides sprint races the breed has developed as a working cattle horse, its agility and instinct making it popular for ranch and rodeo work. They have a short head and small muzzle, with a well developed jaw, a short strong

The mighty Clydesdale grows 17–18 hands.

Quarter Horses are known for their speed, agility and good temperament.

back, deep chest and broad powerful hindquarters from which they get their acceleration. They are usually 14.3–15.1 hands and weigh 500–600 kg.

Thoroughbred

These are the basis of the racing industry and have been selected predominantly for their speed. Usually Thoroughbreds are tall, slender horses with a long, free and easy action. The racing Thoroughbred nowadays tends to be fairly highly strung and excitable, but other strains have been selected for jumping and hunting ability.

Shetland

Originally from the Orkney and Shetland Isles off Scotland, this midget horse is very hardy with a thick mane and tail and coat to protect it in severe weather. It is strong for its size (under 116 cm), with a short back, deep girth and well sprung ribs but a small, refined head. It is sometimes headstrong with an independent nature and needs firm, kind handling.

Welsh Mountain

Originally from the mountains of Wales, this pony has a hardy constitution and is sure footed, free moving and a natural jumper. They usually have a concave face, a deep sloping shoulder and a short strong back. The tail is set high and carried proudly, legs are short and strong and the feet fine. They grow to 12 hands.

Donkeys

Most of New Zealand's donkey population are descended from four animals imported to Ponui Island in the Hauraki Gulf in the days of the early settlers. In spite of the massive in-breeding they seem sturdy, healthy, good-tempered animals. However, they are generally smaller than recent imports from Australia. The Ponui Island donkey is typically 10–12 hands high, while Australian bred donkeys may be bigger, up to 14 hands, but not always so sweet natured.

Donkeys come in grey, brown, or black. All should have a black cross or 'mark of Christ' on

Ponui Island donkeys.

their withers, reputedly from the time a donkey carried Christ through the streets of Bethlehem.

Basic driving technique

There are plenty of good books on riding but, if you really don't know how to make a horse go and have just got one home and are dying to have a test run then try the following:

It's a kick start (actually just a squeeze with your heels) against the belly to slip it into first forward gear.

Steer by holding a rein in each hand, pull the head round with the left rein to turn left and with the right rein to turn right.

Brakes are applied by pulling back on the reins. Start gently and if there is no response you may need to pull harder.

To change gear going forward, more pressure with the heels on the belly should shift it up a speed; pulling back on the reins should drop it down one.

To get it into reverse, stop the forward motion, then carry on tugging gently back on the reins. A trained horse will oblige, but some only have forward gears.

Management

Grazing

Some horses are better doers than others, so you largely have to judge how much to feed your horse or donkey by eye and take into account how much work it is doing. Some horses go slower as they tire and get hungry; others, especially more spirited animals, continue to work just as hard but get skinnier unless you feed them to replace the reserves they are using up.

If you are just riding around home or going to pony club once a week then keep it with enough condition to just cover the ribs, so you can feel them if you run a finger firmly along the horse's side, but not see them. Don't let the horse get fat as that can lead to foundering and laminitis. (See 'Problems', page 144.)

Horses usually spend long periods feeding — up to 12 hours a day or more if feed is short. They will eat a range of grasses, herbs, shrubs and weeds if given a selection and their digestive system is designed for a little and often. They can cope with both long and short grass, wrapping their tongues round long grass as a cow will and cropping off short grass with their teeth like sheep. But horses can be fussy grazers and if you just have them in one paddock they will graze some spots down to bare earth and leave other areas long and leafy. So it's best to rotate them with other stock.

If you want to keep them in the pony paddock near the house so they are easy to catch, fine, but have two pony paddocks and each time you shift the horses out of one, bring the sheep in *en masse* for a couple of days to graze it down evenly. Mature horses pile their dung in one or two areas of the paddock. Those spots will go sour unless you collect the dung and compost it or harrow it to spread it more evenly over the paddock. Bringing in another class of stock will also help vacuum up worms (see 'Problems', page 147) and thus keeps your horses healthier.

Fencing

Just a few tight wires will hold horses in but it is a good idea to make the top one hot or put an outrigger around an existing fence to stop them leaning on it.

If putting up temporary electric fences for horses use bright tape which they can see clearly. A horse that gets a shock and doesn't know where it came from is likely to bolt in panic. Give horses the daylight to get used to wires in new positions.

The main thing to ensure when fencing horses is that the wires are tight, so they cannot get their legs caught up. I am against tethering horses. It is too easy for them to accidentally wrap the tether rope around a leg, and in flicking that leg to free it, end up with a rope burn through to the bone which can be damn hard to get to heal over. If you want to tether a horse then check it at least every couple of hours to sort out any tangle it is in.

Feed supplements

If you are in a mild climate where grass grows all year round your horse may not need any supplements. But in colder areas where the winter grass growth is negligible, or where you want your horse

in tip top condition right through the winter, feed a bit of hay or pellets. It is surprising how small a scoop of pellets a horse needs each day on top of grass to keep it sleek over winter. If your grass stops growing in the cold, feed a mixture of pellets (how much is usually marked on the bag according to the size and type of horse) and good hay for bulk. Most horses will sell their souls for concentrates so hand feeding a bit each day makes them eager to come when called, and helps you keep an eye on their condition and pick up early any illness or injury.

There are many commercial supplements available and horses develop a taste for most of them. The only thing to avoid is feeding too much raw grain, especially wheat, unless it is well crushed or boiled and steeped in water.

Donkeys enjoy supplements, too. Being browsers rather than grazers they are more like goats in their eating habits, and will love any tree prunings, thistles, vegetables, carrots, treebark, eucalyptus leaves or prize rose bushes you offer them. If your donkeys are kept on rich rye grass pasture you should feed them hay as roughage.

Never lure a horse or a donkey to an empty bucket. They will soon learn it is not worth coming up after all. But at the same time don't spoil them — sometimes give them treats, sometimes don't or they will become pushy and bad tempered if you don't produce the goodies they have come to expect every time.

Drenching

This is a most important part of regular horse care and worth doing so you know the food the horse gets is being digested efficiently. (See 'Worms' under 'Problems'.) Drench young horses monthly until they are at least 6 months old. How often you drench after that will depend on how many horses you are running, on what area and whether you use other stock to clean up behind them. But generally a drench spring and autumn will be enough for mature horses and four drenches a year for donkeys.

Feet care

The hoof is a horny box which expands and contracts in response to pressure. The hoof wall, the immediately adjacent part of the sole, the rubbery frog and the bars are the main weight bearing surfaces. (See Fig. 83.) The horny sole is shaped like an arch to make it stronger and give extra protection to the sensitive structures inside the foot. The frog, the thick rubbery triangle at the back of the foot, is like a shock absorber and it needs to be kept in use or it will waste away. The whole foot needs work to maintain blood circulation as blood flow up out of the foot relies on weight being applied intermittently to pump it up into the leg. That is why troubles like laminitis can be helped by gentle exercise as it improves blood circulation around the feet. The wall of the hoof grows from the top at the coronet and it may take eight months or a year for the horn that is growing there now to finally reach the lower border.

Hooves should be picked out at least once a week, or daily during wet weather to make sure they get a chance to air out and dry. Painting the frog, and the groove between it and the sole, with tincture of iodine will help keep it dry and avoid thrush. Overlong hooves should be rasped down every six weeks or the horn walls are likely to split and any cracks are open to damp and infection. As the toe grows out the horse will end up standing further and further back on its heels, which puts a strain on the tendons in the lower leg and will affect the animal's gait. As a general rule rasp the horn flush with the frog. You can rasp the outside rim of the sole lightly, too, though most horses only need attention to the hoof wall. Stop rasping the sole if any pink spots show through.

You must rasp the hoof evenly so the weight-bearing surface is flat and level. (See Fig. 84.) If it is uneven then one part of the hoof wall will be carrying more weight than another, which can cause splitting. To rasp feet you will need a special coarse-toothed horse rasp (a carpentry Surform will do the job but it is rough on the surform).

Picking up the hoof

To pick up the front feet, stand with your back to the horse's head and run your hand down the leg to the fetlock. Grasp the fetlock and pull up. If the horse refuses to lift its foot lean your shoulder into its shoulder and push it slightly off balance so the weight comes off the foot and it is easy to raise up.

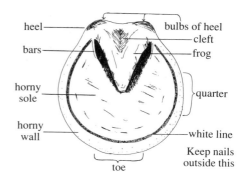

Fig. 83 **Hoof structure**.

Fig. 84 **Rasp hoof so both sides are level**.

First bend it at the knee so the shin is parallel to the ground. Hold it just below the fetlock in one hand and with a spike or hoof knife pick out the dirt, running the spike around the groove between the horn and the sole and up each side of the frog. Then move so you are just behind and slightly to the side of the horse's shoulder and slip the hoof from behind you through your legs and grasp it around the fetlock with your knees. This leaves both hands free to hold the rasp.

To pick up the hind feet, stand level with the horse's rump facing backwards, run your hand down the leg, grasp the fetlock and pull upwards. Sometimes a horse will bring this leg up quickly. Don't be alarmed, just hold onto it lightly and when the horse stops waving it around bend your legs slightly to form a lap, and sit the lower part of the horse's leg over your thigh so the hoof is upside down in your lap, just by your knees. It should stay there leaving both hands free to rasp.

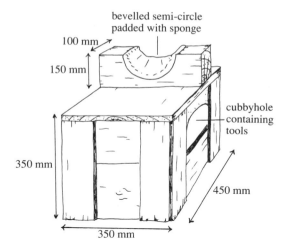

Fig. 85 **Box for shoeing on**.

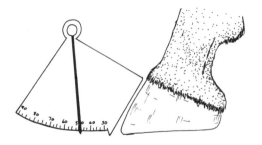

Fig. 86 **Getting the hoof angle right**.

If you have back problems or just find it tiring to stand crouched over gripping a leg, you can build a foot box for your horse. They soon learn to rest their foot on it, especially if it is comfortably padded. (See Fig. 85.)

When rasping the hoof you must bear its proper shape and angle in mind. Ideally there should be a 50° angle in the front hoof and a 55° angle in the back foot. On the donkey the front of the hoof should be twice as long as the back of the hoof. (See Fig. 86.) If the foot has been badly neglected don't try to correct the angle all at one go. It may take several manicures over a period of a few months to eventually get the foot back to a proper shape.

Once you have rasped the horn down level with the sole you can whizz the rasp around the outside edge a couple of times to take off the sharpness, but other than that, *do not* rasp the outside of the hoof wall. The shiny outer layer known as the periople is what keeps water out of the hoof fibre. If you rasp into it you open the foot up to damp and rot. If the feet are very brittle and hard to rasp (sometimes the case with donkeys) you can soften them by hosing them down for half an hour or so beforehand, or standing the donkey somewhere damp. But this toughness means the donkey should not need shoeing.

After rasping or looking at a horse's hoof don't

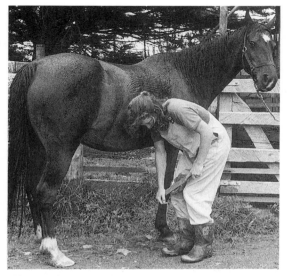

Horses feet should be trimmed every six weeks.

just drop it down, put it down carefully, or the horse or donkey will learn to snatch it back at any opportunity. Also, if the animal leans on you while you are holding the hoof up, don't try to support their weight, just let the hoof get closer to the ground until the horse overbalances. It will learn to carry its weight on the other three legs then.

Shoeing

As you get more familiar with your horse and more adept at its regular feet care you may like to attempt your own shoeing. But be warned: not only is it damned hard work, but you can do a lot of damage in a very short time and generally a good farrier is well worth what he is paid.

If you are determined to do it yourself then I stress the need to learn properly first. Before hammering nails into any feet, get out and work with your farrier a few times. Spend a day going on the rounds with them if they will have you. Don't just have a go because at the end of it you won't even know enough to know if you have done a good job or not. For those who have picked up the clues and want to be reminded of the basic rules:

- First, shape the foot. Rasp it down so the shoe sits on both the horn rim and the adjacent part of the sole. The weight bearing surface must be flat and the heels and quarters level. Don't rasp any of the bars and take care in lowering the heel at all as just taking a little off radically alters the angle of the foot.
- Use a hoof knife or the edge of the rasp to make a groove in the toe for a toe clip if the shoes have them. Do not make the groove bigger than necessary.
- Select the right sized shoe. You will need some idea of the size of your horse's hoof when you go to buy shoes as they range from small Os to 5s. There are different types available too; narrow, light shoes for racing and speed work, and heavier, longer-wearing general purpose ones with a wider bearing surface. (See Fig. 87.)
- Select the right sized nails. If shoeing a big, heavy horse with heavy shoes you need bigger, thicker nails, while smaller, lighter nails will do for a pony.
- Shape the shoe. You may have to alter the size of the curve, the bend in each arm or its width

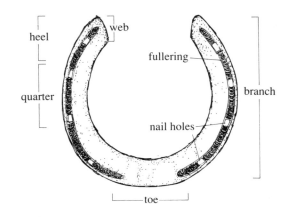

Fig. 87 **General purpose horse shoe**.

to get it to fit the foot (note you always make the shoe fit the foot, not the other way around). To adjust the shoe, put it over an anvil (a short length of railway iron will do) and hammer it to shape. This can take a lot of trial and error and holding it back against the foot to get it right, but the shoe must sit snugly so no edges protrude and the heel bars do not extend beyond the hoof heel. The heel of the shoe should rest on the solid piece of horn immediately behind the angle formed by the wall and the bar in the hoof. If the shoe is too long use a hacksaw to shorten each tip slightly.

- Make sure the holes in the shoe are big enough so the nail heads will bed down securely. Use a punch to enlarge the holes if needed.
- You are now ready to nail the shoe on. You will need a light farrier's hammer as an ordinary carpenter's hammer is too heavy and will just bend the soft nails rather than drive them.
- When nailing, make sure the bevelled side of the nail tip is to the inside of the hoof. This curve will cause it to bend outwards as it is driven and stop it going deeper towards the foot. Check every single nail before you put it near the foot. Face it the wrong way and it will curve in and lame the horse. (See Fig. 88.)
- The nails must enter the hoof just outside the white line between the horn and the sole and be angled so they come out about 25 mm up the wall of the hoof. After you have driven in the

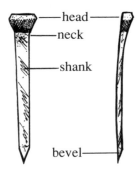

head

neck

shank

bevel

Fig. 88 **Horseshoe nails**.

nail about 25 mm feel around the other side to see if it is coming out yet. If not give a couple more taps and if the tip of the nail still can't be felt it is going in too deep. You must pull it out and start again.

- Most shoes have eight nail holes, but a lot of farriers find six nails are enough to hold shoes firmly for average riding work.
- After driving each nail through, clip off the sharp end before driving the next nail. Then, should the horse get restless and try to claim its foot back, you are less likely to get scarred by the sharp points.
- Once all nails are driven in and clipped short, shift your position so you are facing the same way as the horse and have its hoof sitting up on your knee. Run the edge of the rasp along the lower side of each nail tip to put a groove in it. This makes them bend over neater.
- Then either tap them over gently with a hammer (hold the rasp against the nail head and the shoe to stop the nail being tapped back out) or use clinching pliers to fold the tips over and grip the hoof wall.
- You can then lightly rasp any bulge where the inside nails have bent over to stop the opposite hoof from catching them.

Removing shoes

Sit the foot upright on your knee and rasp off the clinches (these are the bent over ends of the nail on the outside wall of the hoof). But don't rasp any of the outside hoof wall. If you have farrier's clippers and are strong enough, you may now flip the hoof back between your knees as for rasping and

ease the clippers under one arm of the shoe to lever it off. I have never been strong enough to do that, so after rasping the clinches I use a small punch to tap the nail ends back into the hoof wall a little. Then from the under side of the shoe I can pull them out one at a time with the hammer claws. It is slower but avoids putting a lot of leverage on the sole of the foot.

Toe clip

Most bought shoes these days have a toe clip. This is just an extra bit of metal on top of the shoe which fits into a groove you make in the hoof wall and theoretically stops the shoes from swivelling. Once the shoe has been nailed on gently tap the toe clip so it hugs the groove firmly.

Breeding

As with any animal, should you decide to breed from your horse, think about it carefully. If it is a favourite horse or donkey, realise you are increasing the risk of harm coming to her. Though 98 per cent of horses and donkeys manage foaling without any trouble at all, that still leaves 2 per cent that don't. Don't breed indiscriminately. People often make the mistake of putting in foal some horse they don't like much and don't know what to do with. Chances are if it has faults or vices the foal will have them too and the people end up with two horses they don't particularly like. So only breed good animals.

Most districts boast several stallions. Stud fees vary enormously, often with little regard to the real quality of the stallion or jack. Before turning up with your mare at the nearest stud, find out what the stud fee is and whether that includes a live foal guarantee or not. Some studs will have your mare vetted in foal before returning her to you and what happens to her thereafter is your responsibility. Others will save on the vet fees but offer you a refund or a return service if the mare doesn't produce a live foal.

Find out whether the stud owners hand mate horses (the mare and stallion are introduced to each other in a controlled situation and the mating is overseen to make sure neither animal is injured) or paddock mate which means the mare is just run out in the paddock with the stallion. Some sires are good natured and paddock mating is fine, but mares and stallions don't always get along so with valuable stock hand mating is safest.

Mares

Females reach puberty from 12–24 months old, but don't put a filly in foal before she is three, thus ensuring she has ample time to finish her own growing. Mares have a breeding season over spring and summer and during this time cycle every 20 days with each heat period lasting five to six days. This oestrus or heat is often longer early in spring and gets shorter into summer.

Mares usually declare they are in season with a lot of whinnying. They may be naughtier than usual, urinate frequently and 'wink' — flashing the lips of their vagina with their tail held high. Some mares will not show obvious signs of oestrus until a stallion is around. Mares with foals will have a 'foal heat' just a few days after birth and if not mated then will not cycle again until the foal is weaned.

Stallions

Stallions mate effectively from about 15 months old and may mate three times a day with ease.

Where a stud employs hand mating, the mare is usually mated once a day for five or six days. She is then watched to see if she comes back in season in three weeks' time. If not, you can bring her home and calculate her foaling date from the last date of service.

Gestation in horses is about 345 days but varies from 305–365. Spring-born foals are usually carried five days longer than those born in summer and colts carried two to three days longer than fillies. Gestation in donkeys is longer, usually between $11\frac{1}{2}$ and $13\frac{1}{2}$ months.

Pregnancy

The main rule with any pregnant stock is to keep them fit, not fat. The same goes for horses and donkeys — both can be worked well into their pregnancy. Keeping them fit will help them at the birth time, but in the last month just give them light exercise. Increase their rations slightly in the last couple of months of the pregnancy when the foetus will be making its greatest burst of development.

Some horses are very hard to pick in foal unless vetted. Mine had me fooled until the last four weeks. With jennies a pregnant belly differs from a grass belly as it is usually lopsided.

Have your local vet teed up so he or she knows roughly when the mare is due and will not be surprised should you call for help. A horse foaling is very quick and awesomely powerful. After weeks of running and checking on my mare in the middle of the night (nightie, gumboots, umbrella and torch should have been enough to scare her into foaling) she eventually performed one sunny afternoon so I got to see the whole show. I realised if anything had been wrong I would have been helpless against those powerful contractions, so it is vital that you have a vet on call.

Birth signs

Swelling of the vulva and udder are signs that your mare is close, but the most reliable sign is waxing. A week to ten days before foaling she may get tiny little white drops on the ends of her teats. Don't get too excited yet, but about 24 hours beforehand (sometimes not till after foaling) those droplets will suddenly spread and generously cover the sides of the teats in a sort of creamy, buttery wax.

A jenny close to foaling may suddenly look a bit slimmer as the foal moves up into the birth position. The ligaments on each side of her tail will slacken slightly and like the horse she will get deposits of wax on her teats before the birth.

About four hours beforehand, both mare and jenny get increasingly restless. They may have a temperature, and be sweating and uneasy. Labour starts in earnest once they start looking back towards their belly and repeatedly lying down, getting up, and maybe urinating.

The birth

Next the water bag will rupture and the foal should be pushed out shortly after. The mare will lie down

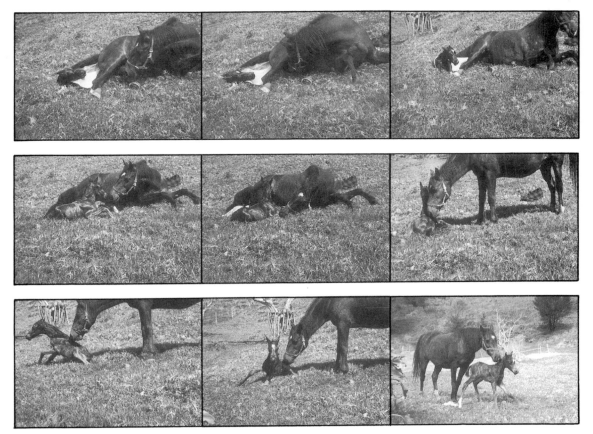

Strider arrives . . . head first. Within fifteen minutes he's tottering to his feet.

to deliver it. Usually there is one grunt and a push to get the head and front feet through, maybe a slight rest and then another big push to get the shoulders through; the rest follows soon after. The process only takes about 15 minutes. Any longer, or if you can see feet but no head or only one front foot, and the horse may need your vet's help. (See also 'Calving', page 77.) The foal is born in a tough white membrane which it should be able to break with its own thrashing around. But the birth sac is surprisingly tough and if you are around, and the mare is not worried by your presence, tear the bag around the foal's nostrils then step back out of the arena again.

Some mares will rest before getting up. Meanwhile, the foal will struggle up onto its chest and work its way out of the birth sac. Within 15 minutes a foal can use its front legs as levers and

get its chest off the ground, but it usually takes about 30 to 45 minutes before the hind legs work and it can stand. During this time the mare should be licking the foal to dry it and talking to it, maybe encouraging it up with nudges and little nips. Once on its feet the foal should start seeking a teat, though how soon it finds it will depend to some extent on the mare.

The foal needs a feed of colostrum within eight hours of birth and it should pass meconium (the dung which was in its bowels before birth) within six to eight hours. If the foal hasn't managed to move its bowels within 18 hours you need a vet's help. Similarly the mare should 'clean' or expel the afterbirth within about four hours. Lay out the afterbirth and check that there are two 'bags' — the birth sac will be pale, the placenta dark and blood coloured.

Foals become fully active amazingly quickly. Within 12 hours they can walk, whinny, trot, gallop, play and nibble grass, wiggle their ears and tail and back into Mum to stop her when they want a feed.

Hand rearing an orphan

If the worst happens and for some reason you end up with a foal and no dam, you become surrogate mother. The first job, be it horse or donkey, is to ensure it gets a feed of colostrum even if that means milking the dead mother. The first 12 hours of its life is the only time the foal can absorb the large immuno-proteins in the colostrum which are essential to help it ward off illness and get a good start in life.

Foals need food a little and often. For the first day with a donkey foal that means about 50 ml every hour. For a horse foal feed 600 ml to 1 litre over the first day with feeds two hourly. Usually the foal will let you know how much it wants at one time as it only takes what it needs.

If colostrum is absolutely unavailable then make up a substitute by adding 20 ml of vegetable oil and one raw egg to a litre of commercial foal milk formula. To give some protection against infection ask your vet about antibiotic feed supplements which you should carry on for six weeks until the foal has had time to build up its own immunity.

For the first couple of weeks feed two hourly at least (yes, all through the night, too). Try to find a good-natured companion horse to take over the emotional welfare of the foal, as this will lighten your load so you just have to supply the food. As the foal grows and drinks more at each feed, space out feed times until by eight weeks you should get by with just four a day. There are commercial milk replacers available for horses. If you cannot get one of these use a milk replacer made for lambs rather than calves. Alternatively mix your own using 500 ml skimmed milk, 500 ml whole milk, one tablespoon of lactose and some vitamin drops.

The foal will soon learn to nibble at grass and you can encourage it onto hard feed by adding some calf weaning supplement in small amounts to one of the day's milk feeds. Milk feeding should continue for at least four months — six months would be better and closer to the situation if the foal's dam was feeding it. Continue solid supplements right through until the following spring.

Handling the foal

If you are planning to eventually break and train the young horse yourself then start 'gentling' it from day one. The sooner the foal accepts you as some sort of aunt or uncle, the easier it will be to attend to it should the need arise, such as for gelding, drenching or in any case of injury.

If you decide to have a colt gelded as a foal it is crucial that he is well handled and familiar with you beforehand so you can keep an eye on the castration incision and be ready to treat him at the first sign of any infection. So put time into your young horse, petting and scratching it from day one, after all it will only be a foal once.

Gelding

Unless you have produced an exceptionally well bred colt or you want a donkey jack for future breeding, it is best to geld horses and donkeys if they are intended as riding animals or pets. Both species can be gelded either as foals or at 12 to 18 months. There are arguments in favour of each. The young foal is easier to handle and once the operation is over it is all behind him and you can go on to become friends. He still has the comfort of his dam and her milk to help him over any shock. Being gelded that young will stop it developing any stallion characteristics. Whether that is a good thing or not will be up to you. Legend has it that Cardigan Bay was gelded as a foal and it didn't slow him down.

Castration must be done by a vet and usually within the first two weeks. Five days to a week is probably the best time. After two to three weeks the testicles retract back into the horse or jack and it is too late; you will have to leave him entire until he reaches puberty and they descend back into the scrotal sac at a year to 18 months old. Horses can be gelded using just local anaesthetic and done standing if they are well handled. But many vets prefer to put them under a general anaesthetic and cast them. With donkeys the artery feeding the testicles is bigger than in a horse and should be tied off to prevent him bleeding profusely. Jacks and colts gelded as adults will be fertile for a couple of months after their operation and it may be six months before they lose the instinct to serve mares.

Problems

A healthy horse should be alert and interested in what is going on. It should stand squarely on four legs. If resting it may relax one hind leg but it should always have weight on both front legs. It should have good appetite and droppings which are moist, well-formed, kidney-shaped pellets. The coat should be shiny (less so in winter when the animal may be fluffy) and no sign of dirt or scour at the back end. The eyes should be clean and bright. At rest horses breathe about 12 times a minute and there should be no noise accompanying breathing, although noise and gurglings from the gut are quite normal.

With regular care, illness is pretty rare in horses — injury is far more likely to be the cause of a call to the vet. Reduce the risk of injury by ensuring the paddocks horses are kept in are free of hazards, that they have company (horses are herd animals) and adequate food and therefore aren't tempted to try to take on fences or gates. Even quite small wounds can be complicated with horses because they are very susceptible to tetanus. (See the following.) Once you have taken care of the risk of tetanus then commonsense first aid is all that you need. Injury is much rarer in the donkey which tends to be pretty astute and errs on the side of caution.

Strains and sprains respond to the same treatment as in people. Run a cold tap over the affected joint or tendon for a good half hour two or three times a day and support the joint firmly with an elastic bandage. Don't work the horse for a couple of weeks, and ease it back into work gradually, checking for any return of lameness.

Bots

The bot fly looks like a cross between a bee and a blowfly and will buzz persistently around horses, irritating them as it lays its eggs on their coat. The eggs are obvious little, white elongated capsules glued firmly to the hair follicles. After about ten days when the horse turns around and licks at them they hatch and the larvae enter the mucous membrane around the horse's mouth and tongue. They stay there for a few weeks but end up hooked into the stomach lining, damaging it and affecting the digestive process. The larvae will stay in the gut for nine or ten months, then drop off and pass out into the dung, going to ground as pupae in the spring and being ready to hatch the following autumn.

Treatment

Most worm drenches these days include a boticide. Best to give an autumn drench about May when the bots should have stopped flying. Keep the horses clear of bot eggs either by shaving them off with a razor or washing them in warm water to encourage the eggs to hatch, then wipe over with a parasiticide.

Brittle hooves

Hooves allowed to get too brittle can split easily, which opens the feet up for infection. Soften hooves with a dressing of Stockholm tar and beeswax, or make up a mixture of 3 parts sulphur sublimate, 4 parts neatsfoot or whale oil, 3 parts cod liver oil and 2 parts castor oil. Rub it onto a dry hoof wall once a day. Encourage growth of the

This fellow earns his keep snigging log thinnings out of the forest.

hoof with good diet and molasses and cod liver oil mixed into any concentrates.

To correct split hooves make sure the feet are trimmed regularly, because if the split wall is allowed to get overlong the split will extend as the cracked sides splay further apart. So keep the hoof short and rasp a small groove at the top of the split at right angles to it. (Normally you never put a rasp to the outside of the hoof.)

Bruising

With half a tonne of dog sausage pounding up and down on four little feet it is not surprising horses go lame occasionally or get bruised feet. Normally the sole and the frog can take pretty powerful impacts without bruising, but a sharp stone may do the damage. A bruise will show up as a dark coloured area under the surface of the sole and the horse will probably be lame in that foot. You can ease the lameness by running cold water over the sole to chill the area. Don't work the horse, but ensure it moves around to maintain blood circulation to the foot. If the bruising is severe you may need to get the vet to pare away the sole and release the blood built up in the bruise site and then treat the wound. Reduce the risk of bruising by careful shoeing and feeding which will stimulate the frog.

Canker of the feet

Canker is a fungal infection of the foot. In early stages it may just affect the frog but will progress to the sole and the wall if untreated. The sole goes crumbly and cheeselike and will smell bad. It is very difficult to treat and is considered a serious unsoundness. The bacteria involved may be allied to the bacteria behind thrush and greasy heel. Thrush usually only affects the cleft of the frog and greasy heel, the heel of the feet.

Treatment

For thrush, clean the cleft thoroughly with plenty of soap and water, dry the foot, then dress the site daily with either sulphanilamide powder, Stockholm tar or a mix of 1 part of formalin and 3 parts of water. If the ground is wet put the dressing on a wad of cotton wool and keep it in place with a leather sole or a 'shoof'.

Canker is more serious and will require your vet's advice. Reduce the risk of canker or thrush by regularly cleaning the feet out and if conditions are damp underfoot, paint the feet with Stockholm tar. Keep the hooves trimmed so the frog always gets adequate exercise, and if the horses are stabled, keep the floor clean and dry.

Colic

This is a general term for stomach upset, indigestion and pain. It may be spasmodic. During the spasm the horse may bite or kick at its belly, paw the ground, try to roll, stand as if trying to move its bowels and groan. It is usually caused by incorrect feeding or watering and sometimes from worms. Prevent colic by keeping to a routine of feeding and watering. Feed little and often (this is what the horse does naturally). Let your horse cool down gently after work before feeding or watering. Don't offer icy cold water.

Treatment

To treat a colicky horse walk it up and down for a couple of hours. Don't let it roll as this may cause a bowel twist. Try drenching it with a bottle of beer. That usually relieves about 80 per cent of colic cases. If there is still no improvement you will need a vet's help as the colic could be due to a bowel twist or a blockage of some sort, or from eating too much too fast, or bad food.

Laminitis

Also known as founder, this is an inflammation of the sensitive parts of the hoof between the horn and the rest of the foot. The small blood vessels in the foot overfill as a result of histamine being released into the bloodstream from one of many causes. It is usually only seen in top-heavy horses, and very fat or unfit ponies. But it may also occur if a horse is suddenly overfed (as may happen if one finds its way to the feed bin), or in a mare with retained foetal membranes. If over-eating is the cause, and it is discovered early on, then anti-inflammatory drugs combined with forced exercise to drive blood out of the feet can help. Put the horse on a soft laxative diet and run cold water over the hooves to ease the inflammation. In severe cases the form of the hoof could change and it may take several years of careful manicuring and shoeing to correct.

Horses with laminitis may adopt a saw horse stance, with their front feet well in front of them and their hind feet closer under the body than normal to get the weight off the front hooves.

Mastitis

Mares in milk are as susceptible to mastitis as other milking animals. The udder will be hot and inflamed, and the milk thick, pus-like and clotted. Seek your vet's advice. Treatment usually involves a course of antibiotics and regular massaging and stripping of the udder (see also mastitis in cattle).

Mud fever

This is a skin problem that occasionally crops up in winter where horses are kept in wet, muddy conditions. The constant wet encourages a fungal growth in the skin until it appears thickened in places and covered with little rough scabs which fall off, taking hair with them. The affected spots may be tender and can spread, becoming quite a serious condition.

As the weather warms and dries, mud fever usually disappears. Prevent it occurring by keeping horses in well-drained paddocks with shifts to fresh ground before an area is pugged up and muddy. If washing your horse be sure to dry its skin thoroughly. Better still, wait for mud to dry then brush it off. Any sore looking areas can be treated with some astringent lotion or a suitable fungicide wash (check with your vet).

Nails in the feet

With this sort of injury tetanus is a real risk (see following). Pull the nail out and assess how deep into the sole it went. If it hasn't penetrated through to the sensitive layers of the foot, the prick may clear up on its own. But if it is deeper the risk is that the entrance to the wound will heal over while there is still infection inside. You can help by soaking the site with hot water and disinfectant to draw out any infection, but if it is already hot and tender you may need a vet's help to pare away the sole and open the site up or to prescribe antibiotics to clear the infection up from inside.

Pneumonia

There are numerous causes of pneumonia, from viruses to incorrect drenching technique which forces liquid into the lungs. Whatever the cause there is usually inflammation of the lungs, the horse's breathing will be fast and shallow, it will be off its food and may develop a temperature and nasal discharge. Serious cases can lead to broken wind, whistling or roaring breathers, laminitis and even death, so pneumonia must be treated. Seek your vet's advice on suitable antibiotics and keep the animal warm and dry with plenty of fresh air, clean water and light feed.

Ringworm

This is a highly contagious skin condition. Cats, dogs, humans, horses and hedgehogs all get it and pass it on. It is caused by a fungus which attacks the skin and grows on hair follicles. It usually shows up as a bare patch, 25–50 mm in diameter with a scaly, bald centre and a scabby, crusty ring with hair lifting in the scabs. Some forms of ringworm are very itchy and the horse may have scratched the spot raw. Prevent the spread of ringworm by not swapping saddlery, blankets or grooming gear between horses. To treat, get drugs from your vet which will attack the fungus from inside the horse, or else dress each lesion generously with tincture of iodine. Clean and disinfect all saddlery blankets and grooming gear and if you are returning your horse to its paddock, scrub and disinfect the posts it leans or rubs against.

Saddle sores

These are the result of an ill-fitting or badly padded saddle. It will first show up as a fluid-filled bump where the saddle either hits the backbone or withers, or ribs to the side of the backbone. If the horse flinches when you climb into the saddle and you suspect a sore, put extra padding under the saddle, but not on the affected spot, so you raise the saddle off it.

Prevent saddle sores by only using good fitting saddles, keeping the padding on them in good condition and using a well-padded saddle blanket. If you continue to use ill-fitting gear on an animal with sores, they may break open and require veterinary help to treat.

Teeth

A horse's teeth do not always wear down as they should and it may be left with sharp edges on the outside of the upper molars and the inner edges of the lower molars. These can make chewing painful. The horse may have cuts to its tongue and cheeks, may salivate heavily and drop a lot of the food out of its mouth and, if bad enough, the horse will lose condition.

Correct the fault by rasping the sharp edges off with a horse dentistry rasp or similar. First stand the rasp in a warm bucket of water so the horse does not object to it so much, then get an assistant to hold the horse's nose and pull its tongue well out to the side away from you. Slide the rasp in between the cheek and the outer edge of the upper molars, slanting towards them slightly. Start rasping slowly, only speeding up as the irregularities are filed down. Rinse the filings off in the bucket of water. Slip your hand up the side of the mouth and check that the sharp edge has been filed down. Repeat the procedure on the other side, and if needed on the inner edge of the lower molars.

Tetanus

Horses are the most susceptible to tetanus of all domestic animals (see 'Clostridial diseases' in sheep). The danger comes when your horse is injured or cut. It may be so small a scrape you can hardly see it. The conditions around a wound are just right for the tetanus bacteria to bloom and it is the toxin they produce which causes the usually fatal lockjaw symptoms of tetanus.

The animal will get steadily stiffer and stiffer until it stands boardlike. It is very hard to treat and

Horses are very susceptible to tetanus and should be immunised regularly.

an affected horse is best put down. Prevention by a regular vaccination programme is the answer. Vaccinate pregnant mares with tetanus toxoid near the end of their pregnancy and they will pass some immunity on to their foals via the colostrum. This should protect the foal till it is 2–3 months old, when it and any other unvaccinated horses should be given a primary course of two injections of tetanus toxoid about four or five weeks apart. This should protect them for a year. Follow this up with an annual booster. If your horse is not immunised this way and suffers any wound or surgery then it

Donkeys, affectionate and docile pets.

will need immediate protection. For this inject with tetanus anti-toxin.

Ticks

Healthy horses on good short feed and in good condition should not be plagued by ticks, but if they are badly infected sponge them with some anti-tick solution (such as Asuntol). Read the instructions carefully to ensure you mix it to the right strength and that it is safe before using on pregnant or lactating mares.

Worms

Strongyles or red worms are the most important. Horses never develop an immunity to them. (See 'Internal parasites' in sheep.) The adult worms live in the large intestine and suck blood before passing their own eggs out in the dung. A heavy load of strongyles will cause anaemia, weakening the horse and making it susceptible to other ills.

Besides red worms, horses carry tapeworms, roundworms, thread worms, lung worms and liver fluke. All contribute to a general loss in condition. Control with regular drenching is essential. Mares should be drenched about a month before foaling and both mare and foal drenched a month after foaling.

How you drench after that will depend to some extent on your grazing management. Many horse studs collect dung daily to reduce the spread of worm infestations. Bringing in other classes of stock to graze paddocks after horses (for example, sheep or cattle) can help vacuum up the infective larvae and your climate will influence the need for worm control. Larvae survive on pasture longer in mild, wet climates than in cold, frosty or very dry areas.

Generally, horses should be drenched once a month during the warm, wet weather until they are 6 months old. After that a drench in spring and again in autumn should keep them healthy, especially if you can give them shifts to fresh ground and bring the sheep in to clean the pony paddock up from time to time.

Donkeys are browsers rather than grazers, and thus can be more susceptible to worms if confined to small paddocks. Donkeys may need about four drenches a year; less if they are getting regular paddock changes and other stock are cleaning up behind them. Drench both horses and donkeys according to weight. Assess this by measuring girth (A), and the length of the back from the withers to the tail (B) in centimetres. Weight in kilograms will be:

$$\frac{2A \times B}{108}$$

13. Chooks, ducks, geese and turkeys

The humble hen is a hard act for other farm animals to beat. She provides eggs conveniently packaged and delivered regularly, and if you cull your laying flock and raise a few young roosters, a steady supply of chicken dinners.

Aside from the benefits to the smallfarmer's stomach the hen can do a good service on the farm, scratching and spreading dung pats and providing nitrogen rich manure of their own under the chookhouse, just perfect for the compost heap.

If you want some bigger birds, well, ducks are no extra trouble and lay bigger eggs. Geese are bigger again and can usually be run free range on the farm, so require no supplementary feeding unless you wish to pen and fatten them for the freezer. Turkeys likewise can generally forage for themselves loose on the farm.

But if you want regular eggs and worthwhile meat production you do have to feed and care for your hens properly. If you expect your chooks to produce, be prepared to put some work and money into feeding and housing them right. Remember they will still need feeding during their moult and it may go against the grain to be buying both feed and eggs.

The same is true of ducks. Some farms do have them running free, but farmers face the task of finding eggs (duck eggs are exceptionally porous so can pick up lots of nasties if laid anywhere not up to Health Department hygiene regulations — and ducks have little respect for regulations). Ducks also dirty stock water supplies.

If geese and turkeys run loose they are unlikely to recognise those boundary fences you built and are just as likely to end up in the neighbour's deepfreeze as your own. They also graze an appreciable amount of grass, 12 geese being about one stock unit, and they foul more ground than they graze.

Breeds

Hens

You may choose your chooks scientifically, working out whether you want an egg producing flock, chicken for the freezer or the best of both worlds. Or you may select them on which you think are the prettiest, or like me, it may all depend on what the neighbours are giving away.

For the first-time chook owners I recommend the dual purpose breeds. With these you can get a steady supply of eggs and once hens have passed their best laying capacity they are still a reasonable size to put in the pot. (See Table 17.)

Bantams

Besides normal sized domestic birds you can consider bantams. These come in all the colours and shapes of the regular breeds but are diminutive versions, weighing about a quarter as much.

Ducks

Once again consider whether you want meat or eggs. Some people do not like duck eggs and others may not be up to the butchering of birds which can easily waddle their way into your affections.

Breed	Bird colour	Size (kg)	Eggs	Rate of lay
Egg producers				
Leghorns	White, also black, blue or brown	1.8	White	Ex.
Minorcas	Usually black, also blue and white	1.8	White	V.G.
Meat producers				
Brahmas	Light, dark or buff	3.6	Brown	Fair
Cochins	White, black or buff	3.4	Brown	Poor
Cornish	White	3.2	Brown	Poor
Dual purpose				
Plymouth rocks	Barred or white	2.4–3	Brown	V.G.
Rhode Island red	Brick red	2.4	Brown	V.G.
Light Sussex	White with black striped neck & tail	2.4–2.8	Brown	V.G.
Australorp	Black	2.4–2.8	Brown	V.G.
Orpingtons	Black or buff	2.4	Brown	Good
Red Shavers	Orange red	2.4	Brown	V.G.

Ex. = Excellent   V.G. = Very good

Table 17. **Hen breeds and features**.

Egg producers
Khaki Campbells
Birds are usually a dark khaki or green colour. They can lay over 300 eggs a year. The eggs are white and only slightly larger than a large hen egg. Surplus ducks and drakes can weigh 1.4–1.8 kg in 8–10 weeks; a fully grown drake weighs about 2.25 kg.

Runners
Birds are usually fawn and white, or white. They have an upright stance and run rather than waddle like other ducks. They can lay 200–250 white or green-tinted eggs a year. Mature ducks weigh only 1.8–2 kg.

Meat producers
Pekins
A creamy white bird with rapid growing rate, weighing up to 2.5 kg at 9 weeks. But they are poor layers, producing only 120–160 eggs a year, usually in cycles of about 24 eggs. Eggs are white.

Muscovy
These are really a separate species and seldom interbreed with other ducks. If they do the resulting offspring are infertile. Muscovies are large, slow-maturing birds, but drakes can weigh up to 4 kg and ducks 2 kg within about 18 weeks. Birds are usually black, white or pied with patches of scarlet skin around their eyes. They only lay 45–100 white tinted eggs a year.

Geese
Embden Geese
A large, white-feathered breed kept for meat production. Adult ganders weigh up to 12–13 kg and geese about 9 kg. If kept for meat the ganders are normally killed at about 14 weeks when they weigh about 6 kg.

White Leghorn hen.

Black Orpington hen.

Rhode Island Red rooster.

White Plymouth Rock rooster.

Minorca rooster.

Light Sussex hen.

Khaki Campbell duck.

Indian runner duck.

A Muscovy mama and brood.

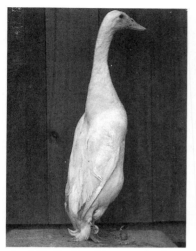

A white Indian Runner duck.

Turkeys come in black and bronze or ...

Sebastion goose.

sparkling white.

China Geese

These are smaller birds. Ganders weigh about 5 kg and geese 4–4.5 kg. They mature rapidly. There is a white variety with blue eyes and orange bill and shanks, and a brown/grey variety with dark, slate-coloured bill, brown eyes and a white faceband and orange shanks.

Toulouse Geese

These are loose feathered so look bigger than they actually are, though adult males can weigh 10–12 kg. They are dark grey on the back, light grey on the breast and have white undersides.

Pilgrims

A medium-sized, docile and pretty bird. The females are greenish grey and males all white with blue eyes. Adult ganders weigh about 6 kg.

Turkeys
Mammoth Bronze

A rich, metallic coloured bird with white barring on the tail. They have a big head with red caruncles (fleshy growths) and large scarlet wattles. There are also white and buff varieties.

153

Beltsville White

A smaller breed with white plumage and black beard, it grows to 4 kg at 14 weeks.

Management

Hens

My childhood memories of only throwing out scraps and the odd bit of mash coincide with memories of only ever picking up the odd egg. In contrast, hens housed and managed with regular inputs of care and food will provide a regular supply of eggs and chicken flesh.

How you decide to house and manage your chooks may depend on how many your family need. Allow everybody an egg a day. Most dual purpose breeds should manage 200 eggs or more a year, so work on about two chooks per person plus young stock coming on for next year.

Now the method I recommend for keeping chooks on the smallfarm is a mixture of confinement and free range. I do not go along with hens being kept in cages and turned into egg laying machines. It may be more economic, but if hens were meant to be in cages they wouldn't have been given wings to fly and legs to scratch with. If hens are confined to one hen house and one small yard all their lives, that yard is likely to end up a dirty mud hole in winter and a disease-ridden dust bath in summer. But a single yard is sufficient if you can let the hens run free outside for a few hours each day.

However, there may be good reasons why you don't want to let hens have free range: maybe you have a vulnerable vegetable garden, maybe the neighbours have a vulnerable vegetable garden . . . okay, then design your hen house so it feeds into a couple of yards. (See Fig. 89.) That way you can let the hens have the run of one pen for a month or so, then close it up and let the grass and ground cover regenerate while they use the adjacent one.

But the best method, I believe, is allowing hens free range for some of the day. For this a movable hen house is ideal as each year it can be shifted to a fresh site. Most egg laying goes on in the morning, so give the chooks breakfast in their house and leave them there until early afternoon. Then let

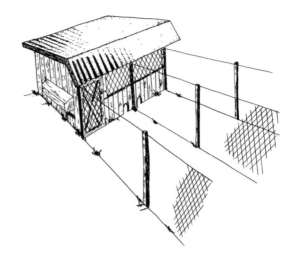

Fig. 89 **Permanent hen house feeding into two runs**.

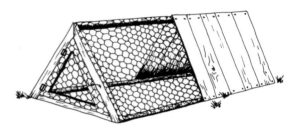

Fig. 90 **Ark for hens**.

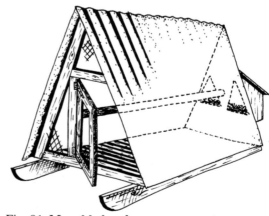

Fig. 91 **Movable hen house**.

154

them out to explore the outdoors and call them in again with their evening feed. Hens allowed free range generally produce darker, richer-coloured eggs with better shells.

Housing

An ark type house (see Fig. 90) is suitable for 8–10 chooks. If you're planning on more than that either build another movable ark or house go to a larger, permanent hen house of the sort shown in Fig. 91.

Things to bear in mind when building a house:

- It must have plenty of ventilation but no draughts. Hens create a lot of moisture and high levels of ammonia and carbon dioxide which need to be removed to keep the flock disease-free. So in an ark design leave the ridge open but protected from rain by a moulding 5 cm above the peak of the house. In a box type house with a sloping roof, leave the top 60 cm or so of the highest wall open, closed in only with netting.
- Have laying boxes accessible from the outside so you don't have to clamber through the house to see if anyone has laid a golden egg.
- Make perches removable so they can be cleaned and disinfected against mites and other parasites.
- Allow at least one nesting box for four hens. The boxes should be just big enough to hold one hen, normally about 30 cm square. It is a good idea to have a 10 cm lip on the front of the box to stop eggs and nesting material from being scratched out. The boxes should be dark.
- In an ark type of house hens should be kept up above the ground, on a floor of either timber slats or metal grating which allows droppings to fall through so hens are not walking in their own mess. In permanent houses it is a good idea to use dropping boards to catch droppings from under the perches and litter elsewhere in the pen.
- Sawdust, straw or pine needles make good litter. Hay is usually not absorbent enough. The litter layer should be gradually added to as hens break it down and it is fouled. At the end of the season the house can be cleaned out and the litter turned into excellent compost.

Feeding

If you want your chooks to lay lots of well balanced and protein-rich eggs you need to feed them a well balanced and protein-rich diet. If you want tender plump chickens for the table you will have to provide the protein and carbohydrate they need to grow and put on weight. For young stock see the paragraph on rearing chickens and feeding instructions.

Laying hens normally require about 100 g of dry feed/bird/day. Bought feeds are carefully formulated to provide hens with a balanced diet so go carefully if you want to experiment with homegrown grains. Corn is easily grown for hens, but is lower in protein than wheat or barley. Introduce grains gradually, starting with a ratio of about 10 of mash to 1 of grain when the birds are at least 8 weeks old (younger birds will not be able to digest whole grain), and increase it gradually to a 1:1 ratio by the time the birds are 20 weeks old. Remember the whole grains you can grow might not be very high in protein so balance them with a higher protein mash. Make sure hens have access

A movable A-frame ark means the hens can be moved to clean range each season.

155

to grit which they hold in their gizzard and which helps to grind down the coarse grain.

Laying birds also require a good source of calcium to replace the calcium carbonate that goes into making eggshells each day. You can provide it in the form of ground up shells, crushed limestone or ground bone meal.

Household scraps are fine as a supplement and something for the chooks to scratch about in. Do not feed more scraps than the birds can clean up in about quarter of an hour or they will not eat their requirements of carefully formulated feed.

Laying cycle

Young pullets normally start laying at about 20 weeks so chickens hatched in spring should be laying by autumn. Of course this varies from breed to breed and bird to bird. The dual purpose breeds generally take a couple of weeks longer to come into lay than the egg-laying breeds.

Once she has started laying, a pullet should continue to produce for a year before moulting. This usually occurs in the following autumn. Commercial poultry farmers often cull chooks once they begin to moult, believing it is not economic to feed them through this period of two to four months. But for a smallfarmer it is a toss up whether it's easier to feed hens through the moult or raise a new clutch of replacement pullets every year. But it is wise to cull chooks before their second moult while they are still worth eating as egg production in their third season will be considerably reduced.

Culling

Do not try to cull hens during the moult. The chances are you will not be able to tell good layers from bad. The bad layers are likely to have moulted early and be looking good, and the hard working hens will be ragged, scruffy looking chooks that don't look worth keeping. So it's best to select your culls while the birds are still in full lay.

Ducks

Egg-producing ducks can be kept on a similar regime to hens — housed part of the day and allowed free range the rest. Ducks and hens can be run together if you do not want to make a separate duck house, but make sure there is enough room so ducks that do not want to roost can stand clear of the firing line from hen perches.

If you are just keeping ducks, you don't need to provide quite such elaborate housing as for hens though they do need some form of shelter from rain and wind. A dirt floor is suitable and a pen, allowing at least 1 m^2/duck, which they can be confined in overnight. Ducks normally lay at night or in the early morning and are notoriously unfussed about where they lay their eggs, so by keeping them in a pen for those hours you have a better chance of finding the eggs and collecting them before they get tainted. While ducks need plenty of good clean drinking water it isn't essential to give them enough to swim in. However, a shallow trough (about 20 cm), which can be cleaned regularly, at the bottom of a well-drained night pen will be enjoyed by the birds and keep their plumage in better condition.

Feeding

Ducks like a wet mash feed as early in the morning as possible. All eggs should be laid by about 9 am and then the birds can be let out to

Feature	Layer	Non-layer
Comb, wattles	Large, full and scarlet	Small, scaly, pale and shrunken
Vent	Large and moist	Small contracted
Abdomen	Large, soft and yielding	Shallow or full of hard fat
Pubic bones (each side of vent)	Slim and pliable	Stiff or hard to find if covered in fat

Table 18. **Characteristics of layers and non-layers**.

range. By 4 pm or 5 pm bring them back into the pen with a feed of grain or pellets. Ducks can see in the dark and will enjoy a feed of scraps or mash left in their trough late in the evening. Because of the very heavy egg production ducks are capable of they need a richer protein diet than hens. This can be supplied by fish or meat meal, milk or fresh grown clover or lucerne. Allow at least 170 g of mash or pellets/duck/day of at least 20 per cent protein. Supplement this with some meat meal or fish meal. Ducks need green feed as well, though they will get sufficient if allowed free range during the day. Like chooks they also need grit to aid digestion and crushed shell to provide calcium and phosphorus for egg shell production.

If you are managing ducks for meat then you might prefer to keep them confined rather than burning up energy and weight wandering around the farm. Domestic ducks are generally not good fliers and a fence 60 cm high is usually enough to keep them in. But it will not be enough to keep cats and dogs out.

When to slaughter

Ducklings begin to develop pin feathers when they are 9–10 weeks old. These are immature feathers which eventually grow full sized but are hard to clean off the carcass. So aim to have your duck-lings up to weight and ready for slaughter before then, about 8–9 weeks. If you have been running your ducklings on pasture they may take longer to reach a slaughterable size. In this case wait until they are 12–14 weeks old; by then the pin feathers will have grown into full feathers and be easier to pluck.

Geese

Geese can live 30 years or more. They also tend to mate for life so new birds introduced to a flock may not be accepted for a while and for breeding purposes a high ratio of ganders to geese (about 1:4) is required. Some of the breeds can be quite aggressive, a point to consider when toddlers are around; nearly all make excellent watchdogs, kick-ing up a great honking and ruckus when strangers arrive. They are also supposed to be useful as

weeders for crops like young strawberries (before they fruit).

On a lot of farms geese are just released in to a back paddock and left to their own devices. They will do quite well like this, but if you want to cull the flock regularly for the freezer it won't hurt to feed them grain once a day, especially in winter when feed is short. This will keep the flock tame and nearer the home, making it easier to find the nests of goslings. Goslings can be reared for the table on pasture alone, but it will be six months before they are up to weight. Alternatively, allow them free range but also 1 kg of grain or fattening pellets/bird/week. On this sort of regime they can weigh up to 4.8 kg in 14 weeks.

Turkeys

With our mild climate, particularly in northern parts of New Zealand, the easiest way to raise turkeys is to buy a couple of breeding pairs, feed them around the farm for a few days so they learn where home is, then let them go. Turkeys do fine on free range and young birds can be killed for the table at about 16 weeks if penned for the last few weeks and fattened on three feeds a day of mash, meat meal, boiled fat scraps and some grain. But beware, chooks and turkeys do not mix due to disease transference between the breeds.

Rearing young

Hens

I think chick rearing should stay with the hens where it belongs. Some of the specialised egg-producing breeds of chooks have had the broodiness bred out of them, but the older breeds, Rhode Island Reds, Black Orpingtons and Ban-tams in particular, usually go broody at some stage in the season and make fine mothers. You will know when a chook is broody: she refuses to get off the nest, makes little tick-tick noises instead of her usual cackle, and shows only a passing interest in food.

Once you have a broody chook decide what you

157

want her to hatch. Often you can get a clutch of fertile eggs from other hen breeders. Maybe they have a variety you want to introduce to your flock or else if you like your own hens and rooster then your own eggs should do fine. A chook can sit up to 20 eggs but 12 or 15 is probably a safer number. Only give a bantam six or seven unless she is sitting bantam eggs.

You won't want your broody hen occupying one of the laying boxes and keeping other producing chooks out, so shift her and the clutch to a brooding pen. A small ark similar to Fig. 90, with a dry, sheltered house of laying box proportions at one end and a small netting run is ideal.

Because a dedicated broody chook will neglect herself it pays to have food and water close to her nest. The enclosed run means she can get some exercise scratching for grain without going far enough to forget her duty to those eggs.

In order to hatch, fertile eggs have to be kept at the correct temperature and humidity, have adequate ventilation (the embryo chicks breathe through the eggshell) and be regularly turned. A good broody chook will take care of all these requirements, but it doesn't hurt to sprinkle a little water on the eggs when you entice the chook off for a feed. If the shells get too dry and hard the chicks can have trouble breaking out.

Hen eggs take three weeks to hatch, and then you have a brood of chicks to worry about. The same ark is ideal for their first few weeks of life as the main danger to them now comes from the outside, namely hawks and cats.

From about six weeks on you can begin letting the chicks and their mother out to range in the day but call them back to their safe house with a feed each night.

Egg type	Incubation time
Chicken eggs	21 days
Duck eggs	28 days
Muscovy duck eggs	35 days
Geese eggs	30 days
Turkey eggs	28 days

Table 19. **Rearing young poultry**.

decided to make her nest. If the mother duck or goose has nested near some water and gets her feet and plumage wet during her daily exercise then that will be enough to dampen the eggs. But if the nest is somewhere very dry the eggs will need to be sprinkled with water occasionally, particularly in the last week of hatching.

Once hatched, get the ducklings or goslings and their mother into some secure pen or ark which will allow them limited range for the first couple of weeks. From then on let them have more range but pen them safely each night. Be aware that while ducklings might enjoy playing in water their fluff is not impervious to it, unlike their mature feathers, so it is easy for them to chill and die from too long in water. Ensure that any trough has rocks in one end so they can scramble out easily.

Curing broody birds

Sometimes a bird will go broody and stop laying when you don't want her to. To cure her put her in a wire cage in a draughty place such as hanging in a tree with water only. Usually a day or two is sufficient.

Ducks and geese

It has been said that a hen makes the best duck mother. Certainly some hens can be more reliable at sitting eggs through to hatching than some ducks, but one of the best sights on a smallfarm is proud mother duck waddling out in front of a line of 20 little quackers. If a duck does decide to go broody it is best to let her sit where she has

Butchering

Birds destined for the pot should be starved for 12 or 24 hours but make sure they have plenty to drink during this time. There are several methods of killing poultry, the obvious being to hold the bird by both legs and lay the head over a chopping block: dispatch it with a sharp axe and toss the bird under a box to thrash around. A slightly more

Type	Age (weeks)	Feed	Amount
Chickens	0–6	Starter mash mixed with milk or water. Some greens if not on range.	Keep in front of them.
	6–18	Growing mash, some scraps and grain, limited range.	Feed morning noon and evening.
	18–	Laying mash, some grain, scraps and free range part of the day.	Feed morning and evening. Up to 100 g/bird/day.
Ducklings	1–2	Very wet mash mix.	Keep in front of them.
	3–9	Growers rations, milk, some grain and scraps.	Keep in front of table birds, or three feeds for future layers.
	9–20	Mash of about 15 per cent protein, scraps and some range.	Feed early morning all they can eat in 20 mins. Allow range from 9 am on.
	20–	Same as above.	Same as above, plus a 4 pm feed and even an extra feed later at night up to 200 g/bird/day.
Goslings	0–3	Same as ducklings.	
	3–	Allow free range and feed some grain.	One evening feed.
Turkeys	0–3	Same as for chickens.	
	3–	Free range.	

Table 20. **Feeding young stock.**

Fig. 92 **Killing a chook.**

sophisticated (and less bloody) method is to grab the hen's legs in the left hand and hold it with its head hanging towards your rear. Hold the neck in the right hand between first and second fingers with the head cupped in your palm, then push your right hand down and bend it back. (See Fig. 92.) Continue pushing until the top joint or vertebrae snaps but stop as soon as you feel the backbone break or you may pull the head off.

Plucking
Birds can be dry plucked immediately, but the preferred method is to scald them first. For this you want a large container of scalding water at 80°C (two-thirds boiling water and one-third cold is about right). Dunk the bird in the water and swish it up and down for about

30 seconds for hens, then proceed to pull all its feathers out. The pin feathers can be removed later by gripping them between your thumb and the edge of a knife.

Dressing

After plucking, wash the bird in cool water and dry the carcass. Cut the shanks off below the hocks. Cut off the head if you haven't already done so with the axe. Cut the skin on the back of the neck all the way down to the body. Cut the neck bone at the shoulder and pull out the neck, the gullet, crop and stomach. Run a finger around inside the shoulder to loosen all the other organs. Next, with the bird on its back, make a horizontal cut about 8 cm long across the abdomen just above the vent (take care not to cut too deep and penetrate the intestines), make another cut completely round the vent, push the vent and intestine into the body and pull it all out through the first cut. The sexual organs (like two small white beans attached to the backbone) and lungs can then be reached and pulled out by hand. Fold the neck skin back neatly and push the legs firmly under the wings. (For roasting it is an idea to skewer them in position.) Cut a small slit in the abdomen flesh and buttonhole this over the parson's nose or tail. Birds should be bagged as moist as possible for the deep freeze.

Bigger birds

The techniques for bigger birds are largely the same. To kill them you can still either chop the head off with an axe or break the neck. Or you can cut the jugular vein at the side of the head, then immediately stick the bird by pushing a sharp knife or sticking skewer into the roof of the mouth and on into the brain at the back of the head. This method is said to loosen feathers and make plucking easier, but you will need an experienced poultry person to show you the right spots to cut and skewer the first time.

Plucking ducks and geese is the same as for hens; they are just bigger birds so take longer. If scalding them, dunk ducks for about two minutes and geese for two or three minutes. You can add a drop of detergent to the water to combat the waterbird's natural oils. Dressing ducks and geese

is the same as for chickens. Turkeys can be butchered the same way, but plucking them is easier and quicker due to fewer and coarser feathers.

Diseases

Happy, healthy birds are disease-resistant and with good management your flock should stay disease free. But there are pests and problems which might crop up. The most likely are these:

Coccidiosis

This is mainly a disease of young birds. Symptoms are diarrhoea, blood streaks in the droppings and dazed, droopy-winged birds. It is highly contagious as the eggs of the coccidia pass out in the droppings and can infect other birds. Perfectly dry conditions can thwart the parasite and chicks allowed fresh range each day are less likely to be affected. Some chicken starter mashes contain a preventative or alternatively you can add a coccidiostat to their drinking water. If treating laying stock with sulphanimides, do not use the eggs for human consumption.

Crop bind

This is the proverbial spanner in the works. More correctly some straw, hay, string or other fibre has bunged up the passage from the crop to the stomach. The bird will be off its food, mopish and will look as if its crop is very full. If you can, get a teaspoon of warm water with a little baking soda dissolved in it down the bird's throat. Then massage the crop and hold the bird upside down by the feet and press and massage the crop to empty it. Put the bird in a cage on her own and starve her. Repeat massaging the crop until the blockage has dispersed.

Entero-hepatitis

This is a liver disease of turkeys with similar symptoms and treatment to coccidiosis in chooks.

It is often called blackhead as it turns the skin on the head and face a dark colour. Add Emtryl to turkey water or feed according to the maker's instructions. Most importantly, to avoid blackhead in turkeys keep them clear of any ground hens have ranged on.

Internal parasites

These include roundworms, tape worms and caecal worms. Birds only pick up worms through pecking at old litter or droppings so infestations can generally be avoided if the birds are allowed clean range. Worms will cause loss of weight, lowered egg production and eventually death. If worms are suspected the flock can be treated with piperazine in their drinking water.

Lice

These are small crawlies which run around on the skin of live birds, and if you are killing infested birds, will start running around on you once their host starts to cool off. Dust birds with a flea or lice powder containing pyrethrum, paying special attention to the vent area.

Prolapse

This usually only occurs in overfat, young laying stock. The oviduct protrudes through the vent and if discovered early enough before the oviduct dries or is damaged you may try washing it in cool water and holding the bird by the feet to allow it to slip back into place. But the bird is probably best destroyed as she could suffer a prolapse again or pass the tendency on if any of her eggs are hatched for next year's flock.

Red mites

These are members of the spider family and tend to live in cracks in the perches, laying boxes or woodwork near where chooks roost. They are grey by day but at night swarm onto the birds and gorge themselves with blood until they turn red. March is the worst time for mite infestation and perches and woodwork should be painted with kerosene or creosote before then. If using litter on the floor of the shed, ensure it is clean and free of mite before building up the litter layer for winter.

Scaly leg

This is caused by another spider parasite which burrows into the leg scales, causing them to puff up with concrete-like deposits. To cure it you may wash off some of the deposits with warm soapy water then dry the legs and apply a soothing type of oil, (such as baby oil), and smear them with Vaseline to trap the parasites.

Chooks living in clean, dry quarters on a balanced diet with some free range are unlikely to fall ill. But if one does and you cannot decide the cause of it, isolate her for a few days as she could recover if it is only a case of crop binding or cold. Otherwise destroy her to prevent any disease spreading to the rest of the flock.

14. Pigs

Pigs fit easily into the smallfarm set up. They don't take up much space, they eat almost anything, they are intelligent and friendly, and they can turn surpluses from the house cow and vegetable garden into pork and bacon. A good sow may produce 16–20 piglets a year which can be sold as weaners or carried on for slaughter.

Put an unringed pig in next year's garden plot and it will take great delight in grazing it down; rooting it up and fertilising it for you. Or else put the pig in last year's garden plot and it will clean up all the stubble and leftovers. Housing does not need to be elaborate though that will depend on your climate. Obviously the better you make the pig house the more years' service it will give.

Pigs are intelligent, they can be trained and learn readily, be it where dinner comes from or to respect the electric fence. With good management, feed and shelter they should be relatively trouble free.

But to keep pigs you need to like them. They are quite different from other animals and some stock, particularly horses, seem frightened by them. But whether that means you shouldn't keep pigs or shouldn't keep horses will be up to you.

Pigs are big, strong animals and can eat anything. That makes them dangerous to other animals that can't get out of the way quick enough, and includes everything from weak sheep to toddlers. They do need regular feeding, at least twice a day, and they eat lots.

Pigs will need a house, and pig-proof fences with a couple of electric outriggers or they may push through and wander where they please. If you keep a sow or two for breeding you have the hassle of finding a boar or keeping one (ever tried loading 100 kg of unco-operative boar onto a trailer?)

Pigs are subject to their share of illnesses and internal parasites, though with good management most of these should be avoided.

Breeds

There are four more common domestic breeds of pig in New Zealand: Berkshire, Tamworth, Large White and Large Black. Besides these are the rare fat little Kunekune and the rangy, wild Captain Cookers. What breed you choose will depend whether you want pigs for bacon or for pork. Let me explain the difference. Pigs, be they reared for pork or bacon, have essentially the same body conformation (body shape). The difference is that porkers reach it at 3–4 months when they weigh about 45 kg and baconers reach it at 6 months when they weigh about 90–100 kg. You want a breed that matures at the right time for the purpose you have in mind. Dark and black-skinned pigs are less popular for pork production as white flesh and skin are preferred on the table. For bacon the colour does not matter.

Berkshire

This is an early maturing type of pig usually kept for its pork. It is mostly black with white face and feet and short legs. It is one of the most popular pigs in New Zealand and is adaptable to a variety

Berkshire sow.

Tamworth sow.

Large White sow.

Kunekune, an endangered species.

of conditions. Some strains are suitable for bacon, for example the Canadian Berkshire.

Tamworth

This is a good hardy pig. It is usually reddish coloured and is late developing so tends to be leaner at light weights and later maturing than the Berkshire, so it is generally kept for bacon. Its hardiness makes it ideal for rearing on pasture.

Large White

This is an indoor pig. Its pale skin makes it susceptible to sunburn if kept outside, so it is not so popular with smallfarmers. It is a late developer so is good for producing lean bacon, but it is not so suitable for pork when younger as it may still be lean and leggy. It is very prolific and sows throw litters of 12 to 14 quite normally.

Large Black

This breed is also known as the Devon. It has characteristic droopy ears. Its black skin makes it less desirable for pork production but it is good for bacon. It is a good-natured pig and generally easy to handle. It is hardy and will thrive on pasture.

Selecting breeding stock

If you want to get breeding pigs of your own then you should select them at the size they will be when you want to slaughter the offspring. For instance if you intend raising porkers, examine prospective breeding stock when they are 3–4 months old and should weigh about 45 kg. Likewise don't select baconers until they are 6 months old. If you start off with piglets, raise several young gilts (young female pigs) and once they reach slaughter weights, just keep the best for breeding from.

Desirable traits

Like any farm stock, some individual pigs will be better at converting the feed and dollars you put into them back into returns in bacon, pork or piglets than others, so the trick is to select the most efficient animals. You want a sow that is highly fertile and a good mother. Be careful on the fertility aspect, though. Some pigs can produce up to 14 piglets a litter, but may not rear all those satisfactorily. Most farmers find a litter of 8–10 is more manageable.

To be a good mother a sow must be able to feed all those babies well. So she needs a good set of teats. The number of nipples varies from 10 to 14. The more a sow has the better she will cope and the less likelihood of you having to feed surplus piggies that have run out of places at the milk bar. The teats should start well up on the sow's chest. Check that none of the nipples is inverted. They should be evenly spaced for effective rearing. Temperament is important in the sow, not only for you if you need to get in there and help her, but more importantly for her babies. A good sow will move carefully around her piglets and lie down and call them for dinner with a couple of grunts. Avoid excessively big sows as they tend to be clumsy and more likely to squash their offspring.

Fertility is mainly up to the sow. She determines how many piglets will be in a litter, but there are a couple of points you need to look out for when selecting a boar. Besides just being a good all-round pig with the right conformation for your pig farming plans, he needs to have all the right sexual bits (two fully developed testes and a healthy penis) and the inclination to carry out his duties.

Selecting piglets for rearing

If you don't want to go into breeding but still want homegrown pork or bacon then buy weaner piglets off other farmers, at about 8 weeks old. If you are allowed to pick from the litter choose the strongest and healthiest looking. As with most farm animals, runts tend to stay that way and you will get better returns for the feed you put into the pigs if you pick vigorous stock to start with.

A piglet should have bright eyes, clean, warm ears (hot or cold ears suggest illness of some sort), his tail should have a jaunty curl in it and his back be straight. The skin will be satiny and soft. A runt may be dirty around the mouth and in the ears, will have skinny little hams (back legs), his tail will droop out straight if he is poorly and his skin may be coarse and hairy. (See Fig. 93.)

Management

Housing

If pigs are to stay healthy and grow to their best potential on the food you give them the housing must not be overcrowded. Eight to nine piglets in a pen is considered the maximum; beyond that they will spend more time fighting and becoming stressed. But don't keep a solitary pig either. Pigs like to huddle for warmth at night and just one pig is not a huddle.

The shelter must be dry, draught-proof but well ventilated, and reasonably insulated, particularly if you are in an area where the weather is particularly hot or cold. From the sleeping quarters the pigs should have access to a yard and dunging area, or to a paddock outside. If you have the pigs confined then the yards should give each pig more space than it gets in the sleeping quarters. After all this is their sunbathing, exercise and feeding area. It is

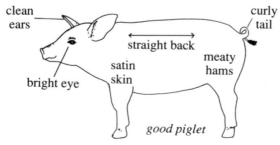

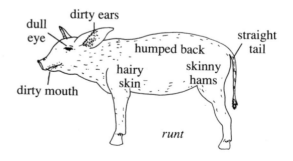

Fig. 93 **A good piglet and a runt**.

164

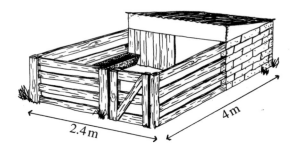

Fig. 94 **Conventional pig sty**.

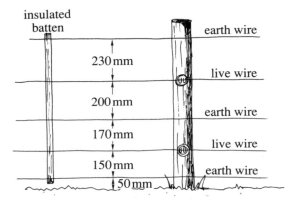

Fig. 95 **Pig fence**.

also where you hope they will excrete and if the dimensions aren't right their natural toilet training can run amok. Basically pigs like to sleep in one area and wander away 3–4m to do their morning business. If the run is too small or too square they might be confused about the best spot to adopt as toilet.

A couple of fattening pigs should live quite happily in a confined pen if their sleeping quarters are about 2.4m by 1.5m and feed into an exercise yard about 2.4m by 2.4 m. (See Fig. 94.) The yard and house complex needs to be built so you can get in and hose it out as required. For this a concrete floor is best, at least in the yard, but wood may be all right in the sleeping quarters so long as your pigs don't soil it. Alternatively stick to concrete and put in straw for bedding. Ventilation is also important. Pigs can actually stand cold better than they can heat, so in summer ensure they have good shade to lie in during the hottest part of the

day. In winter insulate the sty well. One way is to lower the ceiling, using netting and storing hay above it.

If you are running pigs so they have access to pasture, build a house just up above ground level with a warm wooden floor for sleeping on. All the troughs and dunging areas will be outside in the paddock.

Pigs without rings in their noses will merrily root all the ground, munching up weeds, snails and undesirables and turning the ground over for next year's vegetable garden. If you put rings in, the pigs will just graze the area nicely. For this reason they are ideal for keeping orchards clean as they don't seem inclined to ringbark trees or rob low leaves, but you will have to be quick to beat them to any falling fruit.

In the house put a small wooden lip at the doorway about 100 mm high, so if you turn it into a farrowing house the piglets won't wander out and get lost. If using timber for the walls, lay the planks vertically and they are less likely to be chewed. Have a ramp leading up into the house to keep any mud out.

Fencing

Electric fencing is really a must for pigs allowed an area of range. That sensitive snout soon learns to respect a hot wire run around an existing fence about 200 mm above the ground level. If you are building a new fence for the pigs, it does not have to be very high. (See Fig. 95.) Five wires, the top one 800 mm above ground level, will do. Alternatively use pig mesh, which is a low type of netting, but again a hot wire to keep them off the fence is desirable.

Feeding

Pigs will eat most things — some they shouldn't for their sake and some for your sake. Don't feed pigs raw meat scraps. For one thing it is against the law and it can encourage aggressive behaviour in your pigs. They can also pick up disease this way and may transmit those diseases to people. Don't feed pigs milk from cows not tested for TB. What you feed may to some extent depend on what season it is, what is growing in the garden, whether the cow has calved and has surplus milk or the orchard is full of windfalls.

If you are only interested in rearing a weaner or two each year then it is a good idea to buy them in spring when you should have milk from the cow for the young piglets, comfrey coming away in the garden (2.5 kg of comfrey will replace 0.5 kg of meal) and by summer time the growing pig can enjoy your carrot thinnings, empty pea pods, old lettuces and eventually fatten nicely on pumpkins, artichokes, spuds, squash, marrows, turnips and corn.

Feed sources

- Alfalfa, artichokes (Jerusalem) and apples are all enjoyed by pigs. Check that the apples aren't rotten and fermenting.
- Barley is probably the best all-round pig feed. Feed it crushed or steeped in water to soften it. Pigs will fatten nicely on barley and milk alone.
- Bran is too expensive and too laxative to fatten stock on. It is useful fed to breeding sows or sick pigs as a laxative, if mixed into a warm mash.
- Carrots are excellent fed with meal in winter.
- Comfrey is a good food for young pigs, high in minerals and vitamins.
- Corn (and maize) are good pig food and easily grown. Feed it whole on the cob.
- Marrows pigs love.
- Meat meal is a high quality feed made from freezing works by-products, which is rich in protein and valuable as a supplement when other feeds fall short in food value.
- Milk is one of the best foods for pigs and cheap if you have your own cow. Feeding milk is reputed to help keep internal parasites down. Feed up to 5–7 litres/day.
- Molasses can be mixed into pig feed. They enjoy the taste and it has some tonic and laxative effects. But it can be expensive.
- Pumpkins are excellent pig fattening food and easily grown. Feed them cooked or raw.
- Potatoes are good but must be cooked. Four kg of spuds is worth about 1 kg of meal or 4.5 litres of separated milk.

- Sunflower seeds, sugar beet and swedes are all suitable pig fodder.
- Wheat is expensive unless you grow it yourself. Steep it in water or crush it before feeding.

How much?

Let's assume that 4.5 litres of milk or 500 g of meal or 1.8 kg of spuds all equal one meal unit. Then pigs under reasonably good housing conditions and not under any stress from management, disease or whatever should gain the weights shown in Table 21 if fed at these rates.

For the meal portion of the pigs' diet a good mix is 4 parts crushed barley, 2 parts meat meal, 1 part pollard and 1 part bran. As a rough guide feed the quantities in Table 22.

It is hard to put a food value on the bucket of kitchen scraps. Chances are they will just be a supplement and a bit of variety, but the bulk of the pigs' requirements will have to come from meal and milk.

Hygiene

Normally pigs are quite clean animals and will dung in one part of their quarters. If they have range over a paddock then their dunging is no problem. However, pigs are subject to internal parasites like most of the grazing animals, so ground used for pigs one season should be hard grazed by another class of stock and then spelled for six weeks or so before a new lot of pigs go onto it.

The pig house should be regularly mucked out, though the need for this will vary with the weather and the pigs' toilet habits. If the weather is dry and the pigs well trained a few days will not matter, but if the weather turns bad and they are trampling dung through their quarters then clean it up or watch out for disease problems.

Under 3 days old, piglets do their droppings anywhere. But after that they tend to avoid messing their sleeping area but will learn habits from their mother. If she is a 'dirty sow' she will have a 'dirty litter'. You can encourage good dung habits by keeping the pigs in the run of a new pen to empty out before letting them in to the sleeping area. Dampen the area in the new pen where you'd

Age (weeks)	Liveweight (kg)	Daily gain (g)	Meal units required
8	18	500	2.5
10	25	500	3
12	32	500	4
14	40	680	4.5
16	50	770	5
18	60	820	5.5
20	70	820	6
22	82	820	6
24	95	820	6

Table 21. **Weight gain and rate of feed**.

Pig	Meal units
Dry sows and boars	6
Sows in pig	14
Suckling sows	14
Weaners	3
Porkers	4
Baconers	5–6

Table 22. **Feed quantities**.

like them to dung and even put some dung there from the old pen. If they persist with fouling the sleeping quarters, clean them out in the evening and put some bedding or feed pellets where they have soiled.

Note that pig dung is extremely corrosive, so always wash your shovel thoroughly after mucking out.

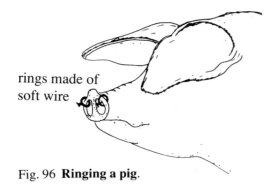

rings made of soft wire

Fig. 96 **Ringing a pig**.

Ringing pigs' noses

If you don't want your pigs to root up their paddock, ring their noses while they are still quite small. The usual story is to use two rings on the top fleshy bar of the snout, one on each side of the central bar of gristle. (See Fig. 96.) Softish wire that is easily bent is best — copper wire is ideal. It needs to be firm enough that you can push it through but soft enough to bend easily without hurting the pig more than necessary.

Equipment

- Two lengths of copper wire or similar about 30 cm long. Sharpen one end of each into a long spike on a grinder.
- Ear muffs (essential as pig squeals can reach 120 decibels and that is enough to do damage to your hearing).
- Someone to hold the pig, also with ear muffs.
- Two pairs of pliers, preferably one pair of long nose, and one with wire cutters included.

The procedure

Have one person hold the piglet very firmly with its snout on a board, bench or stump. The person doing the ringing pushes the wire through the top of the snout (if the wire is good and sharp it is not too difficult). Then bend the wire over and cross it close to the snout (don't use the snout for leverage but grab the wire with the long-nosed pliers). Then grip both ends of the wire where they cross and with the second pair of pliers put several tight twists in the wire and snip the ends off. Then do

167

the other side. Don't make the rings too big or the pig may catch them on things and tear them out. A big pig will take a lot more holding so tie it up against a rail or wall (see Fig. 97) with a loop around its top jaw.

Fig. 97 **Restraining a pig for ringing.**

Castration

Boars reach puberty at about 6 months. They should not be used for service before 7–8 months old and if kept for meat may develop a rank boar flavour before then. If you are planning on killing them for pork at 3–4 months old castration is not necessary. But for baconers which might not be slaughtered until after 6 months it is advisable.

A castrated pig is known as a barrow. They are less aggressive than boars and can be managed more like gilts. Any barrow behaviour problems are usually linked with their rapid growth rate and gutsiness at feed times.

The sooner you castrate the better, with the best time 4–7 days old. Use a very sharp pocketknife or better still a one-sided razor blade or a scalpel. One person holds the pig on a bench or table and pulls the back legs forward while grasping the front legs as well. Swab the scrotal area with iodine (pigs' testicles protrude from the back of the hind legs rather than between them as with lambs or calves). Squeeze the testicle out against the skin with the thumb and forefinger of one hand and cut vertically through the skin to the testicle with the other. Then push the testicle out of the slit. Do the same with the other side and then either clamp the cords (if you have a castration clamp) and cut them, or else tear the cord (a tear clots quicker than a cut) severing the cords as high

up into the pig as possible. Then clean the pig up with iodine and pop it into a clean pen away from uncastrated pigs.

Behaviour problems

Any behaviour problems in your pigs (allowing for some individuality) are likely to be connected with stress or boredom. Stress usually comes from being overcrowded or underfed and frightened. Avoid housing too many pigs in the same pen. There should never be more than 120 kg of pig/m^2 of space. Make sure the trough is long enough to fit everyone.

Boredom can also be prevented. It is unlikely to be a problem if the pigs have access to range outside. But confined pigs can find life a bit ho-hum just waiting around to get fat enough to be slaughtered. So give them a toy, a handful of hay a day, a tin can filled with stones, a ball, a paper sack, anything that will interest them and do no harm.

Breeding

A few good breeding sows producing a couple of litters a year can give a good supplement to other farm income, especially if you have cheap sources of feed for them and their piglets. But don't take the procreation bit too lightly. Birth can be a dramatic and upsetting time and though the small size and shape of piglets makes their birth easier than many other animals, things can and do still go wrong.

Sows

Young female pigs are known as gilts; once pregnant they are sows. Gilts start coming into season (when they will take a boar) from about 170 to 220 days old. Hold off mating until they are at least 8 months old, then check they are a reasonable weight as well — about 110 to 120 kg. The pigs need to be well grown to be strong enough to support the boar through a prolonged mating.

Heat in sows

Sows cycle every 21 days, give or take a few days, and will be in standing heat from anything

168

between 38 to 60 hours. The usual signs that a sow is coming in season are:

- Swollen and reddened vulva about two days before oestrus.
- Mucous discharge.
- Restlessness and less eagerness for food.
- Possibly riding other pigs in the pen.
- When in standing heat she will let you put pressure on her back end.

It is a good idea to flush your sows 10–14 days before mating — that is, feed them slightly more than usual so they are on a rising plane of nutrition when they go to the boar. This can increase the litter size. But you do not want the pig to go to the boar fat. Overfat pigs usually have fertility problems and only manage small litters.

Boars

Boars reach puberty at about 6 months but are usually not worked until they are 7–8 months old. Don't overwork a young boar; four services a week is enough for him until he is a year old, then six times a week is sufficient.

A boar takes as much feeding as another sow would and for most of the year he just eats, but of course he is a vital part of pig rearing. If you have less than five sows, keeping a boar is not worth

Fig. 98 **Moving a pig backwards.**

while. Remember a boar is more aggressive than other pigs, and while he will respond to firm, kind treatment don't ever trust him. Don't let him run amongst other stock (a full grown boar will learn to help himself to a feed of mutton) and keep children away from him. Arrange his feed troughs so you can feed him without actually getting into his pen. Certainly scratch him behind the ears — but from the other side of the fence.

Borrowing a boar can have its hassles, too. Just be sure you are set up with a loading ramp near the pig pen. If you cannot entice a pig where you want it with food, try putting a bucket over its head and manoeuvring it backwards. (See Fig. 98.)

Boars will usually perform better on their own territory. If they just visit your pigs they may waste time establishing dominance in the new territory, so if you have one or two sows and can tell when they are in season it is probably better to take them to visit the boar. Artificial insemination is available for pigs, but you need to be trained in insemination technique. If there are commercial piggeries in your area, the owners or managers may be able to help out on that score.

Mating

This tends to be a relatively drawn-out affair with pigs. The boar will chase the sow around, nuzzling her, leaning on her, grinding and chomping his teeth and making other pig 'small talk'. When he eventually mounts it may be up to 25 minutes before he ejaculates (that is why sows need to be up to reasonable weight before being put to the boar). Pigs produce copious quantities of semen (about 500 ml) and usually one mating is sufficient. But keep a check on the sow 18 to 24 days after mating to check she is not recycling.

The pregnant sow

As with all farm animals the pregnant sow should be kept fit but not fat. The first month after mating is the most critical time. If she gets sick between about the 18th to 32nd day she may abort and come back in season. Reduce her rations slightly after mating and give her a lower energy diet so she does not gain too much fat. But keep her in good condition throughout the pregnancy.

Gestation period is normally 114 days but can

vary from 108 days to 122 days. Sows carrying litters of more than 11 piglets may drop them five days sooner than sows with average litters of nine to ten. Very small litters may be carried longer again. But 3 months, 3 weeks and 3 days is the age-old guide for pigs.

A week before you think she is due, transfer the sow to the pen or house where you want her to farrow so she has time to get used to it.

Farrowing quarters

Your ordinary pig run will do for farrowing, but breeding sows will be happier with some pasture and a nice little pig shelter in the paddock. Nail a piece of 100 mm wide timber across the bottom of the doorway to keep the newborn piglets inside and put a solid bit of timber across at least one wall, spaced about 200 mm above floor level and 450 mm out from the wall. The young piglets will be able to scuttle under this and keep out of mum's way but come out for feeding. This is known as a farrowing rail.

Farrowing

As gestation length can vary it is hard to know exactly when a pig will drop her babies, but likely signs are:
- Vulva swells and reddens about four days beforehand.
- Udder swells and may produce colostrum 24 hours beforehand.
- The sow becomes increasingly restless, getting up and lying down often.
- The sow will chew up bedding and make a nest

Berkshire sow and babies.

with it or paw at the ground if there is no bedding provided.
- Close to birth time she will begin breathing rapidly, up to 90 times a minute compared with 18 to 25 normally.

From a few days before her due date until the piglets are a couple of weeks old you should gradually shift the pig onto a more laxative diet. It will help milk flow and avoid constipation. Only feed lightly on the day you think she will do it. Give her a few armsful of short straw to make a nest with. Just toss it outside the house and she will drag it in and arrange it to her liking. Don't use hay, as the piglets can get caught in it.

The number of piglets a sow can carry means they are born pretty small and their sausage shape makes them easier to pass than some long-legged farm creatures, so farrowing troubles are rare. If your sow is fit and well and not too old (best to cull after 4 years old) you should not have any trouble and not have to interfere.

If you happen to be around at birth time your main job will be to make sure each piglet finds its way from the birth canal to the milk bar. Piglets are usually trying to stand up within a minute of their birth, and are usually active within two minutes. Some may be apparently stillborn, but don't give up on them immediately. If they are chilled, dunk them in a warm bath and dry them off. Use a funnel to give them mouth-to-mouth resuscitation, putting the big end over the piglet's snout. Piglets may come out with quite long umbilical cords and the sow may chew these off close to the belly. But if she is preoccupied, once you are sure there is no more blood in the cord snip it off 40 to 50 mm from the belly and dunk it in iodine.

Once the sow starts farrowing, things usually go quite quickly and she may have bopped them all out, cleaned them and be feeding them in under an hour. But it can take up to eight hours. After the last piglet, the afterbirth should come away in 20 minutes to four hours.

Most pigs make lovely mothers, they flop down, grunt and call the kids to the teat. They can also be fiercely protective. But first-time farrowers might not want to have anything to do with their babies, growling and snapping at them. You will need to step in, remove the babies (they will be all right without a feed for a few hours). Scratch momma pig and make a fuss of her, rub her ears and give her lots of attention until she is lying down to lap it all up. Then put a couple of piglets on her, keep scratching her and if she stays quiet let the other piglets out for a feed too. Then pick them up and take them away again and repeat the process in a couple of hours. After a couple of times the sow should accept her brood.

If there are any real runts in the litter, hand-feed them. Warm cows' milk in a bottle is fine. But leave them with their mothers and litter mates, just giving them the extra bottle until they are big and strong enough to compete. Piglets establish a pecking order along the teat line. The biggest and strongest usually takes the teat nearest the sow's head; the other piglets get relegated further down the line. The same piglet will always feed from the same teat.

Keep the sow on a reasonably laxative diet until the piglets are about 2 weeks old and gradually increase her rations until she is on full feed (6 meal units for herself and 1 for each piglet) by the time they are about 2 weeks old. Some farmers use side cutters and clip the little needle teeth on the piglets so they don't cause the sow so much discomfort. There are eight to do on each piglet, two each side on the top and bottom jaws. Just clip the sharp tip off.

From a fortnight old start giving creep-feeding supplements to the piglets. Put down pellets, mash, or whatever you are using as grower rations, where the sow cannot reach it. Piglets are usually weaned at about 6–8 weeks. If you have been creep-feeding supplements from an early age they should not suffer any setback. To dry off the sow decrease her feed a couple of days before weaning then take the piglets right away, out of her sight and sound or else their squeals will keep her unhappy and in milk. Feed her bulkier and less nutritional feed until her udder has dried up, then let her go back onto normal rations.

Remating

Sows will usually come back into season three to five days after the piglets are weaned. How soon you try to get her back in pig will depend on how many litters you want a year. A good, well-fed pig should manage two litters comfortably.

Killing

If you are raising for home kill then slaughter porkers at about 3–4 months when they should be about 50 kg, but hold baconers for a few months more until they are 95–100 kg. Before killing keep the pig off feed for 12–24 hours but give it plenty of good clean water.

Kill the pig with a rifle bullet in the brain and 'stick it' immediately. Put the knife in just in front of the breastbone and angled back towards the pig at about 45 degrees. Force it down and back to a point about 15 cm below the breastbone. Twist it and cut back towards the head about 5 cm. This should sever the main branching arteries and veins without puncturing the chest cavity. The pig (though quite dead) may thrash around at this stage.

Scraping

Pigs are not skinned, but have to be scraped. For this you need an old bath or tub which you can put the carcass in and swish around in 65°C water for 5 minutes. This should loosen the hair so you can scrape it off. If you don't have a big enough tub you can baste hot water over the pig, but it takes longer.

Start with water about 65°C but keep the pig moving so the skin is not scalded. Keep testing the hair by pulling at it; if it starts to come scrape like mad. Don't use a knife. A blunt metal edge is better. Put the trotters right into hot water, too, and once the toenails have softened pull them right off. The head can be tricky — try scrubbing at it with a clean wire brush. When finished rinse with cold water.

Cutting up

To gut the pig, saw through the breastbone. Insert the gambrel by making a slit 3–5 cm above the foot on each hind leg. Don't cut above the hock or you will ruin good meat. Haul the pig to a comfortable working height. Cut off the head just behind the ears at the first joint of the spinal cord. Cut around the 'bung' or anus, but don't pierce the rectum. Pull it up a little and tie a bit of string around it to stop any dung falling out, then haul the pig up higher. Slit it open down the belly from between the hind legs to the cut you made while sticking it. It's a good idea to hold the knife in one hand and as soon as you have opened up a slit, put the forefinger of the other hand over the tip of the knife so that it doesn't pierce the gut. Cut through the pelvic bone and gently haul everything out. The liver and heart can be rescued, but carefully cut the gall bladder from the liver.

To avoid bone taint in the carcass you want it to cool right through to 4°C reasonably quickly, without freezing it. Cutting it in half down the backbone now and pulling out the leaf fat inside the ribcage can speed cooling.

Dressing

You can either arrange for your local butcher to dress and cure the meat or you can do it yourself. (See Fig. 99.) Start by sawing the pig in half. Next cut the shoulders off, cutting through between the third and fourth rib and through the backbone. Cut off the jowl (this goes into sausage meat) and remove the neckbone from the shoulder. Cut off the shank just above the knee joint. The shoulder can be cured whole, or cut by dividing it between the smallest point of the shoulder-blade bone to give a picnic shoulder (like a small ham) and the butt (the body side of the shoulder), which can be cured or boned out for pork pieces or sausage meat. Remove the hams (back legs) by sawing through at right angles to the backbone just in front of the H or pelvic bone. Cut the shanks off by sawing just below the hock.

This leaves you with just the middle bit of the backbone and ribs. The portion near the backbone is the loin. Separate it from the belly by cutting and chopping along a line about a third of the way from the backbone to the bottom of the belly. Cut the ribs out of the belly meat, square it up, cut out the mammary glands, then roll it up and tie it for curing.

There is a muscle inside the backbone near the end of the hind end of the loin. This is the tenderloin. Cut it out, trim off the fat and slice it up for tenderloin steaks. Cut up between each rib and through to the backbone to divide the loin into chops. If the pig is a porker you will just be interested in roasting the hind legs. But if you plan to cure them as hams remove the H bone and tidy the joint up by cutting off any loose bits of meat.

Curing

Only consider curing meat that was bled out and chilled properly. You can use either a dry or a brine cure.

Brine curing

Sweet pickle brine uses 3.6 kg of salt, 0.9 kg of sugar, 23 litres of boiled cooled water and possibly 50 g of saltpetre (potassium nitrate) which ensures the meat will not develop botulism bacteria. If you plan to freeze the cured meat, the threat of botulism is reduced so you don't need the saltpetre.

Put the meat in a good sized stone crock or new

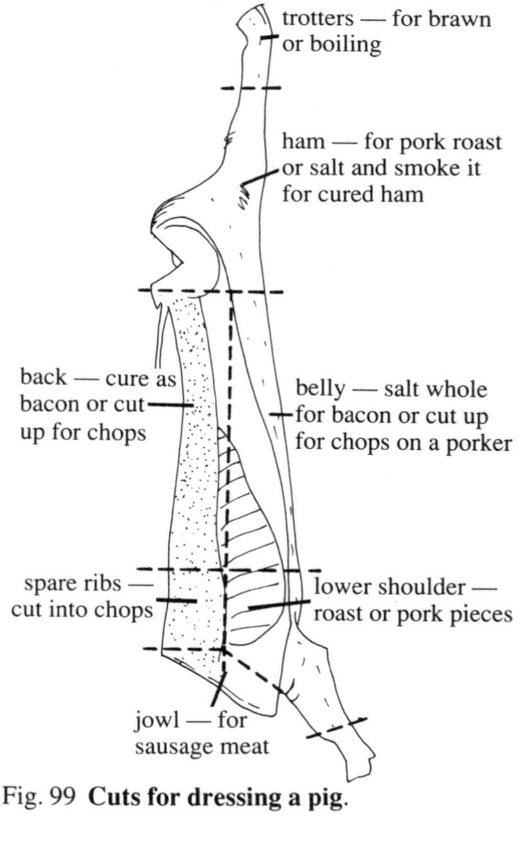

Fig. 99 **Cuts for dressing a pig.**

172

Pigs — friendly and good to eat.

plastic pail (not metal, as the brine will act on it). Pour the brine over the meat and keep it weighed down. (The above quantities should be enough for 45 kg of meat.) It takes about 9 days/kg of meat to cure, so a 6 kg ham will take about 54 days. Every week repack the meat so that it will cure evenly. Should the brine turn slimy at any stage lift the meat out, rinse it off thoroughly and make a new batch of brine. But make it proportionately weaker or the meat will be too salty. At the end of the curing period wash it in fresh water and hang it in a cool, dry place away from flies for a week. You can then eat it as is or smoke it.

Dry curing

Use 2.2 kg of brown sugar, 2.2. kg of non-iodised salt, 50 g of saltpetre, 50 g of cayenne and 50 g of black pepper. Mix it all together and thoroughly rub over the meat. Work it well in, especially around the bones or holes where bones were cut out. Success lies in getting the salt into the meat quickly and thoroughly before the bacteria get there. Keep the meat in the fridge during the process, but don't freeze it. Rub the salt in again next day and repeat every day for a week. Then leave it a week and haul it out and repeat once again. This time repack the meat in a box or crock with drain holes and leave it undisturbed for six weeks. Then take the joints out, scrub them lightly in warm water to take off the excess salt, hang them up for a fortnight somewhere cool and use as is or smoke it.

Hints for smoking

Use a hardwood, not pine. The English have always used oak, the Americans hickory and I guess out here manuka would be hard to beat. Don't cook the meat — it must be far enough up the chimney to ensure the smoke is below 50°C. Cold-smoked meat like this will keep longer than hot-smoked. For bacon that will be stored in the freezer, smoke for 12 hours, otherwise for at least 48 hours.

When cooking home-cured bacon, fry it slowly or it will turn black. Bought bacon contains a special sweetener to prevent this happening.

Problems

A healthy pig will have a round bright eye, with no mucus or weep. The snout should be moist, clean and shiny. The inside of the ears should be clean and warm. The tail should be curled up gaily. Pig dung should be cylindrical pellets, fairly fibrous and a blue-grey to brown colour. Any sign of mucus or blood in the dung suggests something amiss.

Aujesky's disease

Otherwise known as 'mad itch', this is an acute viral infection caused by a herpes virus (it does not affect humans). Most infected pigs show no obvious signs of the disease, but pigs which come into contact for the first time may sneeze, cough, have a fever, tremble, lack co-ordination, go into convulsions, then a coma, and die in 2-7 days. Older pigs show no signs, though pregnant sows may have a bit of fever and abort ten days after contracting it.

Infected pigs shed the virus in their nasal secretions and under ideal conditions it can survive in the environment for up to three months. There is no treatment. The disease is usually controlled by testing pigs for it and killing off any reactors and isolating any piglets away from infected dams.

MAF are currently setting up an accreditation scheme listing clear herds. If you want to breed pigs it would pay to get your foundation stock either from a clear herd or have them tested. Also make sure any boar you bring in has been tested.

Clostridial diseases

Pigs are susceptible to tetanus (especially after castration), black disease, malignant oedema and, less often, to blackleg. Check with your vet which diseases are a problem in your area and vaccinate sows a couple of weeks before farrowing to give passive immunity to the piglets. If sows were not vaccinated then protect piglets especially against tetanus. (See 'Clostridial diseases' in sheep, page 91.)

Dysentery

Diarrhoea in pigs is usually nutritional and should clear up in a couple of days. Maybe you changed their food too suddenly or they ate too much at one time — any of the things which would give your own tummy a hard time. Stressed pigs can also scour. If you have just got new pigs it is better to underfeed them for a few days (try to feed them on whatever they are used to getting and shift them gradually onto a new diet).

Infectious swine dysentery is more serious. The pig may not feed. It may be dirty down the back legs, there may be signs of blood or mucus in the dung, and fever. The pig may be feverish and dehydrated and will get weak, stagger and die without treatment. Make sure the pig has clean water available and seek your vet's advice. Avoid outbreaks by keeping pig quarters clean.

Internal parasites

Management practices can go a long way to keeping worms in check. For pigs in confined quarters, muck out and hose down the sty and yard at least once a week (more often if the weather is wet and dung is getting tramped throughout the quarters). Regular hosing out like this will remove worm eggs before they get to the infective stage.

Prevent sows from infecting their piglets. Drench a pregnant sow about a month before she is due to farrow. If she had access to ground and wallow spots, wash her sides and udder before transferring her to clean farrowing quarters. After farrowing keep the quarters hosed out regularly and once the piglets are a fortnight old transfer them and the sow to clean pasture. Paddocks used for one crop of pigs should be hard grazed by another class of stock and then well spelled before a new litter is let loose there.

Most sheep drenches are effective against pigs' internal parasites. Check the label for dose rates, and if pigs aren't mentioned check with your vet to be sure the drench is safe for use with pigs. Milk-fed pigs are reported to have a higher resistance to worms, possibly as the high lactic acid content of the milk leads to the worms being voided.

Leptospirosis

Pigs are readily infected by wallowing in areas contaminated with urine, either from other infected pigs or infected cows. Note that leptospirosis can cause very serious illness in humans. In pigs pregnant stock may abort or produce dead piglets, but there are often no symptoms in non-pregnant pigs. Control leptospirosis by vaccinating your cows and pigs. Keep the sty clean, dry and hygienic. Pigs can be tested for the disease before you buy them in and this may be worth while especially if you are going to breed them.

Lice and mites

Pig lice grow up to 6 mm long. They spend their entire lifecycle on the pig, but will easily transfer from one pig to another. Mites can also be an irritation as the females burrow into the pig's skin to lay their eggs. Cover the pig with lice powder, paying special attention to behind and inside the ears and between the legs. Repeat the powdering in a fortnight's time to catch any newly hatched lice. Scrub and disinfect your pig houses well between pig litters. If drenching for worms with Ivomec you may find lice no longer a problem.

Oedema

This is usually a disease of pigs kept under good husbandry but seldom affects those allowed free pasture range. The symptoms come on suddenly in the best, fastest-growing pigs. At first they will stagger, lie about and gradually slip into a coma and die. They may scour and walk in circles. It is caused by a toxin produced by E.col bacteria.

Wide spectrum antibiotics may clear up some cases, but death is usual and the disease seems to run its course in a group of pigs within four days. It does appear to be stress related so avoid sudden changes, competition for food and ensure pigs get their quota of rest.

Pneumonia

Pigs can be affected by pneumonia or a pleurisy-peritonitis complex which may have several organisms combining to cause the problem. Outbreaks are usually initiated by stress or draughts. Affected pigs will breathe extra fast, may cough, will appear dull and lose their appetite. Keep them warm and dry and seek your vet's advice on a suitable course of antibiotics. Avoid outbreaks by making sure pig quarters are well ventilated but not draughty, that pigs are not overcrowded and kept free of internal parasites.

Poisoning

Check Appendix D for some of New Zealand's more poisonous plants and make sure there are none growing where your pigs range. Avoid using old demolition timber to build your pig sty if it contains lead-based paints. Don't feed old pickling brine or you can cause salt poisoning. Arsenic is used sometimes as medication to clear up dysentery and you can cause poisoning by over medicating. Get a vet's advice for clearing up dysentery and follow it closely. Green spuds contain toxic alkaloids. Always cook spuds before feeding them to pigs and don't feed them raw potato peelings as the toxin is concentrated in the skins.

Skin troubles

White-skinned pigs are susceptible to sunburn so ensure they have adequate shade in summer. Pigs can go scurfy and have red itchy rashes. This is usually due to poor feeding, especially if pigs are living on garbage. Make sure they get ample green stuff and experiment with different foods in case the rash is from an allergy.

Ringworm outbreaks may occur as reddish round rings of scabby skin caused by growth of mould in the skin tissue. Scrub off all the scabs and scales and rub on strong tincture ofiodine.

Parakeratosis is a skin condition caused by zinc deficiency and may occur in pigs on a high calcium diet, for example milk and bone meal. The calcium seems to accelerate zinc metabolism. The signs are scabby, crusty skin usually behind the ears and on the back of the thighs. See your vet for advice on zinc supplements.

Swine erysipelas

Erysipelas means red skin and this disease produces reddish blotches on the pig. Later it will develop a temperature, may vomit and have diarrhoea and pant. The disease is widespread in New Zealand and is more likely to occur in hot, humid conditions or where animals have their resistance lowered during cold or wet or through parasite infection. It usually affects the fattest pigs and the germs responsible can live for years in the soil. Pigs can be immunised against it after 6 weeks of age; better still, vaccinate pregnant sows 4–6 weeks before farrowing and give the piglets a booster at 9–12 weeks.

Tuberculosis

The incidence of TB will depend on whether pigs can come in contact with TB either through drinking milk from infected cows or grazing ground cows, possums or deer may have infected. TB spreads from pig to pig. Some will show no symptoms and only show lesions once they are slaughtered. Others may be poorly and scour, and boars may have swollen testicles. Control TB by ensuring feed comes from TB-free sources and slaughter any infected stock. Your vet can test stock for TB.

15. Bees

Honey-snap biscuits, honey mead, the health giving and antiseptic qualities of honey and bees-wax candles are all good reasons for keeping bees. Then there is the importance of bees as pollinators of garden, orchard or crop.

There are many agents which will do the job of pollination but none do it as well as bees which will work a range of plants, but stick to one species on any one trip. Bees take up little space and apart from the initial capital costs of getting set up, should not cost much to keep.

The number one put-off for most people is bee stings. One fact is sure, and that is that if you keep bees you will at some time get stung. Bees mean more work around the place and they do take time. They must be visited regularly and maintenance has to be done at the right times of the year. Some of the work can be heavy.

Getting set up for bees is expensive if you have to buy everything in. Keeping bees is so different from other types of farming they add a whole new dimension of learning. But they have such a fascinating social organisation that your research will never be hard work.

Breeds

The bee species (*Apis mellifera*) has many varieties. The light-coloured bees include the Italian bees which are best suited to New Zealand conditions. These are a golden colour with three to five yellow or leather-coloured bands. They are usually quiet and good natured, hard workers, gentle to handle but still good at defending their

hive. Other light-coloured bees include the Cyprian (from Cyprus), the Egyptian, the Syrian and the Holy Land bees from Israel.

Dark varieties include the German or black bees which are basically black with inconspicuous bands of grey hairs. They are fairly excitable. Carniolans are native to Yugoslavia. They are better tempered than German bees and a bit bigger. Caucasian bees look like German bees, but have more marked bands of grey on them. They tend to be gentle but swarm freely.

The bees you are most likely to come across in the bush will probably be hybrids, a mix of black and Italian stock. They are easily irritated. Bees can be selected for desirable qualities the same as you would select any other farm producer from sources known as well mannered and productive.

Bee talk

- Apiary. The place where a number of hives of bees are kept.
- Brood. The unhatched bees that are still larvae in various stages of growth living in cells in the combs in the brood chamber.
- Brood chamber. The lowest section of the hive where the queen lives surrounded by her workers and where she lays eggs.
- Cells. These are the tiny individual six-sided compartments in the honey comb. There are usually about 19 cells to 10 cm. They may be filled with either brood or honey. Drone cells are slightly bigger than worker or honey cells.
- Colony. The inhabitants of one complete hive, including the queen bee, her workers and some

drones. Total population in a colony may vary from 15,000 to 60,000 bees.

- Comb. The intricate structure made by bees out of the wax they secrete; hexagonal cells ready to be filled with brood or honey.
- Drone. The male bee. He is slightly bigger than the infertile female workers but smaller than the queen. The drones are reared at the start of the swarm season and exist solely to mate with any new queen that may develop. The drones have no sting, pollen baskets or wax glands. They are only tolerated if they are needed for mating. At the end of the honey flow they are starved and eventually driven from the hive.
- Escape board. This is a flat board that is placed between the brood chamber and the honey supers. It includes a small metal trapdoor which only works one way to let bees out of the super but not back in. (See Fig. 100.)

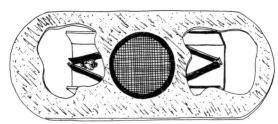

cut away sections show one-way traps

Fig. 100 **Double-end Porter bee escape**.

- Excluder. This is a flat frame grid with holes or spacings just large enough (4.14 mm) to allow the small worker bees to pass but not the larger queen.
- Extractor. The device used to spin honey out from the comb.
- Foundation. These are flat sheets of pure beeswax rolled out by a machine and bear the imprint of the cells built naturally by the bees.
- Frame. Made up of four narrow strips of wood which hold the foundation or comb. They hang in the super and can be removed separately so each comb can be inspected.
- Nucleus. A small basic colony of bees from 500–1000 plus their queen and a few drones.
- Propolis. The tree resin bees gather which they use to glue up cracks and stop draughts in the hive.

- Queen. There is usually only one queen in a colony and her sole function is to lay eggs. After hatching she leaves the hive to mate once and returns and starts laying up to 3000 eggs a day. She can live seven or eight seasons but is most productive in the first two.
- Section. The honey-in-the-comb you buy is section honey.
- Smoker. A tin can puffing unit loaded with an old rotten bit of sacking or dry pine needles. This is burnt to make smoke which will calm the bees and discourage them from attacking the beekeeper.
- Super. These are the boxes of the hive which hold the frames. As the colony builds up its honey store, the beekeeper adds more supers.
- Swarm. What happens when some of the bees in the colony decide it is time to move on and find a new home.
- Veil. The flimsy bit of netting which hangs around the beekeeper's hat and keeps the face free of stings.
- Worker. These are the infertile females who run the hive. They start adult life as cell cleaners, learn to nurse the larvae, clean the hive, evaporate nectar, build comb, act as hive guards, then are promoted to field duties, collecting nectar, pollen, propolis and water. They usually live only six to eight weeks when busy but up to several months if they emerge before the winter. From the female eggs laid by the queen, the workers themselves decide if they will raise the larvae as a queen or a worker. Those to be queens are fed Royal Jelly from the workers' own glands (bee milk). On this rich diet the female larva develops functional sexual organs and emerges in 16 days (21 days for a worker, 24 days for a drone).

Equipment

Bee suit

A beginner would be advised to get or make a bee suit. The veil is usually black mesh. You can make a band of this and attach it around a hat but make sure it hangs well down your chest so you can pull it firmly down over your shoulders and tie it around your upper chest. Bees tend to climb up, so the bottom edge of clothing must be secured. A boiler suit or full-length sleeved overalls will suffice for a suit. If you wear gloves choose ones that are well fitting.

A smoker

Basically it is like a tin can with a pouring spout and a small set of bellows. (See Fig. 101.) These blast air into the bottom of the can which feeds the smouldering fuel and pushes smoke up out the spout.

The hive

Buy your first hive made up or as a kitset. If you are good at woodwork, once you have one hive you can possibly use it as a pattern for making extra supers and frames as your bee colony expands. But the measurements have to be very precise to give bees their proper 'bee space' and make sure the hive seals properly.

Starting from the bottom, the basic hive (see Fig. 102) consists of a base and floorboard. On top of this is the brood chamber box, with ten frames. On top of the brood chamber is the flat queen excluder to keep the queen down in the brood departments. Then come your honey supers. These boxes are basically the same as for the brood chamber. On top of the supers is an inner cover and then finally a waterproof hive lid.

Starting out

There are three main ways of getting into bees:
1. Buy an established hive from a neighbouring beekeeper. That should come complete with all the necessary furniture, bees, beecombs and honey stores.
2. Buy a nucleus colony from a reliable beekeeper and transfer that into a standard prepared hive.
3. Catch a swarm during summer and put it into an empty hive.

If you are lucky enough to find a beekeeper willing to sell a complete hive then check the bees are healthy. Be sure the vendor has a permit to move those bees. The Apiaries Act 1969 makes it an offence to move hives more than 200 m without a permit from the local MAF inspector. Buy a

Fig. 101 **Beekeeper's smoker**.

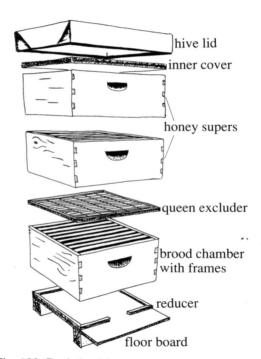

Fig. 102 **Basic beehive**.

complete hive early in the season and check the bees have enough honey stocks to carry them through to the main honey flow.

Probably the best plan for the beginner is to buy a nucleus colony of a good strain of disease-free Italian bees from a reliable breeder. Pop three or four combs from a strong colony with their brood, stores and adhering bees into a small hive box for the journey.

Once your nucleus of bees arrive let them settle down in a cool, dark, airy space for an hour or so, then puff a little smoke over them and transfer all the combs and bees at once into the new hive. Then sit the queen's cage between the combs (if she travelled separately) and release her. Fill a feeder with sugar syrup (see 'Feeding'). Close off the hive opening to about 5 cm until the colony has built up in numbers. The best time to buy a nucleus colony is September/October. The weather needs to be warm and you should wait until there is a good nectar flow or you will need to keep feeding the bees artificially.

The final option of catching a swarm is a pretty exciting way to start with bees. As with buying a nucleus you will need to have a hive prepared. After a bit of a flight, swarming bees usually group in a cluster. The ideal is if they all hang together off a branch. You can go along, put a box under the branch, snip it off, and plop! The bees fall in. If they aren't so conveniently parked you may try gently sweeping them into the box. It is best to wait until the evening to try this trick, for they are less likely to take flight again.

Leave the bees in your box somewhere cool and airy for a while and once they have settled down and formed a cluster inside you can then transfer them to the prepared hive. Just a bottom brood chamber with frames of comb (if you have it) or comb foundation will do. Put a clean sack down in front of the hive and dump the bees out onto it as close to the entrance as possible. They should begin to troop in. If they don't, sweep a few bees in gently and they should call their mates to follow.

Feeding

Unless the nectar flow is well underway your new bees will need feeding as they won't have honey stores yet. Find a reasonably sized tin that has a push-on sealing tin lid (such as a big Maltexo can left from homebrew making), and make a number of small holes in the lid. Fill the tin with honey or syrup (see following), put the lid on firmly and sit it in the hive upside down. Put some sacks or hive

mats over the top of the brood frames to stop heat escaping from the hive, and make a hole in them big enough for the bees to get access to the feeder but not beyond it. Put a spare super box on top of the hive to make room for the feeder.

Another type of feeder is the division feeder which can be made of thin plywood or metal to exactly the same dimensions as the brood frames but shaped as a long, narrow, deep tank which you fill with syrup. (See Fig. 103.) This can be put right into the brood chamber next to the bees. Put some sticks, or brush, down into the honey so bees can climb out and don't drown.

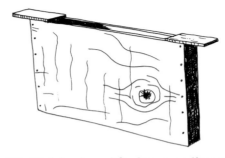

Fig. 103 **Division board feeder same dimensions as frames**.

Syrup

In spring the best syrup to use is made of equal parts sugar and water. It should be given regularly to the bees, about twice a week until they are able to maintain themselves from natural sources. Feeding syrup in spring can stimulate brood rearing so don't overdo it unless the natural sources of nectar are about to come on stream.

Some beekeepers feed bees in autumn, too, if the bees have not built up sufficient stocks to get them through to the following spring. At this time of year feed a thicker syrup, about 2 parts sugar to 1 part of water. Use either white sugar or raw sugar. But don't use brown sugar or molasses as these can lead to dysentery and disease problems.

Making foundation

Eventually, if the bees are doing what they are meant to, you will need to provide them with extra supers full of frames of foundation. You can buy these but it is best to learn to make up your own. If left to their own devices, bees will build their own combs completely. You can help by providing sheets of foundation which will be the backbone of the comb structure. The bees just have to go on and draw the cells out from the foundation until they are deep enough to store honey or brood.

If you have bought kitset frames they should have three or four holes drilled in each end for wiring. The soft foundation sheets need to be wired into the frame or else they may warp or, worse, fall out of the frame once it is heavy with honey. A well made comb may be used for several years.

Wire the frames up (see Fig. 104) so there are three or four parallel lines of wire running the length of the frame. If you can, put some weight on the ends of the frames while wiring up so they bend inward slightly. Once the wires are tied off and the ends allowed to spring back the wires will be stretched taut.

Fig. 104 **Wired Hoffman frame ready for positioning foundation**.

Foundation sheets usually come cut to size. Make sure you order for your type of frame. The next job is to fit the foundation into the frame. Lay it down on the wires so it can slide into the groove on the top bar. Melt some beeswax and, using a teaspoon, dribble the hot wax onto the bar along its length so it binds both the bar and the foundation securely into the groove. Don't worry about the other edges. Next you need to imbed those wires into the foundation sheet or they will get in the bees' way and they will build irregular combs. For this you need a small tool known as a spur wire embedder or some means of heating those wires so they just melt into the foundation. Store your made-up frames and foundation in a spare super box until they are needed.

Managing bees

Look at your duties as a beekeeper by the season.

Spring

Once temperatures start to rise the hive should be checked to see it has enough stores to get through to the honey flow. Generally don't check the hive before September and the air temperature is above 14°C. On the first check look at the brood frames for diseases and clean up the hive, sweeping out any debris on the floor. But checking the honey stores is the most important activity at this time. An average colony will need three good frames to get through spring to the nectar flow.

From September through to early November (depending a bit on your local climate and nectar sources) check the honey stores every fortnight. If you are just two days late with emergency rations of sugar syrup, many of the bees will die. If spring weather is really cold and nectar doesn't start flowing as usual, or windy, so the bees are reluctant to work, you may need to feed more than you'd normally expect.

By artificially feeding in spring you can also stimulate brood rearing. Don't start too soon or you will have lots of workers hatching with no nectar for them to collect.

Brood rearing should wind up and reach its peak by late November and early December. Don't feed more than bees can take up overnight. Feed it lukewarm late in the day and be careful not to spill it around the hive.

If your bees have had the use of more than two boxes over winter, try to arrange things so all the brood combs are in the lower two boxes. You can shift the frames around, but don't remove the combs of pollen which will be next to the brood. Put the pollen combs to the side of the box and fill in any gaps between the brood and pollen frames, with combs or foundation. Put seven or eight good combs of brood in the bottom box, and any other that have brood in the centre of the second chamber. Fill in the empty spaces in that box with empty comb for the queen to lay in. Any combs that were full of honey out of these two boxes can be put in a third super added to the top. This will encourage the bees up to that layer for storing honey once the nectar flow starts.

Summer

By November and early December the nectar flow should be under way and your bees busy. Now your job is to keep giving the bees space to work or they will get overcrowded and may swarm. Add space by putting on extra honey supers. Do it before the top super on the hive is filled up. The procedure is: take the part-filled top super off the hive, put the new one (loaded with frames) on the hive, and the part-filled one back on top. This way the bees pass through the new super to fill up the old one, so are used to it by the time it needs to be used.

Encourage the bees to draw out more combs now for later use by putting some foundation frames in amongst the super that they are currently filling. In a good nectar flow, the bees should draw those combs out overnight. Only put eight or nine in a super which would normally hold ten. This encourages bees to make good deep cells, making decapping easier at harvest time. Come late summer you may harvest your honey. Late February early March is a good time (depending on local nectar sources), and what the bees store after this time, should be left for their winter supplies.

To gather honey, remove the upper supers from the hive, place a bee escape board on top of the lower levels of supers and replace the honey supers. The escape board will let bees currently in amongst the honey get back down to the brood chambers, but will not let them back up. Next day you can remove the top supers and they should be free of bees.

Autumn

If you take most of the honey and don't leave the bees much for winter, then you need to feed them syrup, or if nectar is still flowing, they may be able to build up stores before the cold. Make sure the bees have time to 'ripen' it and cap it before winter, when they will need to cluster to keep warm. Certainly don't feed after May. Once again check the hive for disease, clean the floorboard

and unite any colonies of less than six frames.

At the end of autumn is the time to winter the bees down and ensure they have adequate feed to get through to next season's nectar flow. Give the hive two brood boxes. The bees will cluster on empty brood frames, so put these in the centre of the bottom box with pollen stores and honey on the outside and any remaining brood combs in the centre of the second box, with more honey on the side of them. Remove the queen excluder.

An average sized colony will need 16–20 kg of honey over winter. If you leave them with extra it won't be wasted, but if they run short they will starve. Generally that will be 7–9 full depth frames or 9–11 three-quarter depth frames. How much they need will depend on your climate and the availability of early nectar sources in the spring.

Make sure the hive lid is watertight. Close down the entrance to 5 cm and the hive should be all right from now until spring.

Winter

Bees don't hibernate in winter; they go into a semi-dormant state and still need to eat to stay warm. To help conserve heat the bees cluster around the queen on empty brood frames. Above 7°C the cluster will expand — below that it will contract. Bees on the outskirts of the cluster constantly change places with bees further in. If the hive was adequately prepared for winter, you should not need to open it. Certainly avoid doing so from May to July.

Manipulating the hive

There are two ways to help a weak colony. First, by putting a comb of emerging brood taken from another strong colony into the centre of the weak brood nest. Add an extra comb every 10 days until the weak hive is up to strength and there are enough nurse bees to keep pace with the queen's egg laying efforts. When making space for the extra brood don't remove the pollen combs on the side of the nest, just move them to the side.

Secondly, you can unite weak colonies. One strong hive will produce more than two weak ones. To unite them, put the brood chamber from one hive on top of the brood chamber of another hive with a sheet of newspaper in between. You should kill one of the queens. If you don't they will only fight and one will be killed anyway. The bees will get used to the sound of each other working through the paper and gradually gnaw it away. Leave the bees alone for at least a week before you adjust frames.

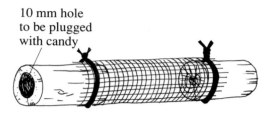

Fig. 105 Doolittle cage for introducing queen.

Introducing a new queen

Normally the bees themselves will determine when their queen is past it and kill her. But sometimes the beekeeper takes over this role of introducing new and better queens. Don't leave the colony without a queen for long or the bees will be even less likely to accept a newcomer.

The simplest method of introduction is to make a small cage known as a Doolittle cage out of two pieces of broom stick, one 25 mm long and one 75 mm long. Drill a 10 mm hole through the length of the longer piece and fill it up with candy (see following). Then cut a 100 mm long strip of wire gauze, wrap it around one plug, wire it up, pop the queen in, slide in the top plug and wire it up too. Pop the cage into the hive next to the brood. The bees will eventually release the queen themselves as they eat the candy. Meanwhile they'll be getting used to her presence. (See Fig. 105.)

Making candy

If you have fresh honey from a disease-free hive, heat it, but to no more than 60°C, then mix it with as much cold, powdered sugar as you can, until it will no longer stir. Put it on a board and knead as you would for bread and mix in powdered sugar until it is stiff enough to stand up. If you don't have honey use inverted sugar.

Increasing the number of hives

Only contemplate dividing up colonies if they are very strong and the nectar is in full flow. Take half the frames containing brood and their attendant bees from the present hive and transfer them to a new brood chamber. Put the old queen in with the new hive and lock the bees in it for a few days to make sure they can identify with their new home.

Introduce a new queen by the cage method to the original hive. If you don't have a new queen the bees will raise a queen cell, but these 'emergency' queens seldom do as well as the best queens. Take care of the two divided colonies as they will not be as strong as before.

Preventing swarming

Swarming usually only occurs if the bees are overcrowded, hungry, the queen is getting old, or if bad weather means field bees are kept in the hive and idle. There are numerous ways of preventing a swarm, such as squashing queen cells before they develop or clipping the queen's wings so she cannot fly off. But management is the best method of swarm prevention:

- Make sure your queen is young and of a good breed. Change her at least every second year and, if buying one, make sure she is from non-swarming strains.
- Use well constructed combs with worker-sized cells. If the cells are big the queen will lay drone eggs, and an overabundance of drones in the hive can cause swarming.
- Make sure there is plenty of brood comb space in the brood chamber for the queen to lay to her full capacity, but keep the brood area compact by shuffling frames, and have it ringed with supplies of honey and pollen.
- Add honey supers as they are needed before the existing honey supers are filled up.
- Keep the hive entrance open in the nectar flow so workers can enter easily and there is no congestion once they are working busily.
- If the bees still insist on making queen cells, destroy those cells. But bees busy on honey storage and with ample space should not be inclined to raise another queen.

Handling bees

Make sure your veil and suit are adequate so that you don't get hassled by stings. Make sure your smoker is going properly. Choose a warm sunny day and visit the hive between 10 am and 3 pm. Not only will a lot of field bees be out working but the propolis glueing the hive together will be soft and easier to break apart.

Use gradual, steady movements. Don't bump or jar the hive and don't flap at the bees. Be gentle but firm. If you start squashing bees they will tell all their buddies about it and call for support. The smoker frightens the bees into thinking the hive is being destroyed. They rush off and fill up their honey sacs from open cells in the hive and once full they are less likely to attack you. After puffing smoke into the hive, give the bees a couple of minutes to get some honey on board.

To examine a frame draw it gently sideways to clear it from the next comb. Use a hive tool or a screwdriver to steadily ease it away and raise it by the lugs at each end. Look at the side nearest you, then turn the frame over as you would a page in an upright book. Revert the frame to horizontal while you examine the other side. The reason for the care is to avoid the frustration of all that comb falling splat onto the ground or back into the hive. Don't hold the hive open longer than needed. Keep records of the hive history and what you do to it on each visit. Avoid encouraging robbing of the hive by other bees, keep the surrounds clean and never drop honey or syrup outside the hive.

The honey harvest

A cup of honey weighs 340 g, whereas a cup of sugar weighs about 200 g. That cup of honey contains about 260 g of sugar, so yes, a cup of honey is sweeter than a cup of sugar. Honey has considerable value not only as a sweetener but also for its antiseptic and hydroscopic qualities. (This means it can remove water from substances it is in contact with so it can act to dry out bacteria causing infection.) It also contains an enzyme which is an effective antibiotic. Of course honey is known as a great energy source; anybody feeling jaded will be picked up with a big glass of hot water containing a couple of teaspoons of honey.

Collecting honey

The beekeeper should only harvest what the bees don't need to get them through the winter. (See 'Summer' management, page 177, for how to collect the honey supers from the hive.) It is best to collect the supers in the evening, and do so quietly so as not to disturb the bees. Get those supers to somewhere bee-proof as quick as possible. Only collect honey that is properly ripe and in sealed-off cells.

Extracting honey

Because each cell of honey has a wax lid on it you cannot get the honey out until the lid is removed. For this you can get special heated 'decapping' knives, but a couple of big kitchen knives sitting in a tub of very hot water will do. Hold the frame up almost vertically and scrape the knife down over the caps, melting and slicing them off. Keep the wax scrapings for melting down into beeswax and swap your knives if they stop slicing the wax cleanly. (See Fig. 106.)

Fig. 106 **Decapping combs**.

The easiest way to extract honey is to use an extractor. This is a drum with an axle the length of it and two or three radial arms off the axle. The frame sits against the arms, you wind the handle and the frames are spun around and the honey hurled out against the walls of the can to settle at the bottom and be drawn off through a tap. (See Fig. 107.)

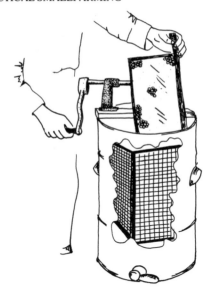

Fig. 107 **Cut away view of hand extractor.**

If your bees had not completely capped over the frames there will be a mix of ripe and unripe honey. To separate the two use a ripener. This may just be a large container with a tap on the bottom. It is a good idea to strain all the honey as it goes into the ripener. But let it dribble from the strainer to the side of the can — don't let it fall directly in or it will become aerated. Stand the ripener in a warm place for a few days and the thinner, unripe honey will come to the top. You can draw off the better quality honey through the tap at the bottom. The rest can be fed back to the bees.

Bottling
Because honey is hydroscopic (it draws water out of the atmosphere) it is important to bottle or seal it as soon as possible.

Used combs
After extracting honey you will be left with a lot of sticky combs. Take the extracted combs back to the hives in the evening and try not to disturb the bees. Put the combs inside the hive under the lid and in a day you will be able to come back and the bees will have cleaned them all up. Make sure the hive getting a comb is well sealed or it will be subject to attack by bees from other hives. Good, strong, well-made combs may be used for several

seasons. Combs that have held brood should not be used for honey next year as they will darken it. Save them for the brood chamber only.

Beeswax
Bees produce wax from glands on their abdomens. The wax comes out as small, brittle, pear-shaped scales which the bee takes and works to soften and mould to build up the comb. During warm weather and a good nectar flow bees can draw out a foundation to full depth overnight.

Each full-size comb contains about 100–150 g of wax; 500 g–1 kg of wax from the cappings of about 100 frames. This wax is worth saving. It may be sold and rendered down commercially or you can render it down yourself by melting it in a pot of water. The wax will met at about 63–66°C and because its specific gravity is less than water it will float and any impurities in the wax will fall out. Use soft rainwater for this job. Once the wax has melted, press a fine strainer down into it while it is still on top of the water and scoop off the liquid wax. Sometimes it will need two treatments to remove all impurities. On the second session scoop the liquid wax into tins or moulds. Cool it slowly or it will crack.

Even if you only get a little wax, don't waste it. It took a lot of bee sweat to make and a little bit added to it each year means you will eventually get enough to do something with.

You can make your own floor wax using 25 g of beeswax, 300 ml turpentine and 125 ml alcohol. Melt the wax and add the other ingredients so it is like a thick paste. Store in a sealed container. Furniture polish uses 600 ml linseed oil, 1.2 litres of turpentine and 60 g of beeswax. Melt the wax in warmed linseed oil and mix in the turpentine.

Pollen
Pollen is the bees' main source of protein. It is a highly nutritious food, rich in proteins, nitrogen, sulphur, phosphorus, carbohydrates and Vitamins A, C, D, E, M, B^1, B^3, B^6 and B^{12}, many of the trace elements, several sugars and valuable enzymes.

If your bees are having a good season, you can

get in on their bounty by 'trapping' the pollen as they bring it back to the hive. They get covered in pollen from the flower, usually while gathering nectar. They carefully scoop the pollen off their bodies and put it in the pollen baskets on their hind legs so by the time they get back to the hive they have little bobbles of pollen on their hind legs. The pollen trap of fine mesh lets the bees into the hive but is small enough to scrape much of the pollen off as they squeeze through. It then falls into a tray and you collect it later. Try a spoonful on your weetbix or just eat it straight from the jar.

Propolis

The last product from the hive is propolis. This is a type of resinous material which the bees collect from buds and joints of trees and use to block up gaps, glue together loose parts of comb and generally make the hive draught free and secure against invaders. Nowadays it is mostly a nuisance to the beekeeper as it glues supers and frames together so firmly it is hard to shift them without jarring the hive. But it has some value as an antiseptic and is a home remedy for cuts and burns.

Bees for pollination

If you are more interested in growing things than in collecting honey you may still find it worth keeping bees (or getting an obliging beekeeper to keep them for you) in your orchard, garden or crop. Table 23 shows the recommended hive population for effective pollination.

Problems

Bees will die from excessive cold, though they usually starve before they freeze. Make sure their hive is weatherproof and that they have adequate food to keep them warm over winter. Besides cold, they can die from overheating. In summer be sure the hive is adequately ventilated and that the bees have a nearby source of clean water.

Brood disease

Let's first consider what the brood should be like. Healthy larvae are a moist glistening white. Once capped with wax they will gradually begin to get adult colours. The eyes change first, from white to pink then dark brown and black.

In American brood disease the larvae collapse and lie along the bottom of the cell. At first the dead are slightly viscous, then become 'ropey'. You can test for this by poking a toothpick into the dead matter and if, as you withdraw the stick, a string of the contents comes out, you have American foulbrood. The capped pupae decay the same way. If you suspect the disease send a specimen of the brood comb to your nearest apiary inspector.

Infected swarms, honey or hive furniture can spread the disease. Likewise, robber bees which attack the weakened hive can catch it and take it home to their own brood. Make sure, if transferring any bees or buying in any stock, that the donor hives are disease free.

To clear American foulbrood you must burn all

Crop	Hives/ha	Crop	Hives/ha
Apple	1–2	Avocado	5–6
Blackberry	2	Blueberry	2
Black currant	3–5	Boysenberry	2
Brassicas	1	Cherry	0.5
Clover (Red)	3–5	Clover (White)	0.3
Kiwifruit	8	Lucerne	3–5
Peaches	0.5	Pear	0.5
Plum	0.5	Raspberry	1.5
Sunflower	1–2		

Table 23. **Recommended hive population for effective pollination.**

infected material. Block the hive entrance, then pour petrol or kerosene over the bees. Shut the lid and the fumes will suffocate the bees. When they are all dead, dig a good-sized hole, light a hot fire in it and burn the hive. Once the fire has burnt down, bury the ashes. Remember *all* honey and comb material is suspect. Don't keep any of it.

European foulbrood

So far this has not been diagnosed in New Zealand.

Sac brood

This is mildly infectious and usually occurs in spring. It is caused by a virus which kills larvae once they have been capped over. They turn a yellowish colour, then brown and black and finally end up as a dried mass on the bottom of the cell which is easily removed. The virus is only active for a month in infected honey or pollen. There is no specific treatment for sac brood, but replace any badly infected brood or comb. It may be as well to requeen with a vigorous queen so she can help the colony regain strength once the trouble clears as the season goes on.

Two hives should supply one household.

Dysentery

Usually this is caused by bees eating fermented or poor quality honey or eating lots in winter to stay warm because the hive is inadequately insulated. It appears as muddy, dark-coloured faeces dropped in and near the hives. It can be avoided if bees have clean, dry housing and plenty of good quality capped honey provisions.

Paralysis

This may occur any time in the honey season. Bees are unable to fly, may tremble, and have a distended abdomen and dark shiny body. Best treatment is to requeen with a good Italian queen.

Nosema disease

This is a type of internal parasite disease caused by a microscopic single-celled animal which drops infectious spores. Once the parasites enter the cells lining the stomach they can multiply rapidly, passing new spores out to infect others. The disease is most common in spring. The signs are a weakened colony for no apparent reason. There is no known cure but you can reduce the likelihood of it occurring by keeping the colony strong, giving good quality winter stores and keeping the surroundings and floorboards of the hive dry. If the colony has been infected, turn the soil around it and sprinkle with quick lime. A strong colony may well recover but a weak one may die out altogether. You can try treating it by adding an antibiotic, fumagillin, in your sugar syrup.

Wasps

Wasps will attack and kill bees and rob the hive. Unfortunately wasp colonies tend to be strong in autumn just as bee colonies are getting weaker at the end of the season. The wasps also work in more severe conditions. They start earlier and work later in the day than bees and will work in colder weather, so may attack a beehive when the bees are clustering against the cold and unable to guard the entrance.

In New Zealand there are both the German Wasp (*Vespula germanis*) and the common wasp

(*Vespula vulgaris*). The two are very similar. You can reduce the danger of wasp attacks by closing the hive entrance down over winter to about 5 cm or even smaller. Destroy wasp nests at night. If the nest is in a hole in the ground pour petrol into it and plug the top of the hole (don't light the petrol, as it is the fumes which will kill the wasps).

If the ground is dry and cracked use an insecticide such as Carbaryl or Sevin. Dust around the entrance after dark, using about 50 g. Don't plug the hole this time, and repeat the treatment after seven days to get any newly emerged young.

Wax moth

The moths lay their eggs in any small cracks or crevices in the hive. Once the larvae hatch they get into the hive and eat a diet of wax, pollen and the remains of brood rearing. They tunnel their way through the comb and enough of them can completely demolish it. To stop them getting into stored combs, make sure the store house is moth-proof. Render down all old combs before the moths find them and fumigate stored hives using carbon bisulphide. Put a couple of tablespoons of the liquid on a sponge in a saucer and stand that at the top of the stack of supers. Fit the hive lid tightly. The liquid turns into an evil-smelling gas on contact with air and will filter down through the supers. It is poisonous to people and quite explosive so use carefully.

Legal points

If you want to start with bees, the person selling or providing the hive or bees must have a permit to move them. Once you have the hives you must register them (even if it is only one hive). The registration forms are available at MAF offices. Beekeeping is restricted in the Bay of Plenty and the Coromandel and you need a special permit if contemplating having hives in those areas.

Obviously if your hives get any brood diseases you must notify your local apiary officer and send a sample of the brood for analysis. If you are going to sell your honey, this is covered under Food and Hygiene Regulations, Weights and Measures Act 1925 and Metrication Regulations 1978. Don't be afraid to check with MAF and get advice from your local apiary officer.

16. Small animals

Rabbits

Rabbits have definite advantages over other animals. A kick from a bunny is less fearsome than a kick from a horse, and furthermore you can eat the rabbit if it is too stroppy! You can farm rabbits for meat or for fibre. A good meat breed doe should be able to wean about 10 times her body weight in baby rabbits each year. The meat is white, tender, easily digested and lower in fat and higher in minerals than other meat.

Fibre-producing rabbits are catching on as one of the best ways to make money on a small block of land. Good rabbits can produce over 1 kg of fibre a year; good fibre was fetching $100–$120/kg at the time of writing. The Angora rabbit will produce 200–250 g/fibre/kg of bodyweight compared with only 50–70 g/kg for sheep. Also, Angora fibre is 99 per cent pure as it has little grease or contamination. By contrast, sheep's wool only yields about 70 to 80 per cent fibre.

But if you want to make a living from fibre-producing rabbits you are looking at considerable initial expense getting in breeding stock and setting up the rabbitry. If you want a fulltime job and respectable income from the rabbits you need about 400–500 of them, and that is a lot of little mouths to feed and water every day. Shearing has to be done every three months. It is a slow job and about as fiddly as sheep shearing is physical.

If you want rabbits for meat you must realise it takes about 3 kg of feed to produce 1 kg of meat.

Whatever sort of rabbits you keep they are a tie. Unlike sheep or cows which you can shift into a fresh paddock and forget about for a week or so, rabbits need daily care and attention.

And as a last word, while sheep and cattle automatically spread their manure, rabbits do it all in the rabbit shed, which means a mammoth clean-out a couple of times a year.

Breeds

Fibre

The Angora is the rabbit grown for its fine fibre (under 10 microns). Note that Angora rabbits produce Angora, while Angora goats produce mohair. These rabbits are now found worldwide, but there are three recognised types:

English Angora

This rabbit weighs 3 kg and produces 350–450 g of fibre a year. It is very fine fibre but tends to mat easily. There are 15 recognised colours.

French Angora

This rabbit weighs between 3.2–3.6 kg and produces 350–500 g of fibre a year. It is the coarsest of the Angora fibres and has a high ratio of guard hairs to undercoat. The French selected the breed especially for fashion garments where some guard hairs are valued.

German Angora

This rabbit is the most important breed for commercial fibre production. It is a bigger rabbit, weighing about 4.5 kg and produces twice as much fibre as either the English or French varieties. Good rabbits produce 1–1.5 kg a year. Purebred German stock are albinos and produce only white

The Angora rabbit, bred for its fibre.

A young New Zealand White rabbit.

Californian rabbits, bred for their meat.

fibre. It is mid-way between the English and French varieties for fibre fineness and ratio of guard hairs to underdown. About two guard hairs to five of down is the desired ratio.

Fur

Farming rabbits for fur has never really caught on, but the best-known species are the Large Blue and the Rex rabbit. Cross these with meat producing rabbits to get pelts worth curing. The Rex has a short velvety coat with no guard hairs or whiskers. It is a small rabbit weighing only 2.7–3.5 kg.

Meat

California

This is an attractive, short-haired white rabbit with black nose, ears and tail. The adult weighs about 4.5–5.5 kg. It is fine boned.

Flemish Giant

This is the biggest of the domestic breeds of rabbit. It originated in Belgium and weighs up to 6.8 kg but is heavily boned and has a heavy pelt so actual meat yield is not what its weight might suggest. It also takes longer to mature (so eats more) than the Californian or New Zealand White.

New Zealand White

This rabbit actually originates from Holland and used to be the Zeeland White. It is a good, meaty rabbit, usually albino with pink eyes. It is fairly big-boned, with bucks weighing 4–5 kg and does 4.5–5.5 kg.

Management

If you plan to keep rabbits for meat on a small scale for home use then work out how many times a week you would eat rabbit, thus how many that would mean a year, divide it by about 28 (a good doe should produce seven or eight babies a litter and four litters a year) and that is roughly how many does you will need. For the home kill operation only one buck should do, but if you keep more than ten does get a couple of bucks.

A small number of rabbits can be kept as a colony, all in one large run. It may be a movable ark with a netting floor, or a permanent run with netting walls that extend well down into the soil. Alternatively, keep the does in their own breeding

189

cages and the buck separate. Allow about 900 cm^2 for each 500 g of rabbit with 450 mm of head room so the bunny can sit up with its ears erect. If possible make the cages larger rather than smaller.

Breeding does also need a nest box. You can make this of untreated wood or ply (note that rabbits will chew on their boxes and could get poisoned if the wood was treated).

A box 300 x 600 mm and 300 mm high is about right for meat rabbits. Put a lid on it so the doe can sit on top of the box and cannot jump straight in and squash her babies. Make the entrance hole 150 mm above the floor of the box so the babies don't come out. Give each doe her own cage to avoid any fighting but the young can stay with the doe until weaning, when they should be ready for slaughter.

If you intend to run fibre rabbits, give yourself room to expand operations as returns allow — or launch into the venture whole hog to begin with and build a proper rabbitry.

The building

This must have good ventilation (one open side covered with wind cloth and ventilation louvres in the gables does the trick). The main problem for Angora rabbits with all that fluff is staying cool in summer, so make sure there is a good air flow through the shed and that the roof is well insulated against the summer sun. But at the same time the shed should not be too breezy.

Cold weather is only a problem to newly born or shorn rabbits. But don't make alterations to the shed for these. Just provide them with a bit of extra bedding.

Cages

House rabbits in individual cages, hung in rows from the ceiling of the shed. Use welded wire mesh (25 x 13 mm on the floor and 50 x 25 mm for the sides and roof). For woollers (rabbits kept just for their fibre) the individual cages should have a floor area of 770 x 450 mm and be 450 mm high. (See Fig. 108.) For breeding does and litters, the cages should be 900 x 600 mm and 450 mm

high, giving each animal a minimum space of 0.7 m^2.

The does also need a nest box of untreated wood or ply, 500 x 250 mm with walls 250 mm high and an opening 180 mm above the floor. Doors in the cage need to be big enough for the rabbits and nest box to be removed easily — about 330 x 420 mm will do. (See Fig. 109.)

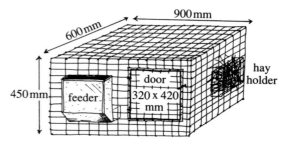

Fig. 108 **Rabbit cage**.

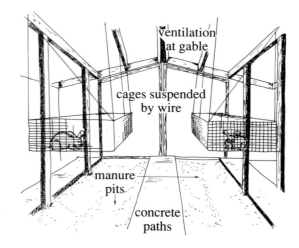

Fig. 109 **Inside a rabbit shed**.

Manure pits

If planning a proper rabbitry then install your cages in long rows with a concrete or shingle walkway giving access to each side of the cage rows. Dig pits 500 mm deep beneath the cages to catch all the droppings. A layer of coarse sand or shingle at the bottom of the pit will improve drainage. Just let the droppings fall in, scoop out any hay to stop the pit filling too fast and it should only need cleaning out once or twice a year. The manure is excellent for putting on the vegetable garden.

Feeding

Rabbits are vegetarians, but you cannot expect them to just live on lettuce or cabbage if you want them to grow high-protein meat or heaps of fibre. It would take about 23 kg of cabbage leaves a day to give the rabbit the protein it needs to put on weight efficiently and of course no rabbit could eat that much. So while rabbits will enjoy a few titbits from the garden and the odd tree pruning or carrot, don't feed them too much of it and make sure they get their concentrated protein rations first. It's a bit like being made to eat all your meat and veges before you were allowed pudding.

Meat rabbits

The aim is to get those young rabbits to slaughterable weights as quickly as possible, preferably by weaning at eight weeks. If you have to carry them on after weaning there will be a week or so when they don't gain weight as they adjust to life without mum, but all that time they will still be gobbling up your expensive feed.

You can grow some feeds yourself, but the easiest way is to dish out commercially prepared pellets which contain all the necessary minerals and vitamins. Dry does and bucks need a feed of about 12–15 per cent protein while pregnant does and does with litters need 16–20 per cent protein.

How much to feed varies from rabbit to rabbit as with people but as a guide:
- Give dry does 3.8 per cent of their bodyweight, for example 190 g for a 5 kg doe.
- Give bucks and young does reared for breeders 6.8 per cent of their bodyweight. A young 2 kg doe would get 130 g of feed.
- Give a pregnant doe or a doe with a litter as much as she wants. It will not be wasted and the kits will start sharing her hard feed from about 18 days old if it is always available.

Fibre rabbits

Feed is the single biggest cost in rabbit farming so the aim is to feed as little as possible while maintaining top fibre production levels. Table 24 is a guide only. If the rabbit appears to be putting on too much weight then cut back on those levels.

Type of rabbit	Intake (g/day)
Pregnant doe, day one to 21	115–125
Pregnant doe, day 21 to birth	150–170
Birth to weaning	Ad lib
Bucks working	110–140
Woollers	100–140

Table 24. **Feeding levels for fibre rabbits**.

Rabbits require some fibre in their diet as well, about 14 per cent, to keep their digestive systems working properly. This is most easily supplied with a handful of hay. Put it in a small hayrack on the side of the cage, *not* on the roof or it will fall in and contaminate the fleeces.

If you want to feed any titbits like cabbage leaves or carrots, do so on a regular basis. Don't suddenly introduce them or you may cause an outbreak of dysentery or bloat. Don't offer the rabbits any mouldy feed and don't leave food in the hopper for more than a couple of days as it

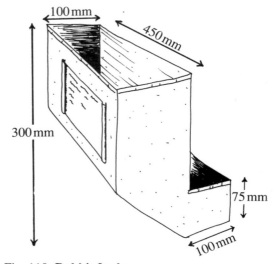

Fig. 110 **Rabbit feeder**.

goes stale. Rabbits should clean up all they are fed in 24 hours or you are feeding them too much. Feeding once a day is sufficient.

Rabbits are not ruminants like sheep or cattle so they cannot burp food back up and chew their cud to break food down further. But they are 'pseudo' ruminants. They produce two types of droppings, a hard pellet which drops through into the manure pit and a soft 'night' pellet (which they eat directly from the anus). It is not a sign of any perversion or deficiency but is a basic part of their digestive process.

If you are not on an automated feed system, the simplest method is to make a feeder box which attaches to the outside of the cage. A trough on the bottom portion slips through to where the rabbits can get to it. (See Fig. 110.)

Water

Water should be provided ad lib. Rabbits tend to knock containers over, and as it takes a long time to fill that many troughs, the best system is to run a water pipe along the line of cages and from that run an individual hose into each cage with a dew drop valve on the end. The rabbits soon learn to use the valve and can drink whenever they like. Always check hoses at the end of the line to make sure those rabbits are getting water too.

Breeding

Baby rabbits are born with their eyes closed.

Whether you are keeping meat or fibre rabbits you want good breeding does to produce a regular supply of weaners for the freezer, or a steady flow of replacement woollers so you can cull heavily and keep only the best animals.

Meat rabbits

A breed like the New Zealand White can be bred once a doe weighs about 3.6 kg. Don't leave her longer than that as a fat rabbit or one that is not bred regularly may be infertile.

Fibre rabbits

By 8 months old you will have had three clips off the does and thus some idea of their value as fibre producers so you can select for the best breeding stock. Does should weigh 3.4–3.8 kg before being mated.

The buck

Keep a ratio of about 1 buck to 10 does. Bucks are sexually mature from 4 months old but wait until they are 8 months before working them, when they should weigh 3.5–3.8 kg. Start them off with experienced does, but not bossy ones. He can be worked every other day while he is young and increased up to twice a day as he matures.

Mating

There is no particular breeding season or 'heat' in rabbits as the doe is developing and disintegrating egg cells in overlapping periods all the time. For best conception rates don't let does get fat or underfed. Don't breed them if they are moulting. Always take the doe to the buck's cage to reduce fighting over territory.

Mating is a quick affair. The buck mounts the doe from behind, grabs a mouthful of fur to steady himself and after ejaculation may scream and topple off the doe sideways. If the doe won't stand for the buck try presenting her to him late in the evening for a few days. If still no luck you can try holding her for him. Use one hand to hold the scruff of her neck and put the other under her belly, raising her back end slightly. The buck may not like your hand there and if still no joy, I'd suggest you keep that doe just as a wooller and breed from more co-operative animals.

Gestation is about 31 days in the rabbit. Within 14 days you should be able to palpate the doe's belly and feel a slight swelling about the size of a 10 cent piece. If she seems to be empty pop her back with the buck, but if she refuses to mate, give her the benefit of the doubt. Give the doe a nest box about five days before the offspring are due. Fill it up with hay and the doe will scratch it about to form a cosy nest.

Kindling

A doe will go off her feed a couple of days before birth and will start to pluck fibre from her body to line the nest and make it warm. Just before birth she may alternate plucking with lying panting in the cage. The first kit should appear soon after she begins licking her vulva. As each kit is born the doe will clean it and let it suckle. The doe may only feed kits once or twice a day, so if you do not see her with her babies don't panic — it doesn't mean she is a bad mother. Check the kits and if they appear rounded and full assume they are getting fed.

Kits are born blind and hairless. Remove any that are dead or deformed. If the doe has a very big litter (more than ten) it may be as well to take a couple off her and try to foster them onto another doe with a smaller litter.

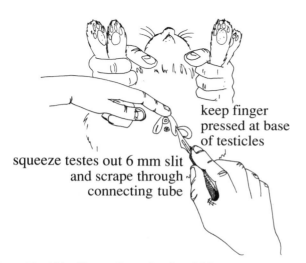

keep finger pressed at base of testicles

squeeze testes out 6 mm slit and scrape through connecting tube

Fig.111 Castrating a buck rabbit.

Kindling problems

If a doe goes over 32 days she may need to be induced. Check with your vet.

Maiden does may have their first litter out on the cage floor. Do not cull for this unless the doe repeats it at her next kindling. If the kits are cold when you find them, dunk them in a bowl of warm water, dry them off and stick them on an electric blanket turned to a low heat for a few hours. Then return them to the nest and cover them with Angora.

If a doe lacks milk or won't feed the kits, they will appear shrivelled and wrinkled. Try and foster the stronger ones on to another doe and stimulate milk production in the mother by feeding wholemeal bread and warm milk. If she consistently has poor milk production then cull her.

Remating

You can remate a doe as soon as the kits are born. This will ensure a steady flow of kits but may wear the doe out quickly. Better to wait until the kits are 4–8 weeks old before remating the dam. An eight-week interval fits in well with shearing for Angoras.

Shear the doe and cut her toenails and mate her one week later. The kits will be born four weeks and weaned 12 weeks later, when the doe will be ready for shearing again and can be remated. This system will give three litters a year.

The kits

By day 3 the kits will begin to grow hair. The eyes should open about day 11. By day 18 they will start to nibble at hard feed. Check new kits a couple of times a day to make sure they are being fed and also check the doe. Her milk glands should feel full and be slightly rounded. Any hardness or heat in the udder could mean mastitis.

Castrating bucks

Does produce the most fibre and castrated males are the next best. So unless you particularly want a young buck for breeding purposes it is best to castrate him. Leave it till the animal is 8 months old, as by then you will have had a few clips off each rabbit and can select the best as breeders.

To castrate, have one person hold the buck on

its back, gripping all four legs at once with the rear end towards whoever has the scalpel. Wash the genital area with a disinfectant, squeeze the testicles into the scrotum and put your fingers at the base of the sac to hold them there. Make a small, 6 mm incision with a scalpel in the end of each side of the sac, cutting through both layers of skin, then squeeze the testes out through the slit and scrape away the connecting tubes. It is better to scrape the tubes rather than just cut through them. (See Fig. 111.) Puff some antibiotic powder onto the wound and let the animal go. It should heal up quickly but keep an eye on it for a few days to be sure no infection sets in.

With meat rabbits being slaughtered at 8 weeks, there is no need to castrate the males as they will be in the freezer long before they are sexually mature.

Killing

If you are keeping rabbits for meat, don't make pets of the young ones. Look after your favourite does and give them names, but realise there will be a lot of young stock passing through and you cannot afford to get attached (or to let the children get attached) to the babies.

The best time to slaughter young rabbits is at 8

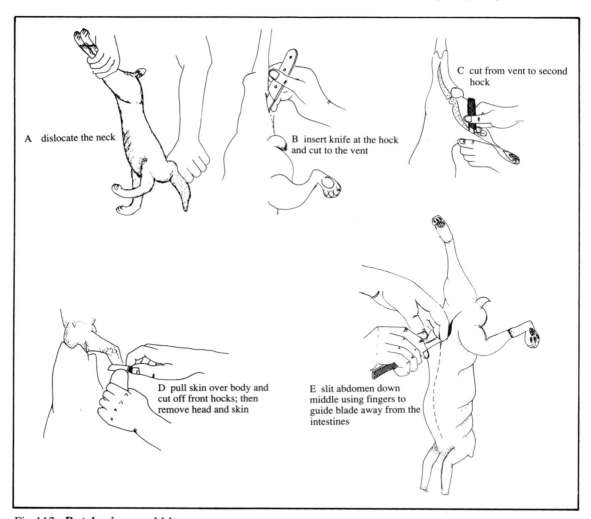

A   dislocate the neck

B   insert knife at the hock and cut to the vent

C   cut from vent to second hock

D   pull skin over body and cut off front hocks; then remove head and skin

E   slit abdomen down middle using fingers to guide blade away from the intestines

Fig.112 **Butchering a rabbit**.

weeks old, so they are taken straight from the mother and processed for the freezer. To kill a rabbit either hit it on the head with a hammer, just ahead of the ears, or dislocate the neck as you would for a chook. Hold the rabbit by the hind legs in one hand with its head hanging down, grab the head in the other hand and twist it backwards at the same time as you force your hand downwards to stretch and break the neck. (See Fig. 112.)

Skinning

Cut off the head to let the rabbit bleed out. Hang it by one hind leg on a small gambrel hook (a bit of wire between the tendons and bone in a hind leg will do). Use pruning secateurs to cut off the feet. Cut the skin around the hock of the suspended leg and slit it down to the groin and do the same for the other hind leg. Then peel the skin off the hind legs, cut it at the tail, and you should be able to pull the skin over the rabbit body as if pulling a glove off. If the head and forefeet have been removed the skin will come right off. Alternatively, pull as far up the neck as you can, remove the head and skin together and cut the skin from around the front hocks then cut off the front feet.

To gut the carcass make a slit in the centre of the abdomen near the groin. Put a couple of fingers into the slit to hold the tip of the knife so it cannot pierce the gut, then extend the slit down to the breastbone. Cut around the anus to loosen it, then pull all the guts out. You can save the liver, heart and kidneys, but carefully cut the gall bladder from the liver.

Either keep the carcass whole for roasting or joint it into six pieces. Make one cut behind the shoulder to chop off the forequarters, another cut in front of the hindquarters, then divide each portion in half down the backbone. Use the meat in any dish you would have used chicken for. But remember rabbit has a very delicate flavour so don't overpower it.

Skins

If you want skins for curing, it is best to leave your meat rabbits until they are 6 months old and slaughter them in winter when the coat will be densest. See Appendix C for curing recipes.

Fibre

Shearing is done every three months or 91 days. Kits can be shorn for the first time at 8–9 weeks old. If shearing is left too long the fibre may start to mat or to moult out. Use the electric clippers especially designed for the job. Scissors will do but they are slower and not so accurate. As a last resort you can pluck the rabbit though this is not feasible for a commercial operation. Plucking must be done when the rabbit is naturally starting to shed its fibre, initially at 12–14 weeks old, thereafter every 12 weeks. You can tell a rabbit is ready for plucking if you part the fibres and can see new growth at the base of the coat. In a coloured rabbit the new growth will be darker.

Shearing

Sit the rabbit on its backside or tie it to a miniature shearing table so it is stretched out flat and all four legs are tied down and it can be flipped over and either its back or belly attended to. (See Fig. 113.) Groom the animal first, combing out any dirt or hay.

- Start with a blow up each back leg to the centre of the back just above the tail. Hang on to the tail and make a pass up each side of it.
- Make a blow up the centre of the back from tail to between the ears.
- Make a series of blows angling from the backbone to the belly. Start on the hind leg then clear the ribs with parallel blows away from the backbone and finally down the front shoulder and leg.
- Clear the near side of the face.
- Turn the rabbit around so the other side is near you and repeat the blows down the unshorn side and face.
- Next face the front of the rabbit and clear the breast area and under the chin.
- Flip the rabbit over so it is belly side up. Check the number of teats.
- Clear the inside of the groin, going from each hock in to the belly. Make a run up each side of the belly from hind leg to front leg, then clear the inside of the front legs going from each hock in to the neck.

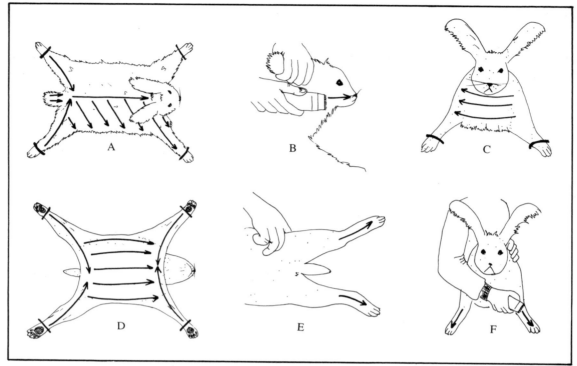

Fig.113 **Shearing Angora rabbits**.

- Now run the handpiece up the belly, making four or five parallel blows. On does lift it 10 mm off the skin so you don't nick the teats.
- Push the hind legs out straight and trim the back feet.
- Untie the rabbit and sit it up so you can run the handpiece over the tops of the front feet.

Don't make any second cuts. If you missed a bit leave it there for next time. Use your free hand to pull the skin back tight under the handpiece to avoid the comb digging in and cutting the rabbit. Pull the fibre clear as it is shorn and sort it as you go.

Grades

- First grade fibre should be clean, mat free and at least 60 mm long.
- Second grade is clean and mat free but under 60 mm.
- Third grade is clean, matted or second cut material.
- Fourth grade is any dirty fibre.

After shearing, clip the rabbit's claws. Weigh the bunny and its fibre and record both details. Give the rabbit a dose of endectocide, like Ivomec. One ml is enough to keep the rabbit free of mites and mange. If it is really cold (under 5°C) give the rabbit some extra bedding in a nest box but don't pamper it unnecessarily.

Store the fibre in cardboard cartons or paper bags with a few mothballs until you can get it to market. Don't keep it too long and don't store it in plastic as it will sweat.

Problems

A healthy rabbit should be bright eyed with a glossy, smooth coat and warm ears. Droppings should be moist but firm. The nose should be clean. Check inside the front legs for any dried mucus. The animals should be alert and interested in life. If they appear depressed or uninterested or if the coat is dull or rough then you have a problem. The following are the more common rabbit afflictions.

Coccidiosis

This is caused by a protozoal organism which lives in the young animal's gut. There are two types, liver and intestinal. If the liver is affected the rabbit is likely to die before you realise anything is wrong. If the intestines are infected the animal may scour. The disease is contagious and spread through droppings and dirty bedding. Most commercial rabbit feeds contain a coccidiostat so the disease is unlikely to be a problem if feeding pellets. But if stock are on home grown fodder, check with your vet for treatment which can be given in the drinking water.

Enteritis

A general term for stomach upsets. The rabbit may appear full and bloated. It may be depressed, possibly scouring, and its coat dull. The trouble may be nutritional, caused by the type of feed, for example too much green feed or a sudden change in diet. Take the rabbit off pellets and feed only hay and water until the faeces have firmed up. Feeding comfrey may help.

Fleas

Flea bites can cause rabbits to scratch and mat their coat. Dust affected animals with flea powder and clean out bedding regularly. Keep dogs and cats out of the rabbitry.

Furballs

These are caused by the rabbit licking itself and swallowing the fibres, which mat into a ball in the stomach and block the works, causing constipation. Prevent fur balls from forming by shearing the rabbits regularly. If a rabbit is constipated treat it twice a day with a teaspoon of vaseline mixed with molasses until its motions are back to normal.

Mastitis

Usually this only occurs in heavy milkers, especially if they produced a small litter and are not being milked out properly. The affected doe will have a swollen, tender udder and teats, and be reluctant to let the kits suckle. Treat her with antibiotics from your vet. If four or more teats are affected it is probably best to cull that doe. Be conscious of hygiene when handling affected does so you don't spread the infection to others. Don't foster young from an infected to a clean doe.

Mites

Rabbits catch ear and mange mites. Ear mites cause the rabbits to scratch at their ears with their hind feet. The ears may exude a brownish wax. With mange mites the rabbit scratches behind the neck and at the back of the head, and there may be dandruff-like flakes in the coat. The fur will become matted so control mites with a drench of 1 ml of Ivomec after each shearing.

Sore hocks

This is caused by rabbits living on rough cage bottoms. Keep the cages smooth, stop manure from building up on the wire, use correct gauge of mesh and regalvanise if the wires get worn and pitted. Rabbits affected will be reluctant to walk on their hind feet. They may have bald patches and sores on the hocks. Bathe the affected feet in warm water with a mild disinfectant solution and apply some soothing ointment like Ungvita or Rawleighs. Some meat breeds are more susceptible to sore hocks. It also appears to be hereditary so cull animals that are always afflicted.

Snuffles

The most common problem in large rabbitries, is caused by bacteria which normally live in the rabbit's nose without causing any harm. But if the rabbit is under stress from poor housing, draughts, noise or bad handling then snuffles can result. Affected animals will sneeze continuously, and have a thick white ooze from the nose. Prevent outbreaks with good housing and hygiene and handle animals at least once a week so they are used to you. Quarantine new stock for three weeks. You may try to treat affected animals with antibiotics from your vet but because snuffles is so contagious, culling is the best option.

Weepy eyes

This can be caused by the snuffles bacteria or by an ingrowing hair. Check the eye first. Pull the lower lid down and if you see an ingrowing hair tweak it out with a pair of tweezers. Smear Golden Eye ointment into the eye if it is inflamed. If you suspect snuffles is the cause, isolate the rabbit and if other snuffles symptoms develop, cull it.

Fitch

Good fitch fur presented for sale correctly can demand big prices on the world fur market. The possibility is there for big returns for fitch farmers. The animals do not take up a lot of space and are one way of converting old cull ewes and fish waste into worthwhile returns. They are intelligent little animals and can make responsive pets with good handling and management.

However, fur is essentially a fashion item and therefore subject to fluctuations in demand and price. This means returns can be variable from year to year so fitch farming is a long-term proposition, not something to get rich quick on. Considerable expertise is needed to give the fitch properly balanced diets and to prepare pelts correctly to get the best returns. It takes about 45 kg of feed to produce one pelt so it is an expensive process unless you have access to cheap meat and fish supplies. There is a big initial capital expense to set up a suitable shed, the cages and the fridges and freezers needed to store their food. Fitch are a tie as they have to be fed daily and handled regularly if they are to be kept quiet and easily manageable.

Breeds

For farming purposes there are two main varieties in New Zealand, the West Highland White and the Finnish. Whatever the variety, select for good, long pelts, a good colour contrast with whiter-than-white underfur and black-tipped guard fur. There should be a regular pattern of dark guard hairs around the shoulders and front legs, and a black line down the back. The underwool should be dense and even over the whole pelt. Breed up a line of similar coloured animals.

Management

Housing

If you are planning on just being a backyard fitch farmer and keeping about 30 for pocket money, then you may already have a building, such as a big barn or a lean-to on the shearing shed, that will suffice. If you plan to go fulltime into pelt production and make that your main income then you will be keeping about 400 animals and need a special building for them.

The main requirement is plenty of ventilation. An open-sided shed is best. Fitch don't mind the cold — it is heat they cannot tolerate. Check with your local authority about regulations covering the farming of animals intensively. Generally new buildings must be 20 m from boundaries and 100 m from existing houses. Put strong netting on the side walls to keep cats and dogs out.

Cages

These can be made of welded wire mesh of 25 mm x 25 mm squares. Cages for pelt animals should be at least 450 mm x 450 mm and 450 mm high. Whelping cages should be about 400 mm x 700 mm and 450 mm high. The whelping cage also needs a nest box attached to the side. (See Fig. 114.)

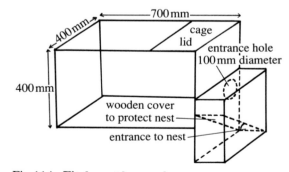

Fig.114 **Fitch nest box and cage**.

Feeding

Fitch are carnivores. Their digestive tract is short so food goes through them fast and absorption of nutrients is minimised. Formulating the right feed is very important as a lot of fitch diseases stem from mineral and vitamin deficiencies. Tables 25 to 28 are guides for formulating feed:

The main rule with feeding is to always supply fresh food. Store mince for up to five days in the fridge; any longer than that and it should be frozen. Don't hang carcasses — mince and freeze the meat straight away. Always freeze and thaw promptly.

Introduce new diets gradually. Add about 5 g salt/10 kg of food during lactation. Don't feed raw eggs as they can cause a biotin deficiency and if feeding whole poultry remove the eggs first. Sheep carcasses should be skinned before they are minced, but poultry do not need to be plucked. If using horsemeat, cut out any fat as it can go rancid quickly and affects the selenium and Vitamin E levels in the feed. If the meat is from a cooked source you may need to add B vitamins. Likewise if the fitch are on a predominantly fish diet they may need supplements of thiamine (Vitamin B[1]). Any cereals must be pre-cooked.

Dollop food on top of the cage for mature stock but put it in a dish inside the cage for young fitch. Make water available ad lib with a main water pipe running the length of the cages and feeder valves to each cage.

Handling

Regular handling will keep fitch quieter and easy to deal with. To pick a fitch up grip it from behind the head around the neck with the thumb and forefinger meeting under the jaw and other fingers around the chest behind the forelimbs.

Element	Dry rations (% min–max)	Wet rations — 60% moisture (% min–max)
Protein	40 +	16 +
Fat	15–40	6–16
Ash (from bone)	5–15	2–6
Non-fat energy and fibre	12–25	5–10
Calcium	1–1.2	0.4–0.5
Phosphorus	1	0.5
Salt	0.5–1	0.2–0.4
Vit E	250 mg/kg of feed	100 mg/kg of feed

Table 25. **Food elements for dry and wet rations.**

Feed stuff	% Dry matter	% Protein	% Fat	% Ash
Cull ewe	37	18	14	3.4
Boned mutton	25	15	9	1.8
Chicken (layers)	47	22	18	4
Chicken (heads, necks, pieces)	45	13	25	4
Beef boned	28	22	4	0.3
Beef liver	29	20	4	1
Fish (gurnard whole)	25	17	10	3
Fish (racks and heads)	20	14	2	4.8
Horse meat	26	20	4	1
Bones	65	20	15	29

Table 26. **Analysis of feed sources.**

Stage	% Fish	% Poultry	% Cereal	% Liver
Non-breeding stock	70	20	10	—
Breeding and gestation	50	30	15	5
Lactation and kit growth	55	30	10	5
Furring	55	30	10	5

Table 27. **Appropriate feed for various stages.**

Age in weeks	Male body weight (g)	Male food weight (g)	Female body weight (g)	Female food weight (g)
5	240	20	230	20
7	460	40	400	40
9	680	70	540	70
11	840	90	620	90
13	970	110	680	110
16	1100	130	740	110
22	1270	120	800	90
26	1350	100	840	90
30	1400	90	860	80

Table 28. **Appropriate feed quantities according to age and sex.**

Breeding

Female fitch are called jills, males are hobs. Fitch have a definite six months breeding season starting about September. They do not have a cycle like other animals. The oestrus in the female is continuous if not mated and shows as an obvious swelling of the vulva. It is important to mate females within a couple of weeks of them coming into oestrus as they are susceptible to uterine infections if left continuously in heat. Plan to mate stock in mid-September or early October, two weeks after the jill's vulva first swells. Kits from this initial mating will be born late in October or early November (gestation is 42 days), weaned at 6 weeks and the jill can be remated in November or December. The first litter will be ready for pelting the following June and the second litter in July/August.

In the male the breeding season shows as an enlargement of the testes which drop down into the scrotum but retract back into the body the rest of the year. Males from 6 months old should be able to serve two to three females a day.

Mating

In fitch this is a fairly drawn-out affair lasting anything from ten minutes to three hours. The female usually ovulates about 30 minutes after mating.

Single-sire mating enables the farmer to decide which males should be crossed with which females, thus controlling the direction of pelt selection. Simply take one female at a time to visit a particular hob and return her to her own cage after mating. Repeat for several days if necessary until mating has taken place. Don't leave the two together all the time.

Group mating makes allowance for fitch preferences but means the farmer is not sure just which hob got which jill in kit. The usual method is to keep three or four females in one cage and put one hob in with them. Every two or three days the hobs are swapped between groups of females.

About a week after mating examine the jill and if her vulva has shrunk down you can assume she is in kit and take the gestation as starting from about day 3 or 4 of mating.

Put the female in her whelping cage about three weeks before birth. Give her a nest box and half fill it with some soft hay or untreated wood shavings that she can arrange into a cosy nest. The young are about 50 mm long at birth and are born hairless and with their eyes shut. The usual litter is six to ten babies. Litters with less than four should be fostered on to another mother. The original dam will be ready to rebreed in 14 days. Also litters with more than ten should have the surplus fostered on to another mother with a smaller litter.

By 3–4 weeks old the kits will have their eyes open and the mother will start to take solid food into the nest for them. Put a false bottom in the cage and put feed out on that for the young fitch. Kits can be weaned at 6 weeks old and the stronger, good milking females rebred. An 8–10 g baby at birth should weigh 250 g at 5 weeks and 600 g at 10 weeks. You will have to carry them on for 160 to 210 days before they will be ready for slaughter with their fur at its prime.

Fitch do moult. The females usually moult midway through their pregnancy and the males once a year in April or May. The males usually moult their first adult coat at 6 to 7 months old.

Pelting

Fitch fur is prime for only a short three week period. Generally fitch born late in October will be ready for pelting the following June and any late or second litters born in December can be slaughtered in July or early August. Most farmers kill fitch using vehicle exhaust run into an airtight box of about 1 m³. Make sure the exhaust is cooled properly before it reaches the box. The alternative is to kill them with an injection, but carcasses from fitch killed this way must not be fed back to other fitch.

Skinning

- Lay the carcass on its back. Use a small sharp knife or scalpel to make a cut in the centre of a back foot pad, down the inside of the hind leg to a point about 25 mm on the belly side of the anus. Do the same with the other hind leg and join the two cuts up.
- Turn the fitch onto its belly and pull the skin a little way clear of the base of the tail exposing the stink glands (these are usually covered in fat). Cut the gland out taking care not to cut it.
- Pull the skin as far up the tail as it will go then cut the muscles around the tail bone and pull the tail right out.
- Next grip the carcass firmly or hook it down onto a skinning spike and pull the hide back over it as far as the front legs. Keep the skin stretched over the head and separate the skin from each leg as close to the feet as you can get.
- Cut around the skin on each foot, leaving just a little bit to cover the foot.
- Continue to pull the pelt towards the head. When it stops at the ears make a little cut on

Young fitch are best fed on a saucer or board.

the back of the head so the skin pulls over and the ears stay on the pelt.

- Pull the skin as far as the eyes and make another small cut the same as the ear cut to clear the eyes.
- After the eye cut the skin will pull up to the nose. Make your final cut just around the nose and the pelt should then come free.

Preparation

Next you can either freeze the pelts and send them off to be commercially fleshed and prepared for sale, or have a go at the preparation yourself. It is the preparation of the hide, almost as much as colour and size, that will determine what it earns in the market place.

Trim off any area of tail that has been chewed or any belly stains. Remove any surplus flesh or fat from the skin. If the pelt is dirty wash it with detergent. Then tumble the pelts in a drum of sawdust or concrete mixer with sawdust for 15 minutes or so to fluff up the fur and remove any grease and excess moisture.

Then mount each fur on a drying board (70 x 900 mm for females and 130 x 1100 mm for a male). Pin the tail out straight but don't stretch the pelt, and stand the boards upright in a drying room at 16–18°C and 60 per cent humidity. Male skins take about 48 hours to dry and females about 36 hours. Then remove the drying board and leave the pelts in the drying room for a further 24 to 36 hours. After that you can freeze the hides until they are dispatched for sale.

Problems

Anaemia

This is most common in breeding and milking females on a predominantly fish-based diet. The animal will show a loss of appetite and weight, jaundice and possibly reddish urine. To treat, increase the amount of ruminant meat in the diet to about 75 per cent and if necessary supplement the food with E and B vitamins, iron and copper.

Distemper

Fitch are susceptible to canine distemper. It can be spread by dogs coming in or around the fitch shed so keep the shed closed to dogs and visitors, especially around whelping time. Affected animals show symptoms 9–10 days after exposure to the disease. They will lose their appetite, their eyes become half-closed and pus develops. A rash appears on their chin and hind legs and the skin may appear reddish. The disease is 100 per cent fatal and the animals usually die 3 to 5 days after the symptoms appear.

Prevent outbreaks by vaccinating. Kits out of unvaccinated dams should be protected at 8 weeks old and again at 12 weeks. If the mothers were vaccinated then one shot at 8 weeks will do. Use a fifth of the recommended dog dose. Give an annual booster to all fitch after that.

Fleas

Keep fitch flea-free or scratching and biting will damage the pelt and reduce returns for it. Treat with a rotenone or pyrethrum based powder at least once a year and clean out old nest material.

Hard udder

Usually this is caused by overfeeding jills after they have whelped. The mammary glands go hard and swollen and the kits will be thin and unfed as the jill is reluctant to nurse them. It is more common in good milking jills, especially if they are overweight at whelping or have small litters. Avoid outbreaks by not increasing the jill's rations until at least two weeks after whelping when the kits will start growing more rapidly. To treat, starve the jill and if she shows no improvement within 24 hours foster the kits onto another dam and check with your vet for any further treatment you can give the jill.

Influenza

Fitch are susceptible to human varieties of 'flu and the symptoms run a similar course as they do in people, with sneezing, a nasal discharge, loss of appetite and possibly a slight temperature. The fitch normally recover in three to five days. Note that 'flu is cross-infectious between people and fitch.

Metritis

This is an inflammation of the uterus. Infection may be transmitted by the male or caused by hay seeds or barley grass working into the vagina. Dirty conditions and prolonged oestrus are sometimes behind outbreaks. Prevent it occurring by always using fertile males and don't leave jills in oestrus for long. Keep cages and nest boxes clean. The symptoms are a yellow pus-like discharge from the vagina. Treat with penicillin or some other antibiotic as recommended by your vet.

Nursing sickness

This is usually a salt deficiency which shows up in jills about the time kits are weaned. They will lose their appetite, lose weight and lack co-ordination.

Avoid this by adding 5 g salt/10 kg feed during lactation.

Rickets

Young fitch from 4–8 weeks old on a high meat ration with little bone content are susceptible to rickets. It shows up as a seal-like posture and gait. They lose weight and are reluctant to move and may have difficulty breathing. Add 5–10 per cent of fresh bone to their rations or 2 per cent of bone flour or dicalcium phosphate.

Scabies

This is a skin disease which makes the feet swell and turn scabby. If untreated the claws will drop out. To treat, cut the claws back and wash the feet in warm soapy water to remove the scabs, then rub them with a sulphur or rotenone based ointment. Carefully wash out and disinfect the cages and nest boxes and burn old bedding.

Appendix A

Milk recipes

Butter

With your own cow or goats you can make butter during the flush of the season and deep freeze it to last throughout the year.

Butter is basically made of the fat of milk while most of the proteins, minerals and sugars are left behind in the buttermilk. First you must separate the cream from the milk. With cow's milk this is easy: just chill the milk for 12 or 24 hours, the cream will rise to the surface and can either be skimmed off or you can put a syphon hose down through the cream and draw off the skimmed milk until only cream remains in the container.

Because of the finer nature of fat globules in goats' milk it is a bit more complicated. You have to use a separator or else make clotted cream. This is done by putting goats' milk in a wide-topped bowl (not plastic) and letting it stand for 12 hours. Then warm it very gently until it crinkles (about 71°C). Remove it from the heat and let it stand for another 12 hours, then skim off the cream that has risen to the top of the pan. Continue the process with milk each day until you have enough clotted cream to make butter.

Making butter is simply done by bashing cream about. You can use anything from a wooden spoon to a churn or an egg beater. In these days of modern technology the best is a liquidiser. Don't use fresh cream for butter — leave it for at least 12 hours. Have the cream at about 19–20°C for churning. Start with a cup or so of the thickest cream in your mixer and work at a slow speed (about 90 rpm). Once the mixer starts to make patterns in the cream add another cupful and so on until all the cream is in, then carry on beating.

The cream will go through three stages, soft whipped cream, stiff whipped cream and then a fairly sudden change to yellow granules of butter in white buttermilk.

Next drain off the buttermilk (don't waste this as it is where most of the food value of the cream has gone), then dump the butter granules on a clean draining board, wash it thoroughly by pouring clean cold water over it and squeezing until the water runs clear. Sprinkle on some salt (about a teaspoon per 500 g of butter) and if you want the butter to keep you now need to work out as much moisture as possible by squeezing the butter down onto the board with a wooden spatula or flat wooden spoon. Fold the butter over and repeat, squeezing down again and again until virtually no more water is coming out. It is the buttermilk which will go rancid so the secret to long-keeping butter is plenty of washing and working. Then mould your butter to your desired shape, wrap it in greaseproof paper and it is ready to use or put in plastic bags and freeze.

Cheese

To make a basic cheese from your surplus milk the only special equipment you need beyond what is in the kitchen is rennet, a dairy thermometer and some cheesecloth.

It takes about 4 litres of milk to make 500 g of cheese, so to make the exercise worth while start with about 6–7 litres of milk. Let the evening milk ripen overnight at about 13°C, warm it slightly and stir the cream back in and add the fresh morning milk. Put it all into a flat metal stainless steel or enamel container. Warm it to about 30°C. Add the rennet according to the maker's instructions and stir it in. Then leave the milk to stand for several hours until the curd forms.

Once the curd is firm enough to be lifted up by a finger it can be cut. The idea is to cut it into 1 cm cubes. So cut it with a pattern of parallel cuts at 1 cm intervals one way, then another pattern at right angles to the first and finally with your knife cutting on the diagonal down into the curd. Stir it all gently to check the pieces are a uniform size.

Next reheat the curd *very slowly*, taking it up only about 1°C every 5 minutes. Heat it to 38°C and hold it there until the curd is as firm as you want it. Stir occasionally to stop the curds lumping together and also to help the whey separate from the curds. After about an hour at this temperature the curd pieces should have firmed up enough to fall apart in your hand without any squeezing. The longer it is held at this temperature the firmer the curds will be. If the curds turn wet and unmanageable, chances are you have left them in the whey too long and they have gone over-acid.

Pour the curds and whey through muslin to drain off the whey. Next add salt (about one tablespoon per 9 litres of milk, or herbs or bacon bits if you want flavoured cheese). If you like crumbly cheese keep the curd pieces loose. If you want a more resilient block of cheese squeeze the curds together into more solid blocks.

At this stage you have cottage cheese. Run cold water through the curds to rinse off any extra whey and the cheese is ready for eating. If you want to go on to make a harder cheese then it needs to be pressed. If you don't have a cheese press you can make a simple one using a large tin can. Drill holes around the bottom so excess whey can drain off and cut a wooden lid which fits tight inside the can and can be pressed down with weights.

First shape the curd into a ball. Then wrap a bandage of cheesecloth around, forming a cake-shaped mass of curds about 15 cm across. Put a couple of thicknesses of cheesecloth above and below the cheese and then put it into your press. Make sure the curds are packed in well, with no cracks extending to the centre of the cheese. Pressure must be even and stay even as the cheese is pressed. The more pressure applied, the harder the cheese. As a simple guideline increase the weights on your cheese and turn it about every 12 hours if you are using small weights like bricks. If you have a wind-up press and can get it up to 200 kg then a couple of hours is all that is needed between each weight change. You may also prefer to change the cheesecloth at each turnover.

To ripen cheese it should be stored somewhere cool but frost free at about 14°C. After pressing it let the rind dry then protect it either with a layer of paraffin wax, lard or cornflour. While ripening, the cheese should be turned every day for the first few days, then every other day until it is hard and ready to use, at about four to eight weeks. The longer it is left, the tastier the cheese.

Useful contacts

Biodynamic Farming and Gardening Association
Sec. Mr David Wright
P.O. Box 306
Napier

CAPRONZ
Pres. Mr Alistair Frizzell
P.O. Box 32
Kirwee

Cashgora Farmers Association
Pres. Mrs J. Wisnewski
Norfolk Rd
R.D. 8
Inglewood

Dairy Goat Cooperative
Mr Dave Stanley
P.O. Box 3016
Hamilton

Donkey Society
Sec. Mrs D. Wilson
Calypso Rd
Makarewa
R.D. 8
Invercargill

Goat Meat Industry Council
Sec. Mr Mike Aspen
P.O. Box 121
Wellington

Herb Federation
P.O. Box 4055
Nelson South

Livestock Improvement Society
Mr Glenn Whittaker
P.O. Box 3016
Hamilton

Mohair Fibres Ltd
P.O. Box 167
Pukekohe

MOPANZ
P.O. Box 641
Whangarei

National Beekeepers' Association
Sec. Mr R. Rowe
P.O. Box 307
Hastings

National Poisons Information Centre
Phone Dunedin 03 474 7000 (Urgent)
or 03 479 1200 Weekdays 9am to 5pm

N.Z. Dairy Goat Breeders Association
Pres. Mrs J. E. Glover
P.O. Box 34
Hikurangi

N.Z. Farm Forestry Association
Sec. Mr Mike Smith
801 Oruanui Rd
R.D. 1
Taupo

N.Z. Opossum Fur Producers Association
Dr A. Keber
P.O. Box 983
Wellington

N.Z. Rabbit Farmers Association
Gillian Absolon
P.O. Box 1681
Palmerston North

N.Z. Tree Crops Association
Sec. Bronna Brown
22 Shandon Street
Roseneath
Dunedin

Smallfarmers Association of N.Z.
Mr G. Caddie
48 Graham Place
Tauranga

N.Z. Pig Breeders Association
Sec. R. Hughes
P.O. Box 1535
Massey University

Appendix C

Tanning Recipes

Hides for tanning need to be carefully skinned without cuts or tears, and all traces of meat and fat removed from the inside. The easiest and cheapest method I know is the baking soda and kerosene cure. For this, wash the skin before curing to remove grease and blood from the coat. Then wring it out, spin dry it, whatever — the aim is to get as much water out of the coat as possible without totally drying the skin out. Then stretch it on a curing board or frame. Just four 150 x 25 mm boards nailed in a big square the size of the skin is ideal as it allows air to circulate both sides. Tack the skin in place, pulling it taut.

Mix up about three tablespoons of baking soda and enough kerosene to turn it into a thick paste and smear that all over the flesh side of the skin. Mix more paste and add it every day, or often enough to keep the skin moist with kerosene for a week to 10 days. Now every day you add paste, scrape the excess of the last lot off and work at the skin with a stick or a scraper.

I use the edge of my mixing spoon and work at the skin, scraping off any more flesh and breaking up the membranes to let the cure penetrate. The more you work it, the softer the end product will be. As the skin cures it will change from being pink skin coloured to a powdery white. The more you work it the whiter it will get. Spend half an hour a day scraping hard at it and don't forget the edges and around the tacks.

After 10 days you can scrape off the excess baking soda, brush the flesh side with a wire brush to clean it up and comb the fur or wool on the other side. Trim the hide to shape (only use a razor blade or scalpel to cut the skin side — don't cut the fur or wool) and the hide is ready for a floor rug or for making into whatever you choose. Unfortunately with this cure you cannot wash the hide as it will shrink and go hard, so just brush any dirt out.

If you want to dehair a skin before curing it, soak the hide in about 50 g slaked lime/litre of water. Lift the skin out and plop it back in and stir it around every day for a week or until the hair starts to slip out. Then remove the hide, scrape the hair off and wash it all in water to remove the lime. Then neutralise it by soaking it in a bath of 75 g of battery acid-strength sulphuric acid in 4.5 litres of water for eight hours or more. Stir it occasionally, then wash the hide well and it is ready for curing.

Alternative recipes

A. Use 100 g of both salt and alum in water instead of soda and kerosene. Rub on and work in the same manner. The skin may take longer to cure with this method. It could also be attractive to flies so keep it somewhere that is flyproof.

B. Put three folds of newspaper down, put the hide fur down on the paper, mix up equal quantities of salt, saltpetre and powdered alum (about a tablespoon each at a time) and rub the mix well into the skin without getting any on the fur or wool. Put three more layers of newspaper on top of the skin, then roll the whole lot up tightly and tie it up. Put it away for 10–14 days.

Unroll the skin, then using a blunt knife, peel off the inside layer of flesh. It should come away easily and leave a soft pliable hide.

208

Appendix D

Poisonous plants

There are numerous plants that are toxic to humans and animals. I have listed those most often found behind cases of poisoning recorded in New Zealand. Learn to identify the plants concerned and if possible eradicate them from your land.

Cestrum. A shrub up to 4 m tall with alternate rather narrow leaves and red, yellow and white fragrant flowers. Cestrum was introduced as a garden plant but has escaped into the general countryside in North Auckland, Coromandel and Bay of Plenty. Symptoms of poisoning are gastro-enteritis and acute pain.

Conium maculatum (Hemlock). A biennial herb up to 2 metres tall with branching hollow stems, lanceolate, fern-like leaves, and white flowers in broad compressed umbels with numerous rays. It is found throughout New Zealand in waste places and on roadsides. Stock are usually not attracted to it because of its smell. All parts are toxic. Children often mistake the leaves for parsley and make peashooters from the hollow stems. Signs of poisoning are salivation, bloating, irregular breathing, convulsions and paralysis followed by death.

Coriaria (Toot or tutu). The classic New Zealand poisonous plant. There are several varieties.

C. angustissima. A subshrub up to 50 cm tall with opposite leaves, black or purple fruit and flowers in axillary racemes. This variety is usually found in rocky places on streamsides and grasslands in the South Island high country.

C. arborea (tree tutu). An evergreen small tree growing up to 6 m with flowers in long drooping racemes of green with purplish juicy fruit. It is found on coastal to montane forests and often forms a pure community.

C. kingiana. A subshrub up to 40 cm tall from a branched rhizome. It has narrow ovate leaves up to 15 mm long with wavy margins, black or purple fruit, and is usually found in grassland and shrubland from Gisborne to Hawkes Bay.

C. plumosa. A subshrub up to 40 cm tall. It is green in summer but dies back in winter. It has opposite leaves up to 8 mm long, black or purple flowers and is found in stony places from Taranaki and Poverty Bay southwards.

C. pteridotes. A subshrub up to 60 cm tall out of a branched rhizome. It has narrow leaves to 25 mm long, flowers in axillary racemes and has black or purple fruit. It is found on the Central Plateau and parts of Taranaki.

C. sarmentosa. A subshrub up to 1 m tall out of a branched rhizome. It is green in summer but dies back in winter. It has broad to narrow ovate leaves about 5 cm long. Flowers are in spreading racemes, it has black or purple fruit and is found on lowland to upper montane areas in both islands.

Hypericum perforatum (St John's Wort). A herb with two-edged erect stems, it grows up to 1 m tall out of underground runners. It has oblong leaves about 3 cm long with numerous glandular dots, yellow flowers, and fruit which ends up as a dry capsule. It is found in waste places, pastures and roadsides in both islands, but is most common in the eastern South Island. It causes photosensitivity in sheep, cattle and horses. The plant is poisonous at all times of the year.

Laburnum anagyroides (Laburnum). A large shrub up to 7 m tall with erect spreading branches with very narrow leaflets growing in groups of three which are silky underneath when young. It has yellow flowers about 2 cm long that are in racemes 10 to 20 cm long. The fruit are black seeds in a 5 cm long pod. It is cultivated throughout the country but is a garden escape in the east coast of the South Island. Children and livestock, especially horses, are all susceptible. The toxin is most concentrated in the seeds and flowers. The signs of poisoning are excitement, nausea, coma, slow breathing, convulsions and finally the heart and lungs stopping working.

Lolium perenne (Rye grass). A grass widely sown as pasture throughout the country which has been connected with the phenomenon of rye grass staggers. This is now thought to be caused by a fungus which grows within the rye grass. It is the toxins produced by the fungus which cause animals to become nervous, excited and show muscle tremor especially when they are being mustered. The animals may be unable to stand up. They may move stiffly in bounds or even throw themselves over backwards. Staggers is seldom fatal and if left alone animals usually recover so long as there is nothing they can injure themselves on or fall into. Try to get affected animals onto an alternative feed source like clover or lucerne, but take care moving stock or you could trigger an outbreak. Sheep, cattle and horses are all affected but outbreaks usually occur only in late summer and autumn on rye grass dominant pastures, especially if pastures have dried up after a drought, or new growth is suddenly coming away after rain. Stock forced to graze paddocks down hard are more likely to develop symptoms than those grazing longer grass, suggesting that the fungus and its toxin are concentrated among dead material at the bottom of the sward.

Myoporaceae (Ngaio). A small tree up to 10 m tall, with thick brown furrowed bark. Branchlets have sticky tips, the leaves lanceolate 4 to 10 cm long and are sharply pointed, a very bright green, almost fleshy and studded with glands. The flowers are white, spotted with purple and appear in bundles of two to six. The fruit is a reddish purple, oblong drupe. It is mostly a coastal plant but is also found in lowland forest as far south as Otago.

The leaves are the most toxic part of the plant and stock will eat them readily if they are blown down. In cattle the signs are a swollen looking head, swollen skin which breaks, dries and sloughs off. In sheep the skin becomes sensitive to light, the ears and face swell. If the animals have eaten a lethal dose they will be badly constipated, pass small, hard, dry, blood-stained faeces, be depressed and have no appetite before dying.

Pennisetum clandestinum (Kikuyu grass). This is a low-growing, dense grass that sends out runners and spreads like a mat. The leaves are slightly hairy and paler green than most other grasses. For years farmers worked to spray out kikuyu but it has since been valued as good summer grazing in drought-prone areas. No toxin has been isolated, but cases of kikuyu poisoning have been reported in cattle in Northland. Outbreaks usually occur where animals graze predominantly kikuyu pasture on sandy, sheltered paddocks after two or three days of warm, wet weather, especially if the pasture has been damaged by army worm or similar. Outbreaks are most common in April, but may occur from February to June. Once the disease starts, stock find kikuyu less palatable. Signs of poisoning are depression, stomach pain, salivation, constipation and dehydration.

Pteridium aquilinum (Bracken fern). This is found throughout the country and most people are familiar with it in scrubland. It is a type of fern with a rhizome root, a stiff stem and very branched, stiff leaf frond. It is a frequent cause of poisoning in cattle. If eaten for several weeks it will cause internal bleeding and bladder cancers. Cattle may appear to be still gaining weight until the symptoms suddenly show with a high temperature, blood in the faeces and from the nose. Younger cattle may swell around the throat and have trouble breathing. In horses it causes tremors, convulsions and death. Young, actively growing bracken is the most dangerous and produces many of the symptoms of radiation poisoning.

Ricinus communis (Castor oil plant). A shrub up to 4 m tall, it is a soft woody plant with attractive five-lobed leaves up to 60 cm long in many shades from green to rich mahogany. It has erect, panicled racemes of flowers, and fruit capsules up to 20 mm long covered with dark, soft spines and shiny, bean-shaped seeds. It is often cultivated and is found as a garden escape in waste areas with a warm climate. The beans are the most toxic part of the plant. All animals are susceptible to poisoning, especially horses. In humans as few as two to four beans could be fatal. In animals signs of poisoning are staggering, convulsions, coma, internal bleeding and death.

Senecio jacobaea (Ragwort). A herb growing to 1 m tall. It is hairy at first, with light green leaves and a tall flower stem ending with a clump of very bright yellow daisy type flowers each about 2 cm across. It is found throughout the country and easily spreads by wind and water. Losses are most likely in horses and cattle, though sheep can also be poisoned. Death might not occur until several weeks after grazing it. All parts of the plant are toxic. Signs of poisoning in cattle are loss of condition, diarrhoea and nervousness. Horses will be dull, unsteady, wander aimlessly and pass dark urine. It may cause liver damage in all stock.

Taxus baccata (Yew). A tree growing to 20 m, often grown in parks and gardens and as a hedge. Leaves, bark and seeds are all poisonous. Avoid using yew as farm shade or shelter and be careful where you dispose of hedge clippings. Signs of poisoning are excitement, vomiting, trembling, staggering and death. Cattle may drop dead as if shot.

Recommended reading

General

Cloudburst: A Handbook of Rural Skills and Technology. Vic Marks, editor. Cloudburst Press, 1977.

Peasants or Plutocrats. Rusty Firth. Published by the author, 1978.

Plants and gardening

The Native Trees of New Zealand. J.T. Salmon. Reed Methuen, 1980.

Organic Gardening in New Zealand. Richard Llewellyn Hudson. Reed Methuen, 1984.

Reader's Digest Illustrated Guide to Gardening. Reader's Digest, 1982.

Simply Living. Gwen Skinner. Reed Methuen, 1983.

Trees for the New Zealand Countryside: A Planter's Guide. John and Bunny Mortimer. Silverfish, 1984.

Animals

Livestock Behaviour: A Practical Guide. Ronald Kilgour and Clive Dalton. Methuen, 1984.

New Zealand Farmers' Veterinary Guide. New Zealand Dairy Exporter, 1972.

Strategies for Success for Sheep and Beef Farmers Donn Armstrong and David Brown. MAF, 1986.

Practical Lambing: A Guide to Veterinary Care at Lambing. A. Eales and J. Small. Longman, 1984.

Australian Angora Goat Husbandry: The Goat Bible. Alma M Bode. Mimosa Press, 1984.

Home Goat Keeping. L.U. Hetherington. E.P. Publishing, 1979.

Raising Milking Goats the Modern Way. Jerry Belanger. Garden Way Publishing, 1975.

The Family Cow. Dirk van Loon. Garden Way Publishing, 1976.

Veterinary Notes for Horse Owners. Horace Hayes. Stanley Hall, 1968 (revised edition).

Donkey Business: A Guide for Raising and Training Donkeys. C. Berry and J. Robinson. Published by the authors, 1981.

Keeping Chooks, Ducks, Turkeys, Geese. M.W. Stewart. New Zealand Farmer, 1979.

Raising Poultry Successfully. Will Graves, Williamson Publishing, 1985.

Pig Production and Breeding Management. C.P. McKeekan. Whitcombe and Toombs, 1951.

Raising the Homestead Hog. Jerome D. Belanger. Rodale Press, 1977.

ABC and XYZ of Bee Culture. A.I. Root. A.I. Root Co., 1974.

Beekeeping in New Zealand. T.S. Winter. Government Printer, 1975.

Practical Beekeeping in New Zealand. A. Matheson. Government Printer, 1984.

Angora Rabbits. Neil Rennie, Terry Reece and Diane Kearvell. New Zealand Angora Imports, 1987.

Index